Algebraic Linguistics;
Analytical Models

MATHEMATICS IN SCIENCE AND ENGINEERING

A SERIES OF MONOGRAPHS AND TEXTBOOKS

Edited by Richard Bellman
University of Southern California

MATHEMATICS IN SCIENCE AND ENGINEERING

In preparation

Algebraic Linguistics;
Analytical Models

SOLOMON MARCUS

UNIVERSITY OF BUCHAREST
AND MATHEMATICAL INSTITUTE
OF THE ACADEMY OF THE
SOCIALIST REPUBLIC ROMANIA
BUCHAREST, ROMANIA

1967

ACADEMIC PRESS   New York and London

ACADEMIC PRESS INC.
111 Fifth Avenue, New York, New York 10003

United Kingdom Edition published by
ACADEMIC PRESS INC. (LONDON) LTD.
Berkeley Square House, London W.1

LIBRARY OF CONGRESS CATALOG CARD NUMBER: 65-28625

PRINTED IN THE UNITED STATES OF AMERICA

Preface

There are two fundamental types of models which are studied in algebraic linguistics: generative and analytic. Simplifying, we might say that within the framework of a generative model, the starting point is a certain grammar, while the object we study is the language generated by this grammar. An analytic model presents an inverse situation; here the starting point is a certain language, i.e., a certain collection of sentences, whereas the purpose of the study is to establish the structure of these sentences, their constitutive elements, and the relations among them within the framework of sentences.

As shown by the title, the present book is devoted to analytic models. These models cover to a great extent the area of descriptive linguistics and therefore present a great interest for linguists.

Special attention has been given to the axiomatic-deductive structure of analytic models. At the same time we have tried to explain the linguistic origin of the notions, the linguistic meaning of the theorems and the manner in which the models studied are used to investigate natural languages.

Most of the examples belonging to natural languages have a hypothetical and explanatory character; here we must take into account that the model is only an approximation of the reality. Hence there exists a certain lack of fit between a phenomenon and its model.

In view of the close connection between analytic and generative models and of the fact that some models have a mixed, generative-analytic character, we have also discussed some questions currently considered as belonging to generative models. An example of this sort is the calculus of syntactic types, discussed in the second part of Chapter III. We have also given those notions and results concerning generative models which permit us to understand the links between the two types of models; these links are pointed out in various paragraphs of the book.

The book is primarily directed to those mathematicians who desire to become acquainted with the mathematical aspects of linguistic structures and to those linguists who wish to know (and to use) one of the most powerful tools for investigating the structure of language: mathematical modeling. The book can also be useful to all those who are interested in the problems of linguistic information processing (automatic translation, informational languages, programming languages, etc.). Thus, the notion of configuration, dealt with in Chapter V, has already been used in construction of some algorithms of automatic translation (see the corresponding references in Chapter V).

In view of the rapid progress of algebraic linguistics, we made a definite effort to take into account the most recent contributions in this field. Of course, we have not presented all analytic models existing in literature. We hope that the selection we have made enables us to confer on the book a certain unity of conception and treatment.

A good portion of the book relies on some of the author's papers, as specified in the references placed at the end of each chapter. On the other hand, the book contains many results published here for the first time (especially in Chapters II, III, IV, and V).

We are very indebted to Professors Miron Nicolescu, Grigore Moisil, and Alexandru Rosetti for their support and encouragement in pursuing the research in the field of mathematical linguistics.

In writing this book we have been stimulated by the proposal made to us by Richard Bellman in June 1964 to publish in his famous series "Mathematics in Science and Engineering" an English version of our previous book "Lingvistică matematică" (Editura didactică și pedagogică, București, 1963). We thought it more appropriate to write an entirely new book, which would reflect the general status of analytic models and our own most recent views. We are deeply grateful to Richard Bellman for the opportunity to publish this book.

Bucharest   SOLOMON MARCUS
November, 1966

Contents

Chapter III. **Parts of Speech and Syntactic Types**

Chapter IV. **Grammatical Gender**

Chapter V. **Configurations**

Chapter VI. **Subordination and Projectivity**

Algebraic Linguistics;
Analytical Models

Chapter I

Languages and Partitions

1. Languages and Grammars

Let Γ be a finite set called the *vocabulary*. The elements of Γ are *words*. Consider the free semigroup T generated by Γ, namely, the set of all finite strings of words endowed with an associative and noncommutative binary operation of concatenation. Since we are considering only finite strings, we shall say *strings* instead of finite strings. A string of words will also be called a string over Γ. The *zero string*, denoted by θ, is a string such that $\theta x = x\theta = x$ for each string x. Without contrary assumption, θ does not belong to Γ.

A subset Φ of T is a *language* over Γ. The semigroup T is the *total* or the *universal language* over Γ.

A *generative grammar* of Φ is a finite set of rules (called *grammatical rules*) specifying all strings of Φ (and only these strings) and assigning to each string of Φ a structural description that specifies the elements of which the string is constructed, their order, arrangement, interrelations, and whatever other grammatical information is needed to determine how the string is used and understood. ([5], p. 285). It is to be noted that in such a grammar the structural description is made with the aid of grammatical rules.

Such a point of view is closely related to the theory of formal systems and to other fundamental chapters of contemporary mathematical logic (such as Turing machines and recursive functions). But we shall consider in this book a quite different point of view: that of an *analytic grammar*.

An analytic grammar of Φ considers Φ given, and its purpose is to obtain an intrinsic description of the strings belonging to Φ, that is, a description of the relations between the words and between the substrings with respect to their position in the strings of Φ. Such a point of view is very closely related to the traditional structural linguistic theory, especially to the so-called descriptive linguistics developed by Bloomfield [2, 3], Harris [13], Hockett [15], Wells [38], and others.

To provide a clearer distinction between a generative grammar and an analytic grammar, let us consider the following example. It is known that a finite-state language may be generated in several ways. If an ambiguous grammar is used, we may detect the so-called constructional homonymy that arises when a sentence has several representing sequences, that is, several different "constructions" ([1], pp. 93–94). Note, for instance, the ambiguous English sentence: *They are flying planes*, which is really two different sentences: (1) *They (are (flying planes))* and (2) *They ((are flying) planes)*. The grammatical structures, or the meanings of these two sentences are different ([5], p. 274); an ambiguous finite-state grammar or a nondeterministic finite automaton may detect this difference ([1], pp. 93–94). Such a situation is the basic concern of generative grammar.

Let us now consider another situation. We shall say that two strings x and y are Φ equivalent if, for each pair of strings u, v, we have either $uxv \in \Phi$, $uyv \in \Phi$, or $uxv \in T - \Phi$, $uyv \in T - \Phi$. A fundamental result of Rabin and Scott ([29], Theorem 1) and a theorem of Bar-Hillel and Shamir [1] imply that Φ is a finite-state language if and only if there are only finitely many Φ-equivalence classes. Such a characterization of the finite-state languages, which involves only the intrinsic structure of these languages, is at the basis of an analytic grammar.

The above example shows not only the difference, but also the close connection between the two types of grammars. Each completes the description given by the other.

The utility of an analytic study of the languages follows also from another fact. Since Γ is finite, the universal language T is denumerable, and, consequently, the set of all languages over Γ is not denumerable. On the other hand, as is noted in [4], the set of all generative grammars over Γ (more precisely, the set of all constituent-structure grammars over Γ) is denumerable. Therefore, there exists a nondenumerable set $\mathscr{L}$ of languages over Γ, such that, for $L \in \mathscr{L}$, there is no generative grammar of L. For such languages, the analytic study of their structure is the only method of grammatical investigation. An analytic study is applicable to every language.

2. Enriching the Structure of a Language

There are many problems concerning a language Φ which can be successfully studied without enriching the structure of Φ, that is, by knowing only that Φ is a determined subset of the free semigroup generated by Γ and being able to say, for each string over Γ, whether it belongs to Φ. An example of such a problem is that of morphologic homonymy. We shall say that the morphologic homonymy of the word x is not greater than the morphologic homonymy of the word y, if for each pair of strings u and v such that $uxv \in \Phi$, we have $uyv \in \Phi$. Moreover, if the converse is not true, that is, if there are two strings u and v such that $uyv \in \Phi$ but $uxv \in T - \Phi$, we shall say that the morphologic homonymy of x is less than the morphologic homonymy of y. Thus, if Γ is the French vocabulary and Φ is the set of all well-formed French sentences, the morphologic homonymy of *beau* is less than the morphologic homonymy of *mince*. Indeed, in each well-formed sentence containing the word *beau* the replacement of *beau* by *mince* also gives a well-formed sentence; but there exists a well-formed sentence containing the word *mince*, such that the replacement of *mince* by *beau* gives no well-formed sentence (compare *je possède une feuille mince* and *je possède une feuille beau*). A systematic development of this idea—which originates with Dobrušin [7, 8] and Sestier [34]—was given in [21–23]. For further developments, see [6, 24, 31, 32].

Another problem which may be studied without enriching the basic structure of the language is that of the morphemic segmentation. If Γ is the set of phonemes of a natural language and Φ is the set of all well-formed sequences of phonemes in this language, then, by counting the possible successors of each initial segment, one can obtain the morphemic boundaries in the considered sequence. Such a procedure was discovered by Harris [12].

We have discussed so far two problems of a pure distributional and syntagmatic character. Other such problems are considered in [24]. But there are many problems which also involve a paradigmatic structure of the considered language, that is, a partition of Γ. Such problems will be considered in Chapters I through IV. The customary linguistic interpretation of the partition of Γ is the decomposition of the set of words in paradigms, the paradigm of a word being the set of its flectional forms. For instance, the paradigm of book is {*book, books*} and the paradigm of great is {*great, greater, greatest*}. In fact, the paradigms do not form a partition of Γ, since there exist distinct paradigms which are not disjoint. Such nonconcordances are unavoidable in all modeling processes.

A triple $\{\Gamma, P, \Phi\}$, where Γ is a finite vocabulary, P is a partition of Γ, and Φ is a subset of the free semigroup generated by Γ will be called a *language with paradigmatic structure*. Since we are considering especially such languages, we shall say, briefly, that $\{\Gamma, P, \Phi\}$ is a language.

The linguistic analysis needed in machine translation requires a richer structure of the considered languages. Here, a language must be considered a system $\{\Gamma, P, \Phi, K, \phi\}$, where Γ, P and Φ are the objects already defined, K is a class of subsets of Γ called grammatical categories (such as the set of words in nominative or the set of words in the past tense), and ϕ is a function which associates to each word x the intersection of all grammatical categories containing x. For a further discussion of this point of view, see [33], pp. 42–43.

3. The Notion of Natural Language

The notion of a language over the vocabulary Γ includes both natural languages and the artificial languages of logic and of computer-programing theory. The notion of a natural language is much more complicated, since its structure is very rich. Kalmár has proposed a definition of the concept of language, especially concerning the natural languages, which was intended to cover all parts of linguistics [16]. He defines a language as an 11-tuple $\{P, R, F, W, C, A, S, M_W, M_S, A_W, A_S\}$, with the symbols as follows:

P is an arbitrary set called the set of *protosemata* (in the case of a spoken language the set of physical sounds used as representatives of phonemes; in the case of a written language the set of geometrical figures used as representatives of letters).

R is an equivalence relation defined on the set of occurrences of the protosemata in the strings of the free semigroup generated by P. The classes of R equivalence are called *semata* (phonemes or graphemes, respectively).

F is a subset of the free semigroup generated by the set of semata (the elements of F are called *word forms*).

W is a subset of the power set of F, that is, a set the elements of which are subsets of F, or a decomposition of the set F into not necessarily disjoint subsets. (The elements of W, or the subsets of F into which it has been decomposed, are called *words,* every word being identified with the set of all its forms).

C is a partition of the set W into subsets called *word classes* or *parts of discourse*.

A is an application of the set C onto some set the elements of which are sets of functions such that if $c \in C$ (that is, if c is a word class) and G is the image of c under application A, then G is a set of functions f defined for all elements w of c (that is, for all words w belonging to the word class c) and for each such w, we have $f(w) \in w$ [that is, $f(w)$ is one of the forms of w]. For example, if c is the class of all nouns (suppose this to be a word class), the elements of the corresponding G are the functions "the nominative of ... ," "the accusative of ... ," etc.; if c is the class of all verbs (supposed to be a word class), the elements of the corresponding G are the functions "the indicative present tense singular second person of ... ," etc. A is called the *morphologic application*.

S is a subset of the free semigroup generated by the set F. The elements of S are called *grammatically correct sentences*.

M_W is a set called the *set of word meanings*.

M_S is a set called the *set of sentence meanings*.

A_W is an application of the set W into the power set of M_W. For any word $w \in W$, we call the elements of the set onto which w is mapped by A_W, the (possible) *meanings* of w.

A_S is an application of the set S into the power set of M_S. For any sentence $s \in S$, we call the elements of the set onto which s is mapped by A_S, the (possible) *meanings* of s.

Tentatively, we can regard the sets M_W and M_S as arbitrary abstract sets; however, to have a better model of natural languages, we suppose them to be sets having some logical structures still to be determined. Approximately, M_W corresponds to the set of concepts and M_S to the set of propositions in the sense of traditional logic. The sets M_W and M_S are common for different natural languages, which makes translation from one to the other possible.

A theory based on this definition needs some structure axioms (the term "structure" being used in a sense similar to that of an algebraic structure). In such a theory, phonology, morphology, syntax, and semantics will appear as subtheories similar to those of the additive group of a ring in relation to ring theory. Thus, P, R, and F define the phonetics, the graphematics, and the phonology; W, C, and A define the morphology; S defines the syntax; M_W, M_S, A_W, and A_S define the semantics. In such a theory, a generative grammar may show how to generate the set F of word forms or the set S of grammatically correct sentences.

The customary nonconcordance between a phenomenon and its

logical model appears also in the above construction. So, in a natural language the parts of discourse are not disjoint, and the passage from physical sounds to phonemes is not simple enough to describe by an equivalence relation. See, in this respect, [17, 27, 28, 36].

The sets M_W and M_S are ambiguous, for we do not have a clear criterion for deciding when two word meanings or two sentence meanings can be regarded as identical. The definition of identity has to be the main part of the determination of the logical structure of the sets M_W and M_S. For the delicate questions of semantics and the possibility of using the methods of generative grammars here, see [18, 28, 39]. We also note the absence, in the above construction, of such a fundamental linguistic notion as morpheme. Finally, let us remark that, according to some recent papers [14, 33], the notion of grammatical correctness, attached to the set S, may be reduced to simpler notions.

By postulating appropriate axioms, the above model can probably be improved, so as to become more adequate to the nonbanal aspects of natural languages.

4. Distribution

Let us first consider the most simple notion of a language, given as a pair $\{\Gamma, \Phi\}$. The strings which belong to Φ are called *marked strings*. In many linguistic problems we are concerning with various partitions of Γ, that is, decompositions of Γ into nonvoid mutually disjoint sets.

The most important partition of Γ which arises in linguistics is the so-called partition in *distributional classes*, defined as follows. Two words a and b will be considered in the same distributional class if for each pair of strings x, y, the relation $xay \in \Phi$ implies $xby \in \Phi$, whereas the relation $xby \in \Phi$ implies $xay \in \Phi$.

The notion of distributional class becomes more intuitive if we introduce the notion of *context*. A context over Γ will be defined as an ordered pair of strings over Γ and will be denoted by $\langle x, y \rangle$, where $x \in T$ and $y \in T$. A word a is *allowed* by the context $\langle x, y \rangle$ if the string xay belongs to Φ. Denote by $\mathscr{S}(a)$ the set of all contexts with respect to which a is allowed. It follows immediately that two words a and b belong to the same distributional class if and only if $\mathscr{S}(a) = \mathscr{S}(b)$, that is, if and only if a and b are allowed by the same contexts. This notion has its origin in descriptive linguistics (see, for instance, [9] and [13]).

If we interpret Γ as the English vocabulary and Φ as the set of well-formed English sentences, the words *book* and *chair* are in the same distributional class, whereas *book* and *books* are not. If we interpret Γ as the French vocabulary and Φ as the set of well-formed French sentences, the words *mince* and *maigre* are in the same distributional class, whereas *grand* and *mince* are not; indeed, the sentence *j'ai une feuille mince* is well-formed, whereas *j'ai une feuille grand* is not. One of the principal tasks in the study of a language is the establishment of its distributional classes.

It is easy to see that two different distributional classes are disjoint; thus these classes define a partition S of Γ, called the *distributional partition* of Γ. The first mathematical study of this notion was made in 1958 [19] and will be the point of departure in the following considerations. A distributional class is called, in [19], a *family*. We shall use these two denominations as equivalent.

The properties defined exclusively in terms of contexts and of distributional classes are the simplest and the most elegant in a linguistic description. We may consider the following situations concerning the reciprocal distribution of two words a and b: (1) $\mathscr{S}(a) \subset \mathscr{S}(b)$ (where $\subset$ means that the inclusion is strict); in this case we shall say that a and b are in *defective distribution*. If Γ is the French vocabulary and Φ is the set of well-formed French sentences, then $a = grand$ and $b = mince$ are in defective distribution. (2) $\mathscr{S}(a) \cap \mathscr{S}(b) \neq 0, \mathscr{S}(a) - \mathscr{S}(b) \neq 0 \neq \mathscr{S}(b) - \mathscr{S}(a)$; in this case we shall say that a and b are in *equipollent distribution*. If Γ is the English vocabulary and Φ is the set of well-formed English sentences, then $a = a$ and $b = the$ are in equipollent distribution. (3) $\mathscr{S}(a) \cap \mathscr{S}(b) = 0$; in this case we shall say that a and b are in *complementary distribution*. (4) $\mathscr{S}(a) = \mathscr{S}(b)$; in this case a and b are in *identical distribution* (that is, they belong to the same distributional class).

The most frequent type of distribution in a natural language is that of equipollent distribution. But the three other types are very significant from the linguistic point of view. Let us consider, for instance, the French word *grand*. It is an adjective with values singular and masculine. The words which belong to $S(grand)$ are also singular, masculine adjectives, but there are singular, masculine adjectives which do not belong to $S(grand)$; such adjectives are *mince*, *large*, *maigre*, and others. It is possible to find a formal procedure which detects all adjectives with the values singular and masculine? The answer is affirmative and involves the consideration of defective distribution. Indeed, let us consider all adjectives *a* such that *grand* and *a* are in defective distribution. Denote by $\mathscr{A}(grand)$ the set of these adjectives. The union $S(grand) \cup \mathscr{A}(grand)$ contains all adjectives with the values singular and masculine for two reasons. First there exists no word *a* such that *a* and *grand* are in defective distribution; second, *grand* and *a* are in defective distribution if and only if *a* is a singular, masculine adjective and $a \notin S(grand)$ since *a* must have a greater morphologic homonymy than *grand*.

The above considerations may be generalized. Consider, in a natural language, a word *b* for which no word *a* exists such that *a* and *b* are in defective distribution. Then, the union $S(b) \cup \mathscr{A}(b)$, (where $\mathscr{A}(b) = \{a; b$ and *a* are in defective distribution}) is exactly the set of words whose set of values contains those of *b*.

The complementary distribution is very important in the phonological descriptions, where two individual sounds which differ only by their position (such as an initial *a* and a final *a*) are in complementary distribution [17, 36, 37].

5. *P*-Structures; Derivative of a Partition

A more complex concept considers a language to be a triple $\{\Gamma, P, \Phi\}$, where *P* is a partition of Γ other than into distributional classes. Formally, we may also admit the possibility that $S(x) = P(x)$ for each $x \in \Gamma$, but this situation is of no linguistic interest.

In a language with paradigmatic structure there are three species of properties: (1) properties of a purely distributional (syntagmatic) character, which involve only the sets Γ and Φ (such properties are, for instance, those discussed in the preceding section); (2) properties of a purely paradigmatic character, which involve only the set Γ and the partition *P* (such properties appear, for instance, in the description of flectional forms in Latin, Russian, and other flectional languages; see a model description of these phenomena in [25] and in Chapter III of [24]); (3) properties of a mixed character, which involve all three components Γ, *P*, and Φ. We are concerned in the first five chapters of this book especially with properties of the third species. Thus we need some preliminary notions and propositions.

If *P* is a partition of Γ, each set of *P* will be called a *cell* of *P* or a *P-cell*.

If the partition P is written

$$\Gamma = \bigcup_{i=1}^{n} P_i;$$

then each P_i denotes a cell of P and the number of cells is equal to n. Since the sets P_i are mutually disjoint, each word belongs to a single cell. We denote by $P(a)$ the cell of P containing the word a. It follows that, for two distinct words a and b, we have either $P(a) = P(b)$ or $P(a) \cap P(b) = 0$.

As we have remarked, the customary interpretation of the set $P(a)$ in a natural language is the consideration of $P(a)$ as the set of flectional forms of the word a. This situation suggests the introduction of the so-called *unit partition* of Γ, in which each cell is formed by a single word. With the interpretation just adopted for P, a language whose partition P is the unit partition is a language without morphology; following traditional terminology used in the classification of natural languages, such a language will be called an *amorphic language* (for instance, Chinese). This type of language will be studied in Chapter II.

Another simple partition of Γ is the *improper partition*, which has a single cell identical to Γ.

The starting point of linguistic analysis is the unit partition of Γ. Each process of abstraction involves an equivalence relation which leads to a partition with fewer cells. This situation makes the following definition natural.

Let us consider two partitions P and Q of Γ. We shall say that P is finer than Q if $P(a) \subseteq Q(a)$ for each $a \in \Gamma$.

The unit partition is finer than every other partition of Γ, and each partition of Γ is finer than the improper partition. If we interpret $P(a)$ as the set of all flectional forms of a, partition P seems to be finer than the partition of Γ into the parts of discourse. This idea will be expanded in Chapter III.

If $x_1 x_2 \ldots x_n$ is a string over Γ, the sequence $P(x_1)P(x_2)\ldots P(x_n)$ is called the *P-structure* of the string $x_1 x_2 \ldots x_n$. If $P_i \subseteq \Gamma$ for $1 \leqslant i \leqslant s$ and there exists a string $x_1 x_2 \ldots x_s$ over Γ, such that $P_i = P(x_i)$ for $1 \leqslant i \leqslant s$, then the sequence $P_1 P_2 \ldots P_s$ is called a *P-structure*. This *P-structure* is *marked* if the string $x_1 x_2 \ldots x_n$ may be chosen so it belongs to Φ. In other words, the *P-structure* $P_1 P_2 \ldots P_s$ is marked if there exists a marked string $x_1 x_2 \ldots x_s$ such that $P_i = P(x_i)$ for $1 \leqslant i \leqslant s$.

The P-structures may be composed by concatenation. This operation leads to a new P-structure.

Let us consider two P-structures $\mathscr{P}_1 = P(x_1)P(x_2)\ldots P(x_n)$ and $\mathscr{P}_2 = P(y_1)P(y_2)\ldots P(y_m)$. We shall say that $\mathscr{P}_1$ and $\mathscr{P}_2$ are P-equivalent and we shall write $\mathscr{P}_1 \sim \mathscr{P}_2$ or $\mathscr{P}_1 \leftrightarrow \mathscr{P}_2$, if, for each pair of P-structures $\mathscr{P}_3, \mathscr{P}_4$, the P-structures $\mathscr{P}_3\mathscr{P}_1\mathscr{P}_4$ and $\mathscr{P}_3\mathscr{P}_2\mathscr{P}_4$ are either both marked or both unmarked.

The P-equivalence of two P-structures may be easily illustrated when P is the unit partition, denoted by E. In this case, the E-structures are strings over Γ, and an E-structure is marked if and only if the corresponding string is marked. Thus, the strings f and g are E-equivalent if and only if, for each pair p, q of strings, the strings pfq and pgq are either both marked or both unmarked. In other words, two strings f and g are E-equivalent if and only if they are allowed by the same contexts. Thus, the classes of E-equivalence define a partition of T, and it is easy to verify the following two properties:

If f is a marked string and g is E-equivalent with respect to f, then g is also a marked string.

If $x \in \Gamma$, $y \in \Gamma$, and $x \in S(y)$, then x and y—considered strings—are E-equivalent and conversely. If the words x and y are E-equivalent, they belong to the same distributional class.

A string f will be called *parasitic* (with respect to the considered language) if there exist no strings g and h such that the string gfh be marked.

A string which is unmarked but not parasitic will be called a *semimarked* string.

It is easy to verify the following properties.

If the string f is parasitic, each parasitic string is E-equivalent with respect to f and each string E-equivalent with respect to f is parasitic.

If the string f is semimarked, each string g, E-equivalent with respect to f, is also semimarked.

We may now specify in a new manner a notion considered in the first section. Indeed, the notion of Φ-equivalence, introduced in Section 1, is identical to the notion of E-equivalence in T. It follows that a language is a finite-state language if and only if there are only a finite number of E-equivalence classes in T. Since the parasitic strings form a single E-equivalence class, a language is a finite-state language if and only if there are only a finite number of E-equivalence classes of nonparasitic strings.

Let us consider two partitions P and Q of Γ. We shall say that P is regularly finer than Q if P is finer than Q, and for each triple of words x, y, z the inclusions $P(x) \subseteq Q(z) \supseteq P(y)$ imply the P-equivalence $P(x) \leftrightarrow P(y)$.

The simplest example of a regularly finer partition is that of the unit partition E; this partition is regularly finer than the partition S into distributional classes. Indeed, we have $E(x) = \{x\}$, $E(y) = \{y\}$, and the inclusions $\{x\} \subseteq S(z) \supseteq \{y\}$ imply $x \in S(z)$, $y \in S(z)$; hence $S(x) = S(y)$ and x and y are E-equivalent. For each partition P of Γ, let us consider the partition P' whose cells are defined by

$$P'(x) = \bigcup_{P(y) \leftrightarrow P(x)} P(y) \qquad \text{(for each } x \in \Gamma),$$

where the union is taken with respect to all words y for which $P(y) \leftrightarrow P(x)$.

By its own definition, the partition P' is such that P is regularly finer than P'. The partition P' is called the *derivative* of the partition P. Its linguistic significance will become clearer in the following chapters.

It may be remarked that the partition S into distributional classes is the derivative of the unit partition $E : S = E'$. Indeed, for each $x \in \Gamma$ the set $S(x)$ contains all words y that are E-equivalent with respect to x.

It is easy to see that, if P is regularly finer than Q, then Q is finer than P'; it follows that, if we consider the set Π of partitions of Γ, ordered by the relation "finer than," the set $\Pi(P)$ of those partitions Q, for which P is regularly finer than Q, has P' as a maximal element.

6. *P*-Domination and Some of Its Properties

In the following, we shall establish some fundamental facts concerning the derived partitions. We shall use, in a systematic manner, the following generalization of the relation of P-equivalence between two P-structures:

Let P be a partition of Γ. We shall say that $P(x)$ *P-dominates* $P(y)$, and we shall write

$$P(x) \rightarrow P(y),$$

if, for each pair of P-structures, $\mathscr{P}_1$ and $\mathscr{P}_2$, such that the P-structure $\mathscr{P}_1 P(x)\mathscr{P}_2$ is marked, the P-structure $\mathscr{P}_1 P(y)\mathscr{P}_2$ is also marked. It is easy to see that $P(x) \leftrightarrow P(y)$ if and only if $P(x) \rightarrow P(y)$ and $P(y) \rightarrow P(x)$.

Lemma 1. Let A and B be two partitions of Γ such that A is finer than B. Let $x_1 x_2 \ldots x_n$ be a string such that $x_i \in \Gamma$ for $1 \leqslant i \leqslant n$. If the A-structure

$$A(x_1)A(x_2) \cdots A(x_n) \tag{1}$$

is marked, then the B-structure

$$B(x_1)B(x_2)\cdots B(x_n) \tag{2}$$

is also marked.

PROOF.   Since (1) is marked, there exists a marked string $y_1, y_2, \ldots, y_n$ with $y_i \in \Gamma$ for $1 \leqslant i \leqslant n$ and such that $A(x_i) = A(y_i)$ for $1 \leqslant i \leqslant n$. Since A is finer than B, we have $A(x_i) \subseteq B(x_i)$; therefore $A(y_i) \subseteq B(x_i)$ and $y_i \in B(x_i)$ for $1 \leqslant i \leqslant n$. Thus, $B(x_i) = B(y_i)$ for $1 \leqslant i \leqslant n$ and (2) is marked.

REMARK.   Without proof, lemma 1 is given in [19], p. 205.

Lemma 2.   Let A and B be two partitions of Γ such that A is finer than B. Let $x \in \Gamma$ and $y \in \Gamma$. If, for each $u \in \Gamma$,

$$A(u) \subseteq B(x) \tag{3}$$

implies

$$A(u) \rightarrow A(y), \tag{4}$$

then

$$B(x) \rightarrow B(y). \tag{5}$$

PROOF.   Let $x_1 \ldots x_{n-1}xx_{n+1} \ldots x_p$ be a string with $x_i \in \Gamma$ ($1 \leqslant i \leqslant p$, $i \neq n$) and such that

$$B(x_1)\cdots B(x_{n-1})B(x)B(x_{n+1})\cdots B(x_p) \tag{6}$$

is marked B-structure. There exists a marked string

$$y_1y_2 \cdots y_{n-1}y_ny_{n+1} \cdots y_p \tag{7}$$

($y_i \in \Gamma$ for $1 \leqslant i \leqslant p$) whose B-structure is (6); therefore,

$$B(y_i) = B(x_i) \qquad (1 \leqslant i \leqslant p, \ i \neq n), \tag{8}$$

$$B(y_n) = B(x). \tag{9}$$

Since (7) is marked, it follows that the A-structure

$$A(y_1)\cdots A(y_{n-1})A(y_n)A(y_{n+1})\cdots A(y_p) \tag{10}$$

is also marked. Since A is finer than B, we have

$$A(y_i) \subseteq B(y_i) \qquad (1 \leqslant i \leqslant p). \tag{11}$$

In view of (9), it follows that

$$A(y_n) \subseteq B(x). \tag{12}$$

Hence (3) is satisfied for $u = y_n$ and, consequently, (4) is also satisfied for $u = y_n$:

$$A(y_n) \rightarrow A(y). \tag{13}$$

From (13) and since (10) is a marked A-structure, it follows that

$$A(y_1) \cdots A(y_{n-1})A(y)A(y_{n+1}) \cdots A(y_p) \tag{14}$$

is also a marked A-structure. From (11) and in view of Lemma 1, we deduce that

$$B(y_1) \cdots B(y_{n-1})B(y)B(y_{n+1}) \cdots B(y_p)$$

is a marked B-structure; hence, in view of (8), the B-structure

$$B(x_1) \cdots B(x_{n-1})B(y)B(x_{n+1}) \cdots B(x_p) \tag{15}$$

is also marked. But (15) is obtained from (6) by replacing $B(x)$ by $B(y)$; therefore, (5) is proved.

In the same way we obtain the next lemma.

Lemma 2′. Let A and B be two partitions of Γ such that A is finer than B. Let $x \in \Gamma$ and $y \in \Gamma$. If for each $u \in \Gamma$,

$$A(u) \subseteq B(y) \tag{3′}$$

implies

$$A(u) \rightarrow A(x), \tag{4′}$$

then

$$B(y) \rightarrow B(x). \tag{5′}$$

From Lemmas 2 and 2′ we deduce another lemma.

Lemma 3. Let A and B be two partitions of Γ such that A is finer than B. Let $x \in \Gamma$ and $y \in \Gamma$. If, for any $u \in \Gamma$, the inclusion $A(u) \subseteq B(x)$ implies $A(u) \rightarrow A(y)$ and, for any $v \in \Gamma$, $A(v) \subseteq B(y)$ implies $A(v) \rightarrow A(x)$, then

$$B(x) \leftrightarrow B(y). \tag{16}$$

A corollary follows from Lemma 3.

Corollary 1.   Let A and B be two partitions of Γ such that A is regularly finer than B. Let $x \in \Gamma$ and $y \in \Gamma$ such that $A(x) \leftrightarrow A(y)$. Then, we have (16).

PROOF.   Let $u \in \Gamma$ be such that $A(u) \subseteq B(x)$. Since A is finer than B, it follows that $A(x) \subseteq B(x)$ and, since A is regularly finer than B, we have $A(x) \leftrightarrow A(u)$; therefore, $A(u) \leftrightarrow A(y)$, which implies that $A(u) \rightarrow A(y)$.

Now let $v \in \Gamma$ such that $A(v) \subseteq B(y)$. By changing u to v and x to y in the above considerations, we deduce that $A(v) \rightarrow A(x)$. Thus, all the hypotheses of Lemma 3 are satisfied and (16) follows.

REMARK.   Corollary 1 was established, in another way, by Kulagina ([19] Lemma 2).

Lemma 4.   Let A and B be two partitions of Γ such that A is regularly finer than B. Let $x \in \Gamma$ and $y \in \Gamma$ be such that

$$B(x) \rightarrow B(y) \tag{17}$$

and let $u \in \Gamma$ and $v \in \Gamma$ be such that

$$A(u) \subseteq B(x), \tag{18}$$

$$A(v) \subseteq B(y). \tag{19}$$

Then

$$A(u) \rightarrow A(v). \tag{20}$$

PROOF.   Let

$$A(z_1) \cdots A(z_{m-1}) A(u) A(z_{m+1}) \cdots A(z_s) \tag{21}$$

be a marked A-structure. There exists a marked string

$$u_1 \cdots u_{m-1} u_m u_{m+1} \cdots u_s \tag{22}$$

whose A-structure is (21); thus

$$A(u_i) = A(z_i) \qquad (1 \leq i \leq s, i \neq m), \tag{23}$$

$$A(u_m) = A(u). \tag{24}$$

Since the string (22) is marked, the B-structure

$$B(u_1) \cdots B(u_{m-1}) B(u_m) B(u_{m+1}) \cdots B(u_s) \tag{25}$$

is also marked. Since A is finer than B, we have

$$A(u_i) \subseteq B(u_i) \qquad (1 \le i \le s). \tag{26}$$

From (24) and (26), it follows that

$$A(u) \subseteq B(u_m). \tag{27}$$

From (18) and (27), we deduce

$$B(x) = B(u_m). \tag{28}$$

From (28) and, since (25) is a marked B-structure, it follows that the B-structure

$$B(u_1) \cdots B(u_{m-1})B(x)B(u_{m+1}) \cdots B(u_s) \tag{29}$$

is marked. In view of (17), we deduce that the B-structure

$$B(u_1) \cdots B(u_{m-1})B(y)B(u_{m+1}) \cdots B(u_s) \tag{30}$$

is marked. There exists a marked string

$$v_1 \cdots v_{m-1} \, v_m \, v_{m+1} \cdots v_s$$

such that

$$v_i \in B(u_i) \qquad (1 \le i \le s, i \ne m) \tag{31}$$

and

$$v_m \in B(y). \tag{32}$$

Therefore, the A-structure

$$A(v_1) \cdots A(v_{m-1})A(v_m)A(v_{m+1}) \cdots A(v_s) \tag{33}$$

is marked. From (31) and (32), and since A is finer than B, it follows that

$$A(v_i) \subseteq B(u_i) \qquad (1 \le i \le s, i \ne m) \tag{34}$$

$$A(v_m) \subseteq B(y). \tag{35}$$

From (19), (26), (34), and (35), and since A is regularly finer than B, we deduce

$$A(u_i) \leftrightarrow A(v_i) \qquad (1 \le i \le s, i \ne m), \tag{36}$$

$$A(v) \leftrightarrow A(v_m). \tag{37}$$

From (36) and (37) and since the A-structure (33) is marked, it follows that the A-structure

$$A(u_1) \cdots A(u_{m-1})A(v)A(u_{m+1}) \cdots A(u_s) \tag{38}$$

is marked. But in view of (23), the A-structure (38) may be written

$$A(z_1)\cdots A(z_{m-1})A(v)A(z_{m+1})\cdots A(z_s).\qquad(39)$$

Since the A-structure (39) may be obtained from the A-structure (21) by replacing $A(u)$ by $A(v)$, relation (20) follows. Lemma 4 is completely proved.

Changing x by y in hypothesis (17) of Lemma 4, we obtain Lemma 4'.

Lemma 4'. Let A and B be two partitions of Γ such that A is regularly finer than B. Let $x \in \Gamma$ and $y \in \Gamma$ be such that

$$B(y)\to B(x),\qquad(17')$$

and let $u \in \Gamma$ and $v \in \Gamma$ be such that we have the inclusions (18) and (19). Then

$$A(v)\to A(u).\qquad(20')$$

From Lemmas 4 and 4' two lemmas follow.

Lemma 5. Let A and B be two partitions of Γ such that A is regularly finer than B. Let $x \in \Gamma$ and $y \in \Gamma$ be such that

$$B(x)\leftrightarrow B(y),\qquad(40)$$

and let $u \in \Gamma$ and $v \in \Gamma$ be such that we have the inclusions (18) and (19). Then

$$A(u)\leftrightarrow A(v).$$

7. Comparable Partitions with the Same Derivative

Theorem 1. Let A and B be two partitions of Γ such that A is finer than B. We have $A' = B'$ if and only if A is regularly finer than B.

PROOF. Let

$$A:\Gamma=\bigcup_i A_i\qquad \text{and}\qquad B:\Gamma=\bigcup_j B_j$$

be the considered partitions. We have, for each $x \in \Gamma$,

$$A(x)\subseteq B(x).\qquad(41)$$

Suppose first that $A' = B' = P$ and that P is given by

$$P : \Gamma = \bigcup_k C_k.$$

Let

$$A_i \subseteq B_j \supseteq A_l. \tag{42}$$

Since $P = B'$, B is finer than P; hence there exists a cell C_k of P, such that $B_j \subseteq C_k$. It follows that $A_i \subseteq C_k$ and $A_l \subseteq C_k$. Since $P = A'$, we have

$$A_i \leftrightarrow A_l; \tag{43}$$

therefore, two cells of A contained in the same cell of B are A-equivalent and A is regularly finer than B.

Let us now suppose that A is regularly finer than B; this means that (42) implies (43). It will be shown that $A' = B'$. In view of (41), the equality $A' = B'$ is equivalent to the fact that, for each $x \in \Gamma$, we have

$$X(x) = Y(x), \tag{44}$$

where

$$X(x) = \bigcup_{A(y) \leftrightarrow A(x)} A(y) \quad \text{and} \quad Y(x) = \bigcup_{B(z) \leftrightarrow B(x)} B(z).$$

We shall prove equality (44). Let $u \in X(x)$. There exists $y \in \Gamma$ such that $u \in A(y)$ and $A(y)$ is A-equivalent to $A(x)$. In view of Corollary 1, it follows that $B(y)$ is B-equivalent to $B(x)$; hence $B(y) \subseteq Y(x)$. On the other hand, (41) implies, for $x = y$, that $u \in B(y)$; therefore, $u \in Y(x)$ and

$$X(x) \subseteq Y(x). \tag{45}$$

Now let $v \in Y(x)$. There exists $z \in \Gamma$ such that $v \in B(z)$ and $B(z)$ is B-equivalent to $B(x)$. We have $B(v) = B(z)$; hence, in view of (41) (for $x = v$) it follows that $A(v) \subseteq B(z)$. From (41) and using Lemma 5 (with $y = z$ and $u = x$), we deduce that $A(x)$ is A-equivalent to $A(v)$ and, consequently, $A(v) \subseteq X(x)$ and $v \in X(x)$. Therefore,

$$Y(x) \subseteq X(x). \tag{46}$$

From (45) and (46) it follows (44) and Theorem 1 is proved.

Corollary 2. If D is any partition of Γ, then $D' = D''$.

PROOF. Since D is regularly finer than D', we may apply Theorem 1 and obtain $D' = (D')' = D''$.

REMARK. In another way, Corollary 2 has been established in [19], p. 206.

8. Partitions with the Same Derivative

In the preceding Section we have given a necessary and sufficient condition that two comparable partitions of Γ have the same derivative. We shall now consider the same problem in the general case when the partitions are arbitrary.

Theorem 2.   Let A and B be two partitions of Γ. We have $A' = B'$ if and only if there exists a partition P of Γ such that A and B are regularly finer than P.

PROOF.   Let $A' = B'$. Partition $P = A'$ satisfies the desired conditions. Conversely, consider a partition P satisfying the desired conditions. In view of Theorem 1, we have $A' = P'$ and $B' = P'$; hence $A' = B'$.

Theorem 3.   Let

$$A : \Gamma = \bigcup_i A_i \qquad \text{and} \qquad B : \Gamma = \bigcup_j B_j$$

be two arbitrary partitions of Γ. We have $A' = B'$ if and only if the following condition is satisfied:

If

$$A_i \cap B_j \neq 0 \tag{47}$$

and

$$A_k \cap B_l \neq 0, \tag{48}$$

then

$$A_i \leftrightarrow A_k \tag{49}$$

implies

$$B_j \leftrightarrow B_l \tag{50}$$

and (50) implies (49).

PROOF. First let $A' = B'$ and put $P = A'$. If (49) is satisfied, there exists a cell G of P, such that

$$A_i \subseteq G \supseteq A_k. \tag{51}$$

From (47) the existence of a cell H of P follows, such that

$$B_j \subseteq H \supseteq A_i. \tag{52}$$

From (51) and (52) we deduce $H = G$; thus

$$B_j \subseteq G. \tag{53}$$

From (48) follows the existence of a cell L of P, such that

$$A_k \subseteq L \supseteq B_l. \tag{54}$$

Inclusions (51) and (54) imply $L = G$; therefore

$$B_l \subseteq G. \tag{55}$$

From (53) and (55) we deduce (50); hence, (50) follows from (49).

Since the hypotheses are symmetric with respect to A and B, it follows also that (50) implies (49).

Now let us suppose that we have (47) and (48) and that (49) is equivalent to (50). We shall prove that $A' = B'$.

Let $x \in \Gamma$ and $y \in \Gamma$ be such that there exists a cell M of A', for which

$$x \in M, \tag{56}$$

$$y \in M. \tag{57}$$

We have

$$A(x) \cap B(x) \neq 0, \tag{58}$$

$$A(y) \cap B(y) \neq 0. \tag{59}$$

From (56) and since $x \in A(x)$, it follows that

$$A(x) \subseteq M. \tag{60}$$

From (57) and since $y \in A(y)$, it follows that

$$A(y) \subseteq M. \tag{61}$$

Thus (60) and (61) imply

$$A(x) \leftrightarrow A(y). \tag{62}$$

From (58), (59), and (62) we deduce, in view of the hypothesis, that

$$B(x) \leftrightarrow B(y);$$

hence there exists a cell N of B', such that

$$x \in N \qquad \text{and} \qquad y \in N. \tag{63}$$

We have proved that (56) and (57) imply (63); therefore, if two words belong to the same cell of A', they belong to the same cell of B'. Since the hypotheses are symmetric with respect to A and B, it follows that two words which belong to the same cell of B' also belong to the same cell of A'. Thus, $M = N$ and $A' = B'$.

From Theorem 3, Corollary 3 follows immediately.

Corollary 3.   Let A and B be two partitions of Γ, such that A is finer than B. We have $A' = B'$ if and only if the following condition is satisfied:
   If

$$A_i \subseteq B_j \tag{64}$$

and

$$A_k \subseteq B_l, \tag{65}$$

then

$$A_i \leftrightarrow A_k \tag{66}$$

implies

$$B_j \leftrightarrow B_l \tag{67}$$

and (67) implies (66).

Now let us remark that Corollary 1 and Lemma 5 imply Corollary 4.

Corollary 4.   Let A and B be two partitions of Γ, such that A is regularly finer than B. If we have (64) and (65), then (66) is equivalent to (67).

Corollaries 3 and 4 immediately imply Theorem 1.

9. Conditions That a Partition Be a Derivative

It is obvious that the derivative of a partition P depends not only on Γ and P, but also on the set Φ of marked strings. Thus, the notion of derivative concerns those properties of the language which involve both paradigmatic and syntagmatic aspects.

In a language $\{\Gamma, P, \Phi\}$ the derivative P' is uniquely determined. On the other hand, if Q is a partition of Γ, it is possible to have several languages $\{\Gamma, P, \Phi\}$ such that $P' = Q$. For instance, if $Q = S$, there exist at least two languages $\{\Gamma, P_1, \Phi\}$ and $\{\Gamma, P_2, \Phi\}$ such that $P'_1 = P'_2 = S$; indeed, in view of Theorem 1, we may take $P_1 = E$ and $P_2 = S$, whereas if Φ is suitably chosen, $E \neq S$.

If Q is any given partition of Γ and Φ is any given set of marked strings, does there always exist a partition P of Γ such that $P' = Q$ (with respect to Φ)? The negative answer to this question follows from a proposition.

Proposition 1. The unit partition is a derivative if and only if each family is formed by a single word.

PROOF. Let us suppose that E is a derivative with respect to Φ and let P be such that $P' = E$. It follows that P is finer than E; hence $P(x) \subseteq E(x)$ for each $x \in \Gamma$; but $E(x) = \{x\}$. Therefore $P(x) = \{x\}$ for each $x \in \Gamma$ and $P = E$. This equality implies $E' = E$. On the other hand, we know that $E' = S$. Thus, $S = E$, and each family $S(x)$ is formed by the unique word x.

Let us now suppose that $S = E$. Since we always have $E' = S$, it follows that $E' = E$; thus, E is a derivative.

Given a partition P of Γ, does there always exist a set Φ of strings over Γ, such that P is a derivative with respect to Φ? The affirmative answer follows from the next proposition.

Proposition 2. Let P be a partition of Γ. There exists a set Φ of strings over Γ, such that P is the derivative of the unit partition of Γ.

PROOF. Let us suppose that P is given by

$$\Gamma = \bigcup_i P_i.$$

We shall define the set Φ as follows: The string $x_1 x_2 \cdots x_p$ belongs to Φ if and only if $p = n$ and $x_i \in P_i$ for $1 \leqslant i \leqslant n$. It is easy to see that for each $x \in \Gamma$ we have $P(x) = S(x)$, hence $P = S$. But it is known that $E' = S$; therefore, $E' = P$.

It would be interesting to solve a problem.

PROBLEM. Let P be a partition of Γ and let Φ be a set of strings over Γ. Find a necessary and sufficient condition that P be a derivative with respect to Φ.

We shall say that the partition P of Γ is *proper* if the number of its cells is at least equal to 2 (in other words, if P is not the improper partition of Γ).

Proposition 3. Let us suppose that the zero string θ is an element of Γ and let Φ be a set of strings over the vocabulary Γ. A necessary and sufficient condition that no proper partition of Γ be a derivative with respect to Φ is that either Φ be void, or each string over Γ belongs to Φ.

PROOF. Let us suppose that the single partition of Γ which is a derivative with respect to Φ is the improper partition. We shall show that Φ is either void or formed by all strings over Γ. Indeed, let Φ be non-void and let us admit the existence of a string $x = a_1 a_2 \cdots a_i \cdots a_n$ over Γ, which does not belong to Φ. It follows that the E-structure $E(a_1)E(a_2) \cdots E(a_i) \cdots E(a_n)$ is unmarked. It is known that $E' = S$; on the other hand, in view of our assumption, E' is the improper partition. It follows that S is the improper partition; that is, for each x we have $S(x) = \Gamma$. Since Φ is not void, there exists a string $y = b_1 b_2 \cdots b_m$ belonging to Φ. If $m \leq n$, then y is obtained from x by replacing a_i by b_i when $1 \leq i \leq m$ and a_i by θ when $m < i \leq n$. Since all words form a unique family and since x is unmarked, it follows that y is also unmarked; but this is false, since $y \in \Phi$. If $n < m$, then x is obtained from y by replacing b_i by a_i when $1 \leq i \leq n$ and b_i by θ when $n < i \leq m$. Since y is marked, it follows that x is also marked; but this is false, since x does not belong to Φ. Therefore, in any case the assumption $0 \subset \Phi \subset T$ is contradictory.

Let us now suppose that either $\Phi = 0$ or $\Phi = T$. It is easy to see that, in both cases, all words form a single family. Let P be any partition of Γ. Since we have $P(x) \leftrightarrow P(y)$, for each pair of words x, y, it follows that P' is the improper partition of Γ.

The proof of Proposition 3 suggests the introduction of a new notion, as follows: A P-structure $\mathscr{P}$ will be called *perfect* if it is marked and if each string whose P-structure is $\mathscr{P}$ is a marked string ([31], pp. 122–123).

Theorem 4. Consider a language $\{\Gamma, P, \Phi\}$. The partition P is finer than S if and only if each marked P-structure is perfect.

PROOF. Let us first suppose that P is finer than S and let $\mathscr{P} = P(x_1)P(x_2) \cdots P(x_n)$ a marked P-structure. We shall show that $x = x_1 x_2 \cdots x_n$ is a marked string. Since $\mathscr{P}$ is marked, there exists a marked string $y = y_1 y_2 \cdots y_n$, such that $P(x_i) = P(y_i)$ for $1 \leq i \leq n$. Since P is finer than S, it follows that $x_i \in P(y_i) \subseteq S(y_i)$ for $1 \leqslant i \leqslant n$. Therefore, x is obtained from y by replacing each term y_i of y by a word belonging to $S(y_i)$. Since y is marked, it follows that x is also marked.

Let us now suppose that each marked P-structure is perfect. We shall show that P is finer than S. Indeed, let $b \in P(a)$. It must be proved that $b \in S(a)$. Let $x = a_1 \cdots a_{i-1}aa_{i+1} \cdots a_n$ be a marked string containing a and let $y = a_1 \cdots a_{i-1}ba_{i+1} \cdots a_n$. Since $b \in P(a)$, y has the same P-structure $\mathscr{P}$ as x; since x is marked, $\mathscr{P}$ is marked. Hence $\mathscr{P}$ is perfect and y is a marked string. Conversely, if y is marked, its P-structure $\mathscr{P}$ is marked, and thus is perfect; since $P(b) = P(a)$, $\mathscr{P}$ is the P-structure of x; thus x is marked. It follows that $b \in S(a)$ and Theorem 4 is proved.

Corollary 5.   Each marked S-structure is perfect.

PROOF.   Since S is finer than itself, we may apply Theorem 4.

REMARKS.   The part of sufficiency in Theorem 4 and Corollary 5 were given by Revzin [31 pp. 179–180].

Theorem 4 shows that a partition P whose P-structures are all perfect, has each of its cells contained in a family. But we have already remarked that the customary interpretation of the partition P is that in which $P(x)$ is the set of flectional forms of x. Since two different flectional forms of the same word are not, ordinarily, in the same family, it follows that a perfect P-structure is not in the spirit of the paradigmatic structure of a natural language.

10. Mixed Cells; Union and Intersection of Two Partitions

Let us consider a language $\{\Gamma, P, \Phi\}$. A chain between the words a and b is a finite sequence of words $x_1, x_2, \ldots, x_i, x_{i+1}, \ldots, x_n$, such that $x_1 = a, x_n = b$ and

$$x_i \in S(x_{i+1}) \cup P(x_{i+1}) \qquad \text{for} \qquad 1 \leqslant i \leqslant n-1.$$

The number n is the length of the chain. We shall consider that for each word a there exists a chain of length one between a and a.

Let us denote by $R(a)$ the set of those words b such that there exists a chain between a and b. It is easy to see that (1) $a \in R(a)$; (2) if $b \in R(a)$, then $a \in R(b)$; if $b \in R(a)$ and $c \in R(b)$, then $c \in R(a)$. Thus, the sets $R(a)$ for $a \in \Gamma$ define a partition R of Γ, called the *partition in mixed cells*. For each $a \in \Gamma$, we have $S(a) \subseteq R(a) \supseteq P(a)$. Hence the partitions P and S are finer than R.

Proposition 4. There exists a language $\{\Gamma, P, \Phi\}$, where neither P nor S are regularly finer than R.

PROOF. Let $\Gamma = \{a, b, c\}$, $P(a) = P(b) = \{a, b\}$, $P(c) = \{c\}$, $\Phi = \{ab, ac\}$. We have $S(a) = \{a\}$, $S(b) = S(c) = \{b, c\}$ and $R(a) = R(b) = R(c) = \Gamma$. On one hand, $S(a) \subseteq R(a) \supseteq S(b)$, but $S(a)$ and $S(b)$ are not S-equivalent, since $S' = S$ (in view of Corollary 2) and $S(b) \neq S(a)$. Thus, S is not regularly finer than R. On the other hand, $P(a) \subseteq R(a) \supseteq P(c)$, but $P(a)$ and $P(c)$ are not P-equivalent, since the P-structure $P(a)P(c)$ is marked, whereas the P-structure $P(c)P(c)$ is unmarked. Thus, P is not regularly finer than R.

The partition into mixed cells is a particular case of a general operation, the so-called union of two partitions. If A and B are two partitions of Γ, we shall say that the finite sequence of words $x_1, x_2, \ldots, x_n$ is an *AB-chain* which connects the words a and b if $x_1 = a$, $x_n = b$, and

$$x_i \in A(x_{i+1}) \cup B(x_{i+1}) \qquad \text{for} \ 1 \leqslant i \leqslant n-1.$$

We shall also say that the pair $\{a, b\}$ is *AB-connected*.

A subset Γ_1 of Γ is called *AB-connected* if for each pair $\{a, b\}$ of words in Γ_1 there exists an AB-chain which connects a and b. The subset Γ_2 of Γ is called *saturating AB-connected* if Γ_2 is AB-connected, but no AB-connected subset Γ_1 of Γ exists such that Γ_2 can be strictly contained in Γ_1.

Each word a belongs to a saturating AB-connected subset of Γ, namely to that subset which contains all words b such that the pair $\{a, b\}$ is AB-connected. Since the union of several AB-connected subsets of Γ having a common word is also an AB-connected subset of Γ, it follows that the saturating AB-connected subsets of Γ are pairwise disjoint; the corresponding partition of Γ is called the *union of the partitions A* and B ([11], Section 4).

Now it is easy to see that the mixed cells of Γ are the cells of the partition which is the union of P and S; that is, the union of P and S is R.

Another operation with partitions is the intersection of two partitions, defined as follows: If A and B are two partitions of Γ, the *intersection* of A and B is the partition whose cells are the intersections between any cell of A and any cell of B.

It is obvious that the intersection partition of A and B is finer than A and than B, whereas both A and B are finer than their union.

Proposition 5. There exists a language $\{\Gamma, P, \Phi\}$, where the intersection Q of P and S is not regularly finer than P.

PROOF. Let us consider the same language as in the proof of Proposition 4. It is easy to see that Q is the unit partition E. We have $b \in P(a)$. Hence $E(a) \subseteq P(a) \supseteq E(b)$, but $E(a)$ and $E(b)$ are not E-equivalent, since $S(a) \neq S(b)$. Thus, E is not regularly finer than P.

The union and the intersection of two partitions are used in the abstract theory of automata ([11], Section 4, and [10]).

11. Classes and Their Structure

Let us denote by $K(a)$ the set of words b such that at least one of the following two conditions is fulfilled: (1) $P(a) \cap S(b) \neq 0$; (2) $P(b) \cap S(a) \neq 0$. The set $K(a)$ is, by definition, the *class* of a. Since $a \in P(a) \cap S(a)$, it follows that $a \in K(a)$ for each $a \in \Gamma$. Since Condition 2 is obtained from Condition 1 by replacing a by b and b by a, it follows that $b \in K(a)$ implies $a \in K(b)$. Thus, the relation ρ, defined by $a \, \rho \, b$ if and only if $a \in K(b)$, is reflexive and symmetric.

Proposition 6. There exists a language $\{\Gamma, P, \Phi\}$ where the relation ρ is not transitive.

PROOF. Let $\Gamma = \{a, b, c, d\}$, $P(a) = \{a, b\}$, $P(c) = \{c, d\}$, $\Phi = \{ad, bb, ab, bc, bd, dc, db, dd\}$. We have $S(a) = \{a\}$, $S(b) = S(d) = \{b, d\}$, $S(c) = \{c\}$. Since $P(d) \cap S(c) = \{c\} \neq 0$ and $S(d) \cap P(a) = \{b\} \neq 0$, it follows that we have $c \, \rho \, d$ and $d \, \rho \, a$. But we do not have $c \, \rho \, a$, since $P(a) \cap S(c) = P(c) \cap S(a) = 0$.

Proposition 7. We always have

$$S(x) \cup P(x) \subseteq K(x) \subseteq R(x).$$

26 — I. Languages and Partitions

PROOF. The proof follows directly from the definitions.
Let

$$M(x) = \bigcup_{y \in P(x)} S(y), \qquad N(x) = \bigcup_{y \in S(x)} P(y). \qquad (68)$$

Theorem 5. In any language $\{\Gamma, P, \Phi\}$ and for each $x \in \Gamma$ we have $K(x) = M(x) \cup N(x)$.

PROOF. Let $u \in K(x)$. If $P(x) \cap S(u) \neq 0$, there is a word $v \in S(u) \cap P(x)$; hence $u \in S(v)$ and $v \in P(x)$. Therefore, $u \in M(x)$.

If $P(u) \cap S(x) \neq 0$, let $w \in P(u) \cap S(x)$; hence $u \in P(w)$ and $w \in S(x)$. Therefore, $u \in N(x)$. Thus, we have proved the inclusion

$$K(x) \subseteq M(x) \cup N(x).$$

Let us now consider $u \in M(x) \cup N(x)$. If $u \in M(x)$, there exists a word $y \in P(x)$ such that $u \in S(y)$; hence $y \in P(x) \cap S(u)$. Therefore, $P(x) \cap S(u) \neq 0$ and $u \in K(x)$. If $u \in N(x)$, there exists a word $y \in S(x)$, such that $u \in P(y)$. Hence $y \in S(x) \cap P(u)$, and it follows that $S(x) \cap P(u) \neq 0$ and $u \in K(x)$. We have thus proved the inclusion

$$M(x) \cup N(x) \subseteq K(x),$$

and Theorem 5 is established.
For any subset Γ_1 of Γ, let

$$S(\Gamma_1) = \bigcup_{x \in \Gamma_1} S(x), \qquad P(\Gamma_1) = \bigcup_{x \in \Gamma_1} P(x).$$

Proposition 8. For any $x \in \Gamma$, we have

$$M(x) = S(P(x)), \qquad N(x) = P(S(x)).$$

PROOF. The proof follows immediately from the definitions.
Let us put, for each $x \in \Gamma$,

$$H(x) = \bigcup_{K(y) \cap K(x) \neq 0} K(y).$$

Proposition 9. In any language $\{\Gamma, P, \Phi\}$ we have, for each $x \in \Gamma$, $H(x) \subseteq R(x)$.

PROOF. Let $z \in H(x)$. There exists $y \in \Gamma$ such that $z \in K(y)$ and $K(y) \cap K(x) \neq 0$. Let $t \in K(y) \cap K(x)$. In view of Proposition 7 and since R is a partition of Γ, we have $t \in K(x) \subseteq R(x)$, $y \in K(t) \subseteq R(t) = R(x)$, $z \in K(y) \subseteq R(y) = R(x)$; thus, Proposition 9 is proved.

12. Partitions of the Free Semigroup Generated by Γ

In various problems we must consider some partitions of the set T — the free semigroup generated by Γ. An example of such a partition is that used in Sections 1 and 5 in connection with the so-called finite-state languages. Let us recall these facts, using a new terminology and a more systematic presentation.

The unit partition E of T is, by definition, that partition for which $E(x) = \{x\}$ when $x \in T$. Two strings x and y belonging to T are called *E-equivalent* with respect to the subset Φ of T, if for any $u \in T$, $v \in T$, we have either $uxv \in \Phi$, $uyv \in \Phi$, or $uxv \in T - \Phi$, $uyv \in T - \Phi$. The set $\mu(x) = \{y$; x and y are E-equivalent with respect to Φ} will be called the *T-distributional class* of x or the *T-family* of x (with respect to Φ). A language {Γ, Φ} will be called a *finite-state language* if there are only finitely many T-distributional classes with respect to Φ. This definition agrees with the customary one, as is shown in [1] and [29].

Let us denote by μ the equivalence relation in T, defined by the disjoint sets $\mu(x)$. By μ we also mean the partition of T into the sets $\mu(x)$.

An equivalence relation r in T is called *invariant from the right* if, for any $x \in T$, $y \in T$, $z \in T$ such that xry, we have $xzryz$; r is called *invariant from the left* if, for any $x \in T$, $y \in T$, $z \in T$ such that xry, we have $zxrzy$. An equivalence relation r in T is called a *congruence relation* in T if it is invariant from both the left and the right.

We shall define a binary relation δ in T, as follows: $x \, \delta \, y$ if for any $z \in T$ we have either $xz \in \Phi$, $yz \in \Phi$, or $xz \in T - \Phi$, $yz \in T - \Phi$.

Proposition 10. δ is an equivalence relation in T, invariant from the right.

PROOF. Since it is obvious that δ is an equivalence relation, let us show that it is invariant from the right. Given $x \in T$, $y \in T$, $z \in T$ such that $x \, \delta \, y$, let $u \in T$ such that $xzu \in \Phi$. Since $x \, \delta \, y$, it follows that $yzu \in \Phi$. Now let $w \in T$ such that $xzw \in T - \Phi$. It follows that $yzw \in T - \Phi$. Hence $xz \, \delta \, yz$ and δ is invariant from the right.

Proposition 11. There exists a language {Γ, Φ} in which δ is not invariant from the left.

PROOF. Let $\Gamma = \{a, b, c\}$, $\Phi = \{ba, ca, aab, ac\}$. It is easy to see that $b \, \delta \, c$; but ab and ac are not δ-equivalent, since $aab \in \Phi$, whereas $aac \in T - \Phi$.

We shall define a binary relation λ in T as follows: $x \lambda y$ if for any $z \in T$ we have either $zx \in \Phi, zy \in \Phi$, or $zx \in T - \Phi, zy \in T - \Phi$.

Proposition 12. λ is an equivalence relation in T, invariant from the left.

PROOF. Since it is obvious that λ is an equivalence relation, let us show that it is invariant from the left. Given $x \in T, y \in T, z \in T$ such that $x \lambda y$, if $u \in T$ and $uzx \in \Phi$, then $uzy \in \Phi$. If $w \in T$ and $wzx \in T - \Phi$, then $wzy \in T - \Phi$. Therefore, $zx \lambda zy$ and λ is invariant from the left.

Proposition 13. There exists a language $\{\Gamma, \Phi\}$ where λ is not invariant from the right.

PROOF. Let $\Gamma = \{a, b, c\}$, $\Phi = \{ab, ac, baa, ca\}$. It is easy to see that $b \lambda c$; but ba and ca are not λ-equivalent, since $baa \in \Phi$, whereas $caa \in T - \Phi$.

Proposition 14. The partition μ is finer than the intersection of the partitions δ and λ, but there exists a language $\{\Gamma, \Phi\}$ and two strings $x \in T, y \in T$ such that $x \delta y, x \lambda y$, although x and y are not μ-equivalent.

PROOF. If $x \mu y$, then, for any $u \in T, v \in T$, we have either $uxv \in \Phi$, $uyv \in \Phi$, or $uxv \in T - \Phi, uyv \in T - \Phi$. Taking as u the zero string, we deduce that $x \delta y$. Taking as v the zero string, we deduce that $x \lambda y$.

Now let $\Gamma = \{a, b, c\}$, $\Phi = \{ab, ac, ba, ca, aba\}$. We have $a \delta b$ and $a \lambda b$, but not $a \mu b$, since $aba \in \Phi$, whereas $aaa \in T - \Phi$.

Theorem 6. μ is a congruence relation in T.

PROOF. Since μ is an equivalence relation in T, it remains to show that μ is invariant from both the left and the right. Let $x \in T, y \in T, z \in T$, and $x \mu y$. Let $u \in T, v \in T$ such that $uxzv \in \Phi$. Since $x \mu y$, it follows that $uyzv \in \Phi$. On the other hand, let $u' \in T, v' \in T$ such that $u'xzv' \in T - \Phi$. Since $x \mu y$, it follows that $u'yzv' \in T - \Phi$. Hence $xz \mu yz$ and μ is invariant from the right. In a similar manner, we prove that μ is invariant from the left.

Proposition 15. The relation r for which $r(x) = \{x\}$ for any $x \in T$ is a congruence relation in T.

PROOF. Obvious.

Theorem 7. Let r be an equivalence relation in T. r is a congruence relation in T if and only if, for any $x \in T$, $y \in T$, $z \in T$, $w \in T$ such that xrz and yrw, we have $xyrzw$.

PROOF. Let r be a congruence relation in T and let $x \in T$, $y \in T$, $z \in T$, $w \in T$ such that xrz and yrw. Since r is invariant from the right, we have $xyrzy$. Since yrw and in view of the invariance of r from the left, we have $zyrzw$. Using the transitivity of r, we deduce $xyrzw$.

Suppose now that for any $x \in T$, $y \in T$, $z \in T$, $w \in T$ such that xrz and yrw, we have $xyrzw$. Let us show that r is invariant both from the right and from the left. Since r is reflexive, we may take $w = y$ and deduce $xyrzy$. Hence r is invariant from the right, Using the reflexivity of r again, we may take $z = x$ and deduce $xyrxw$; hence r is invariant from the left. Theorem 7 is proved.

Given two subsets A and B of T, we denote by AB the set of strings xy, where $x \in A$ and $y \in B$. Given an equivalence relation r in T, let us denote, (as done this far) by $r(u)$ the r-equivalence class containing the string u. From Theorem 7 we shall deduce another characteristic of the congruence relations.

Theorem 8. An equivalence relation r in T is a congruence relation in T if and only if for any two strings $x \in T$ and $y \in T$, there exists a string $u \in T$ such that $r(x)r(y) \subseteq r(u)$.

PROOF. Let r be a congruence relation in T and let $x \in T$ and $y \in T$. If $z \in r(x)$ and $w \in r(y)$, then, in view of Theorem 7 (necessity of the condition), we have $xyrzw$. Hence, by putting $u = xy$, we have $zw \in r(u)$. Since zw is an arbitrary element of $r(x)r(y)$, the required inclusion follows.

Now suppose that, for any two strings $x \in T$ and $y \in T$, there exists a string $u \in T$ such that $r(x)r(y) \subseteq r(u)$. This means that, for any $z \in r(x)$ and $w \in r(y)$, we have $zw \in r(u)$. In particular, we have $xy \in r(u)$. Hence $r(xy) = r(u)$ and $zw \in r(xy)$, that is, $xyrzw$. In view of Theorem 7 (sufficiency of the condition), r is a congruence relation in T.

Another form of Theorem 8 is now given.

Theorem 8′. An equivalence relation r in T is a congruence relation in T if and only if, for any $x \in T$ and $y \in T$, we have $r(x)r(y) \subseteq r(xy)$.

A partition P of T is called *automatic from the right (from the left)* if, for any cell P_i of P and for any $x \in \Gamma$, there exists a cell P_j of P such that $P_i\{x\} \subseteq P_j (\{x\}P_i \subseteq P_j)$. A partition P of T is called *invariant from the right (from the left)* if the corresponding equivalence relation is invariant from the right (from the left). A partition P of T is called *semigroupal* if the corresponding equivalence relation is a congruence relation.

Theorem 9. A partition of T is semigroupal if and only if it is invariant both from the left and from the right. A partition of T is invariant from the right (from the left) if and only if it is automatic from the right (from the left).

PROOF. The first assertion follows immediately from the definitions and from Theorem 8. Since it is obvious that any partition invariant from the right (from the left) is automatic from the right (from the left), it remains to prove the converse of this assertion. Let P be automatic from the right and let $x = a_1 a_2 \cdots a_n$ be a string of T. Given a cell $P(y)$ of P, there exists a cell P_1 of P such that $P(y)\{a_1\} = P_1$; then there exists a cell P_2 such that $P_1\{a_2\} = P_2$. Hence $P_2 = P_1\{a_1, a_2\}$. Continuing in this way, we find, after n steps, some cell P_n of P, such that $P(y)\{a_1 a_2 \cdots a_n\} = P_n$; hence $P(y)\{x\} = P_n$. Since x is an arbitrary element of T, it follows that P is invariant from the right.

One proceeds in a similar way when P is automatic from the left.

Proposition 16. If A and B are two semigroupal (invariant from the right, invariant from the left) partitions of T, the intersection of A and B is also a semigroupal (invariant from the right, invariant from the left, respectively) partition of T.

PROOF. This proof follows immediately from the definitions.

Theorem 10. If A and B are two partitions of T, invariant from the right (from the left), their union P is also a partition of T invariant from the right (from the left).

PROOF. If x and y are two strings belonging to the same cell P_j of P, there exists an AB-chain $x = x_0, x_1, \ldots, x_n = y$, that is, $x_i \in A(x_{i+1}) \cup B(x_{i+1})$ when $0 \leqslant i \leqslant n-1$. Since A and B are invariant from the right, we have, for any $z \in T$, $x_i z \in A(x_{i+1}z) \cup B(x_{i+1}z)$ when $0 \leqslant i \leqslant n-1$. Hence the pair $\{xz, yz\}$ is AB-connected. Since xz and yz are two arbitrary elements of $P_j\{z\}$, it follows that $P_j\{z\}$ is AB-connected. Therefore it is contained in some cell of P and P is invariant from the right.

One proceeds similarly when A and B are invariant from the left.

Corollary 6. If A and B are two semigroupal partitions of T, their union P is also a semigroupal partition of T.

PROOF. It is enough to take account of Theorems 9 and 10.

Let P be a partition of T. Denote, as done so far, by $P(x)$ that P-cell which contains the string $x \in T$. If $x_1 x_2 \cdots x_n$ is a sequence of strings, then $P(x_1), P(x_2), \ldots, P(x_n)$ is the P-*structure* of this sequence. Given a sequence of P-cells $P_1, P_2, \ldots, P_n$, that is, a P-*structure*, we shall say that it is *marked* with respect to $\Phi \subseteq T$, if there exists a sequence of strings $x_1, x_2, \ldots, x_n$ belonging to T, such that $P_1 = P(x_1)$, $P_2 = P(x_2), \ldots, P_n = P(x_n)$ and the composed string $x_1 x_2 \cdots x_n$ belongs to Φ. If such a sequence of strings does not exist, we shall say that the sequence (or the P-structure) $P_1 P_2 \cdots P_n$ is *unmarked* (with respect to Φ).

Given two P-cells $P(x)$ and $P(y)$ of the partition P of T, we shall say that $P(x)$ P-*dominates* $P(y)$ [or that $P(y)$ is P-*dominated* by $P(x)$] with respect to $\Phi \subseteq T$, if for any two strings $u \in T$ and $v \in T$, such that the P-structure $P(u)P(x)P(v)$ is marked, the P-structure $P(u)P(y)P(v)$ is also marked.

If $P(x)$ P-dominates $P(y)$ and $P(y)$ P-dominates $P(x)$ with respect to Φ, we shall say that $P(x)$ and $P(y)$ are P-*equivalent* with respect to Φ.

Let P be a partition of T. For any string $x \in T$, denote by $P'(x)$ the union of all P-cells $P(y)$, such that $P(x)$ and $P(y)$ are P-equivalent with respect to Φ. It is easy to see that the sets $P'(x)$ define a new partition of T; it is denoted by P' and called the *derivative* of P (with respect to Φ).

Proposition 17. The partition of T into T-distributional classes is the derivative of the unit partition of T.

PROOF. The statement follows immediately from the definitions.

Given two partitions A and B of T, we shall say that A is *finer* than B if for any string $x \in T$ we have $A(x) \subseteq B(x)$. A is said to be *regularly finer* than B if A is finer than B and if, for any $x \in T$ and for any $y \in B(x)$, the A-cells $A(x)$ and $A(y)$ are A-equivalent.

Most of the results concerning the partitions of Γ remain true when Γ is replaced by T. We give here only some of these results, which will be used later. Since the corresponding proofs are essentially the same when Γ is replaced by T, no proof will be given.

The following results will be considered with respect to a fixed language $\{\Gamma, \Phi\}$. A and B will always denote partitions of T.

Lemma 1′. If A is finer than B, then for any marked A-structure $A(x_1), \ldots, A(x_n)$ (where $x_i \in T$ for $1 \leq i \leq n$) the B-structure $B(x_1), \ldots, B(x_n)$ is also marked.

Lemma 2″. Let A be finer than B and let $x \in T$ and $y \in T$. If $A(u) \subseteq B(x)$ implies that $A(y)$ is A-dominated by $A(u)$, then $B(x)$ B-dominates $B(y)$.

Lemma 3′. Let A be finer than B and let $x \in T$ and $y \in T$. If $A(u) \subseteq B(x)$ implies that $A(u)$ A-dominates $A(y)$ and if $A(v) \subseteq B(y)$ implies that $A(v)$ A-dominates $A(x)$, then $B(x)$ and $B(y)$ are B-equivalent.

Corollary 1′. If A is regularly finer than B and if there exist $x \in T$ and $y \in T$ such that $A(x)$ and $A(y)$ are A-equivalent, then $B(x)$ and $B(y)$ are B-equivalent.

Lemma 4″. Let A be regularly finer than B. If there exist $x \in T$ and $y \in T$ such that $B(x)$ B-dominates $B(y)$ and if $u \in T$ and $v \in T$ are such that $A(u) \subseteq B(x)$ and $A(v) \subseteq B(y)$, then $A(u)$ A-dominates $A(v)$.

Lemma 5′. Let A be regularly finer than B. If there exist $x \in T$ and $y \in T$ such that $B(x)$ and $B(y)$ are B-equivalent and if $u \in T$ and $v \in T$ are such that $A(u) \subseteq B(x)$ and $A(v) \subseteq B(y)$, then $A(u)$ and $A(v)$ are A-equivalent.

Lemma 6. Let A be finer than B. We have $A' = B'$ if and only if A is regularly finer than B.

Corollary 2′. For any partition A, we have $A' = A''$.

Let P be a partition of T; let $\Phi \subseteq T$, $x \in T$, and $y \in T$. We shall say that $P(x)$ and $P(y)$ are *P-equivalent from the right* with respect to Φ, if for any $w \in T$, the P-structures $P(x)P(w)$ and $P(y)P(w)$ are both either marked or unmarked. Denote, for each $x \in T$, by $P_d'(x)$ the union of all $P(y)$ such that $P(x)$ and $P(y)$ are P-equivalent from the right with respect to Φ. The corresponding partition P_d' is called the *derivative of P from the right,* with respect to Φ. Considering the unit partition E of T, the E_d'-cells are called the *T-semifamilies* with respect to Φ. It follows for any $x \in T$, that, $E_d'(x)$ contains exactly those strings $y \in T$ for which, for any

$w \in T$, the strings xw and yw belong either both to Φ or both to $T - \Phi$.
In a similar manner we define, with respect to a given set $\Phi \subseteq T$, such facts as "*A is regularly finer than B from the right*," "*P(x) P-dominates P(y) from the right*," and others. Lemmas $2''$, $3'$, $4''$, $5'$, 6, and Corollaries $1'$ and $2'$ remain true when the A-domination (B-domination, A-equivalence, B-equivalence) is replaced by the A-domination from the right (B-domination from the right, A-equivalence from the right, B-equivalence from the right, respectively), "regularly finer" is replaced by "regularly finer from the right," and "derivative" is replaced by "derivative from the right." The corresponding results will be denoted by Lemmas $2''_r$, $3'_r$, $4''_r$, $5'_r$, 6_r and Corollaries $1'_r$ and $2'_r$, respectively.

In a similar manner we define the corresponding notions "from the left," and we obtain corresponding results, denoted by Lemmas $2''_l$, $3'_l$, $4'_l$, $5'_l$, 6_l and Corollaries $1'_l$ and $2'_l$.

13. Bibliographic Remarks

The notions of P-structure, regularly finer partition, and derivative of a partition — studied in Section 5 — were introduced by Kulagina [19]. Without proof, Theorems 1 and 2 (Sections 7 and 8) were given by Uspenskiĭ [35]. Some notions and results contained in Sections 8 and 9 were previously presented in [20]. The notions of mixed cells, chain, and the partition R studied in Section 10 were introduced by Revzin [30]. The operations of union and intersection of two partitions and the notions of automatic partition and semigroupal partition have been defined and studied by Gluškov [10, 11]. Corollary 6 is proved in Section 4 of [11]. Proposition 16 is an analog of Theorem 10 of [11]. The notion of class and the corresponding sets $K(x)$ are considered by Kulagina in [19]. The notions of invariance from the right, invariance from the left, and congruence relation, studied in Section 12, are due to Rabin and Scott [29]. Theorems 6 and 7 of Section 12 are proved in [29]. Lemmas $1'$, $2''$, $3'$, $4''$, $5'$, 6, $2''_r$, $3'_r$, $4''_r$, $5'_r$, 6_r, $2''_l$, $3'_l$, $4''_l$, $5'_l$, 6_l and Corollaries $1'$, $2'$, $1'_r$, $2'_r$, $1'_l$, $2'_l$ are proved in Chapter 4 of [26].

REFERENCES

1. Y. Bar-Hillel and E. Shamir, Finite state languages: Formal representation and adequacy problems, in Y. Bar-Hillel, "Language and Information. Selected Essays on Their Theory and Application." Addison-Wesley, Reading, Mass., 1964, pp. 87–98.

2. L. Bloomfield, A set of postulates for the science of language. *Language* **2**, 26–31, (1926).

3. L. Bloomfield, "Language." New York, 1933.

4. N. Chomsky, Three models for the description of language. *IRE Trans. Inform. Theory* **2**, 113–124 (1956).

5. N. Chomsky and G. A. Miller, Introduction to the formal analysis of natural languages, *in* "Handbook of Mathematical Psychology" (R. D. Luce, R. R. Bush, and E. Galanter eds.), Wiley, New York, 1963, pp. 269–321.

6. C. V. Crăciun, Sur la notion de racine dans la théorie algébrique de la grammaire. *Rev. Roumaine Mat. Pures Appl.,* **10**, (3) 323–331 (1965).

7. R. L. Dobrušin, The elementary grammatical category (in Russian). *Byul. Ob'edin. Probl. Mašinnogo Perevoda No. 5,* 19–21 (1957).

8. R. L. Dobrušin, Mathematical methods in linguistics. Applications (in Russian). *Mat. Prosveščenie* **6**, 52–59 (1961).

9. H. A. Gleason, Jr., "An Introduction to Descriptive Linguistics." New York, 1956.

10. V. M. Gluškov, The abstract automata and the decomposition of free semi-group (in Russian). *Dokl. Akad. Nauk SSSR* **136** (4), 765–767 (1961).

11. V. M. Gluškov, The abstract theory of automata (in Russian). *Usp. Mat. Nauk* **16** (5), 3–62 (1961).

12. Z. S. Harris, From phoneme to morpheme. *Language* **31** (2), 190–222 (1955).

13. Z. S. Harris, "Structural Linguistics." Univ. Chicago Press, Chicago, 1961.

14. A. A. Hill, Grammaticality. *Word* **17** (1), 1–10 (1961).

15. C. F. Hockett, "A Course in Modern Linguistics." New York, 1958.

16. L. Kalmár, Une définition de la notion de langue (unpublished).

17. S. Kanger, The notion of a phoneme. *Statistical Methods in Linguistics No. 3,* 43–48 (1964) (Stockholm).

18. J. Katz and J. Fodor, The structure of a semantic theory. *Language* **39**, 170–210 (1963).

19. O. S. Kulagina, On one method of defining grammatical notions on the basis of set theory (in Russian). *Probl. Kibernetiki* **1**, 203–214 (1958).

20. S. Marcus, Asupra unui model logic al părții de vorbire. *Studii Cercetari Mat.* **13** (1). 37–62 (1962).

21. S. Marcus, Sur un modèle logique de la catégorie grammaticale élémentaire, I. *Rev. Mat. Pures Appl.* **7** (1), 91–107 (1962).

22. S. Marcus, Sur un modèle logique de la catégorie grammaticale élémentaire, II. *Z. Math. Logik Grundlagen Math.* **8** (3–4), 323–329 (1962).

23. S. Marcus, On a logical model of the elementary grammatical category, III (in Russian). *Rev. Math. Pures Appl.* **7** (4), 683–691 (1962).

24. S. Marcus, "Lingvistică matematică." Editura didactică și pedagogică, București, 1963.

25. S. Marcus, The logical aspect of linguistic oppositions (in Russian). *Probl. Strukt. Lingvistiki* **2**, 47–74 (1963).

26. S. Marcus, "Gramatici și automate finite." Editura Academiei R. P. R., București, 1964.

27. G. E. Peterson and F. Harary, Foundations of phonemic theory, *in* "Structure of Language and Its Mathematical Aspects." *Proc. Symp. Appl. Math.* **12**, 139–165 (1961).

28. H. Putnam, Some issues in the theory of grammar, *in* "Structure of Language and Its Mathematical Aspects." *Proc. Symp. Appl. Math.* **12**, 25–42 (1961).

29. M. O. Rabin and D. Scott, Finite automata and their decision problems. *IBM J. Res. Develop.* **3**, 115–125 (1959).

30. I. I. Revzin, On some aspects of the contemporary theoretic researches concerning mechanical translation (in Russian). *Byul. Ob'edin. Probl. Mašinnogo Perevoda No. 7*, 1–12 (1958).
31. I. I. Revzin, "Language Models" (in Russian). Izd. Akad. Nauk SSSR, Moskow, 1962.
32. I. I. Revzin, Some formal properties of the verb paradigm (in Russian), *in* "Issledovanija po Strukturnoĭ Tipologii." Izd. Akad. Nauk SSSR, 1963, pp. 94–103.
33. I. I. Revzin, Some problems concerning the theory of language models (in Russian). *Nauchn-tekhn. Inform., No. 8*, 42–46 (1964).
34. A. Sestier, Contribution à une théorie ensembliste des classifications linguistiques. Premier congrès de l'Association française de calcul, Grenoble, 1960; Paris, 1961, pp. 293–305.
35. V. A. Uspenskiĭ, On defining the part of speech in the set-theoretic system of the language (in Russian). *Byul. Ob'edin. Probl. Mašinnogo Perevoda No. 5*, 22–26 (1957).
36. V. A. Uspenskiĭ, One model for the notion of the phoneme (in Russian). *Vopr. Jazykoznanija No. 6*, 39–53 (1964).
37. E. Vasiliu, "Fonologia limbii române." Editura ştiinţifica, Bucureşti, 1965.
38. R. S. Wells, Immediate constituents. *Language* 23, 81–117 (1947).
39. P. Ziff, "Semantic analysis." Cornell Univ. Press, Ithaca, N.Y., 1960.

NOTE ADDED IN PROOF

An extensive study of the morphologic homonymy, by the method sketched in Sections 2 and 4, may be found in Chapter V of our forthcoming book, "Introduction Mathématique à la Linguistique Structurale", Gauthier-Villars, Paris, and Mouton, The Hague. Concerning the same question, see L. Nebeský (Conditional replacement of words, *Prague Bull. Math. Linguistics* (3), 3–12 (1965)) and B. H. Mayoh (Simple structures defined on a transitive and reflective graph, *Rev. Roumaine Math. Pures Appl.* 11 (1), 43–51 (1966); Grammatical categories, to appear in the same journal). A more general treatment of some questions studied in Sections 5–8 was given by M. Novotnyĭ (On algebraization of the set-theoretic language models (in Russian), *Probl. Kibernetiki* 15, 235–244 (1965)). A notion of quasi congruence, which generalizes the congruence relation studied in Section 12, was introduced by V. Amar and G. Putzolu (On a family of linear grammars, *Inform. Control* 7, 283–291 (1964)). A graph theoretical generalization of the results concerning morphologic homonymy is given by C. Raischi, Asupra unui model algebric al categoriilor gramaticale, to appear in *Studii şi cercetări matematice* 18 (1967).

Chapter II

Linguistic Typology

In this chapter we deal with some restrictions imposed on a language. These restrictions are of three types. We first have restrictions concerning only the set Φ of marked strings, that is, restrictions of a purely syntagmatic character. We then have restrictions concerning only the partition P of Γ, that is, restrictions of a purely paradigmatic character. Finally, and most frequently, there are those restrictions which concern both the set Φ and the partition P. Each of these restrictions yields some class of languages, and we shall investigate the relations between these classes and their significance as models of various natural languages. The latter will be accomplished in Section 8 of this chapter and in the next two chapters.

1. Adequate Languages

A language $\{\Gamma, P, \Phi\}$ is said to be *adequate* if for each $x \in \Gamma$ we have $S(x) \subseteq P'(x)$. The simplest example of an adequate language is obtained when P is the unit partition of Γ.

Theorem 1. There exists a language which is not adequate.

PROOF. Let $\Gamma = \{a, b, c, d\}$, $P(a) = \{a, b\}$, $P(c) = \{c, d\}$, $\Phi = \{ad, bd, cd\}$. We have $S(a) = \{a, b, c\}$, $S(d) = \{d\}$. We shall show that $P'(a) = P(a)$; since $S(a) - P(a) = \{a, b, c\} - \{a, b\} = \{c\} \neq 0$. the theorem will be established.

It is easy to see that $P(c)$ is not contained in $P'(a)$, since the replacement of $P(c)$ by $P(a)$ in the marked P-structure $P(a)P(c)$ yields the unmarked P-structure $P(a)P(a)$. Thus, $P'(a) = P(a)$.

36

Theorem 2. If $\{\Gamma, P, \Phi\}$ is adequate, the partition R is finer than the partition P'.

PROOF. For each $x \in \Gamma$ we have, by hypothesis, $S(x) \subseteq P'(x)$ and, in any case, $P(x) \subseteq P'(x)$. Let us put $R_1(x) = S(x) \cup P(x)$. It follows that $R_1(x) \subseteq P'(x)$. If we put, for any set $\Gamma_1 \subseteq \Gamma$,

$$S(\Gamma_1) = \bigcup_{x \in \Gamma_1} S(x), \qquad P(\Gamma_1) = \bigcup_{x \in \Gamma_1} P(x),$$

$$R(\Gamma_1) = S(\Gamma_1) \cup P(\Gamma_1),$$

then we may define by induction the sets $R_2(x) = R(R_1(x)), \ldots, R_{n+1}(x) = R(R_n(x)), \ldots$.

Let $A \subseteq P'(x)$. Since $R_1(x) \subseteq P'(x)$, it follows that $R(A) \subseteq P'(x)$. Hence $R_n(x) \subseteq P'(x)$ for each $x \in \Gamma$ and for each positive integer n. But it is easy to see that

$$R(x) = \bigcup_{n=1}^{\infty} R_n(x);$$

therefore, $R(x) \subseteq P'(x)$ for each $x \in \Gamma$ and Theorem 2 is proved.

Theorem 3. If $\{\Gamma, P, \Phi\}$ is adequate, then R is regularly finer than P'.

PROOF. Let $x \in \Gamma, y \in \Gamma, u \in \Gamma$ such that

$$R(x) \subseteq P'(u), \tag{1}$$

$$R(y) \subseteq P'(u). \tag{2}$$

It must be shown that

$$R(x) \leftrightarrow R(y). \tag{3}$$

Let

$$R(z_1), \ldots, R(z_{i-1}), R(x), R(z_{i+1}), \ldots \tag{4}$$

be a marked R-structure. There exists a marked string

$$\phi = w_1 \cdots w_{i-1} w_i w_{i+1} \cdots w_n \tag{5}$$

whose R-structure is precisely (4). It follows that

$$R(w_j) = R(z_j) \qquad (1 \leq j \leq n, \quad j \neq i), \tag{6}$$

$$R(w_i) = R(x). \tag{7}$$

On the other hand, we have $P(w_j) \subseteq R(w_j)$ for $1 \leqslant j \leqslant n$; hence the P-structure

$$P(w_1) \cdots P(w_{i-1})P(w_i)P(w_{i+1}) \cdots P(w_n) \tag{8}$$

is marked, as a consequence of the fact that the string ϕ given by (5) is marked. From (6) and (7) we deduce

$$P(w_j) \subseteq R(z_j) \qquad (1 \leqslant j \leqslant n, \quad j \neq i), \tag{9}$$

$$P(w_i) \subseteq R(x). \tag{10}$$

Using inclusions (1), (2), (9), (10), and in view of Theorem 2, we obtain

$$P(w_j) \subseteq P'(z_j) \supseteq P(z_j) \qquad (1 \leqslant j \leqslant n, \quad j \neq i), \tag{11}$$

$$P(w_i) \subseteq P'(u) \supseteq P(y). \tag{12}$$

From (11) and (12) we deduce

$$P(w_j) \leftrightarrow P(z_j) \qquad (1 \leqslant j \leqslant n, j \neq i), \tag{13}$$

$$P(w_i) \leftrightarrow P(y). \tag{14}$$

From (13) and (14) and since the P-structure (8) is marked, it follows that the P-structure

$$P(z_1) \cdots P(z_{i-1})P(y)P(z_{i+1}) \cdots P(z_n)$$

is marked. Since $P(a) \subseteq R(a)$ for each $a \in \Gamma$, it follows that the R-structure $R(z_1) \cdots R(z_{i-1})R(y)R(z_{i+1}) \cdots R(z_n)$ is marked. But this R-structure is obtained from (4), by replacing $R(x)$ by $R(y)$. Hence $R(x)$ R-dominates $R(y)$. In view of the symmetry of hypotheses (1) and (2) with respect to x and y, it follows that $R(y)$ R-dominates $R(x)$, and relation (3) is proved.

Theorem 4. If $\{\Gamma, P, \Phi\}$ is adequate, then $R' = P'$.

PROOF. Theorem 1, Chapter I says: "If the partition Q is finer than P, then $P' = Q'$ if and only if Q is regularly finer than P." Let us take, in this theorem, P' for P and R for Q. Since, in view of Theorem 3, R is regularly finer than P', it follows that $P'' = R'$. But P is regularly finer than P'; thus, again using Theorem 1, Chapter I, we obtain $P'' = P'$. Hence $R' = P'$, and Theorem 4 is proved.

The converse of Theorem 2 is true, as is shown by the next theorem.

Theorem 5. If R is finer than P', the language $\{\Gamma, P, \Phi\}$ is adequate.

PROOF. In view of the definition of R, we have $S(x) \subseteq R(x)$ for any $x \in \Gamma$. On the other hand, since R is finer than P', it follows that $R(x) \subseteq P'(x)$. Hence $S(x) \subseteq P'(x)$ for any $x \in \Gamma$ and Theorem 5 is proved.

It follows immediately that the converses of Theorems 3 and 4 are also true.

Corollary 1. If R is regularly finer than P', then $\{\Gamma, P, \Phi\}$ is adequate.

Corollary 2. If $P' = R'$, then $\{\Gamma, P, \Phi\}$ is adequate.

A word x is said to be *adequate* if $S(x) \subseteq P'(x)$. A language is said to be *locally adequate* if each of its words is adequate. It follows immediately that a language is adequate if and only if it is locally adequate.

Proposition 1. There exists a language in which no word is adequate.

PROOF. Let $\Gamma = \{a, b, c, d\}$, $P(a) = \{a\}$, $P(b) = \{b\}$, $P(c) = \{c, d\}$, $\Phi = \{ab, cb, ad, cd\}$. It is easy to see that $S(a) = \{a, c\}$ and $S(b) = \{b, d\}$. We have $P(x) = P'(x)$ for each $x \in \Gamma$. Since $S(x)$ is contained in $P(x)$ for no $x \in \Gamma$, it follows that no word is adequate.

The above example is the simplest possible, since we have another proposition.

Proposition 2. If Γ contains fewer than four words, then for any P and any Φ, the language $\{\Gamma, P, \Phi\}$ possesses at least one word which is adequate.

PROOF. If S is the improper partition of Γ, then $P'(x) = \Gamma$ for each $x \in \Gamma$ and the considered language is adequate, hence locally adequate. If S is not the improper partition, there exists a word $a \in \Gamma$ such that $S(a) = \{a\}$. Therefore $S(a) \subseteq P(a)$ and a is an adequate word.

Lemma 1. If L, P, and Q are partitions of Γ such that L is finer than P and P is finer than Q and if $L' = Q'$, then $L' = P'$.

PROOF. In view of Theorem 1, Chapter I, Lemma 3 will be proved if we can show that L is regularly finer than P. To this aim, let x, y, and u be three words such that $L(x) \subseteq P(u) \supseteq L(y)$, and let us put $H = L' = Q'$. Since Q is finer than H and P is finer than Q, it follows that P is finer than H.

Hence $P(u) \subseteq H(u)$ and thus $L(x) \subseteq H(u) \supseteq L(y)$. Since $H = L'$, L is regularly finer than H. Therefore, $L(x)$ and $L(y)$ are L-equivalent. It follows that any two L-cells contained in the same P-cell are L-equivalent, and we have that L is regularly finer than P.

Theorem 6.   Let $\{\Gamma, P, \Phi\}$ be an adequate language. If the classes $K(x)$ define a partition K of Γ , then $K' = P'$.

PROOF.   The partitions P, K, and R fulfill all hypotheses of Lemma 1. Indeed, P is finer than K, K is finer than R, and, in view of Theorem 4, $P' = R'$. Thus, Lemma 1 implies $K' = P'$; Theorem 6 is proved.

2. Homogeneous Languages

A language $\{\Gamma, P, \Phi\}$ is said to be *homogeneous* if the relation $S(x) \cap P(y) \neq 0 (x \in \Gamma, y \in \Gamma)$ implies $S(y) \cap P(x) \neq 0$.

A word x is said to be *homogeneous* if, for any $y \in P(x)$ and any $z \in S(x)$, we have $S(y) \cap P(z) \neq 0$. If each word is homogeneous, the considered language is said to be *locally homogeneous*.

Theorem 7. $\{\Gamma, P, \Phi\}$ is homogeneous if and only if it is locally homogeneous.

PROOF.   Let us consider $\{\Gamma, P, \Phi\}$ homogeneous, and let $y \in P(x)$ and $z \in S(x)$. It follows that $x \in P(y) \cap S(z)$. Hence $P(y) \cap S(z) \neq 0$. In view of the homogeneity, we deduce that $S(y) \cap P(z) \neq 0$. Therefore x is an homogeneous word. But x is arbitrarily chosen in Γ; thus, $\{\Gamma, P, \Phi\}$ is locally homogeneous.

Let us now suppose that $\{\Gamma, P, \Phi\}$ is locally homogeneous and let $u \in \Gamma$, $v \in \Gamma$ such that $P(u) \cap S(v) \neq 0$. There exists $w \in \Gamma$ such that $w \in P(u) \cap S(v)$; hence $u \in P(w)$ and $v \in S(w)$. In view of the local homogeneity, w is an homogeneous word. Therefore, $S(u) \cap P(v) \neq 0$, and the considered language is homogeneous.

Theorem 8.   Each homogeneous language is adequate.

PROOF.   (1) We shall first establish the following property: If $y \in S(x)$

and $y' \in P(y)$, there exists a word $x' \in P(x)$ such that $y' \in S(x')$. Indeed, since $y \in S(x)$, we have $x \in S(y)$. On the other hand, we have $y' \in P(y)$. In view of the homogeneity and in view of the preceding theorem, the considered language is locally homogeneous. Hence the word y is homogeneous. Thus $P(x) \cap S(y') \neq 0$. Any word $x' \in P(x) \cap S(y')$ satisfies the required condition.

(2) Let $y \in S(x)$. We shall show that $P(x)$ and $P(y)$ are P-equivalent. Let

$$\cdots P_1 P(y) P_2 \cdots$$

be a marked P-structure containing $P(y)$; there exists a marked string

$$\cdots v_1 y' v_2 \cdots$$

such that

$$\ldots, v_1 \in P_1, y' \in P(y), v_2 \in P_2, \ldots.$$

In view of (1), we deduce the existence of a word $x' \in P(x)$ such that $y' \in S(x')$. Hence the string

$$\cdots v_1 x' v_2 \cdots$$

is marked. It follows that the P-structure

$$\cdots P_1 P(x) P_2 \cdots$$

is marked, that is, $P(y)$ P-dominates $P(x)$. To establish that $P(x)$ P-dominates $P(y)$, it suffices to remark that the result of (1) may be formulated as follows: If $x \in S(y)$ and $x' \in P(x)$, there exists a word $y' \in P(y)$, such that $x' \in S(y')$.

REMARK. It is interesting that the "local variant" of Theorem 8 is false. Precisely, we have the next proposition.

Proposition 3. There exists a language $\{\Gamma, P, \Phi\}$ and a word $x \in \Gamma$ such that x is homogeneous, but not adequate.

PROOF. Let us consider the language used in the proof of Theorem 1. Since we have $P'(a) = P(a)$ and $S(a) - P(a) \neq 0$, it follows that the word a is not adequate. On the other hand, we have $S(a) = \{a, b, c\}$, $P(a) = \{a, b\}$, $P(c) = \{c, d\}$, $P(b) \cap S(a) = \{a, b\} \neq 0$, $P(c) \cap S(a) = \{c\} \neq 0$, $P(c) \cap S(b) = \{c\} \neq 0$, $P(a) \cap S(b) = \{a, b\} \neq 0$. Hence a is homogeneous.

Theorem 9. There exists an adequate language which is not homogeneous.

PROOF.   Let $\Gamma = \{a, b, c, d\}$, $P(a) = \{a, b\}$, $P(c) = \{c, d\}$, $\Phi = \{ad, bb,$ $ab, bc, bd, dc, db, dd\}$. We have $S(a) = \{a\}$, $S(b) = \{b, d\}$, $S(c) = \{c\}$. It follows that $P(a) \cap S(d) = \{b\} \neq 0$, whereas $P(d) \cap S(a) = \{c, d\} \cap \{a\} = 0$. Hence the considered language is not homogeneous.

Let us show that $S(x) \subseteq P'(x)$ for each $x \in \Gamma$. If either $x = a$ or $x = c$, the inclusion is obvious, since we always have $x \in P'(x)$. Now let $x = b$. It is easy to see that $b \in S(d)$; it must be shown that $P(b)$ and $P(d)$ are P-equivalent. Since the length of each marked string is equal to 2, it follows that each marked P-structure has two terms. But the only P-structures having two terms are $P(b)P(b)$, $P(d)P(d)$, $P(b)P(d)$, and $P(d)P(b)$. It is easy to see that all these P-structures are marked; hence $P(b)$ and $P(d)$ are P-equivalent and Theorem 9 is proved.

Lemma 2.   If $\{\Gamma, P, \Phi\}$ is homogeneous, $x \in \Gamma$ and $y \in \Gamma$, then $y \in R(x)$ if and only if $P(x) \cap S(y) \neq 0$.

PROOF.   Let us first suppose that $y \in R(x)$. There exists a chain $x = x_1, x_2, \ldots, x_i, x_{i+1}, \ldots, x_n = y$, that is, we have

$$x_{i+1} \in S(x_i) \cup P(x_i) \qquad \text{for } 1 \leqslant i \leqslant n-1. \tag{15}$$

We shall show, by induction, that

$$P(x) \cap S(x_j) \neq 0 \qquad \text{for } 1 \leqslant j \leqslant n; \tag{16}$$

the particular case corresponding to $j = n$ is precisely the required relation.

For $j = 1$, relation (16) is true, since $x_1 = x$; thus $x \in P(x) \cap S(x_1)$. Let us suppose that (16) is true for each $j \leqslant i$. Since the language is homogeneous, it follows that

$$P(x_j) \cap S(x) \neq 0 \qquad \text{for } j \leqslant i. \tag{17}$$

In view of (15) we have $x_{i+1} \in P(x_i)$ or $x_{i+1} \in S(x_i)$. If $x_{i+1} \in P(x_i)$, then $P(x_i) = P(x_{i+1})$ and, in view of (17), for $j = i$, it follows that $P(x_{i+1}) \cap S(x) \neq 0$. This implies, in view of the homogeneity of the language, that

$$P(x) \cap S(x_{i+1}) \neq 0. \tag{18}$$

If $x_{i+1} \in S(x_i)$, we have $S(x_i) = S(x_{i+1})$. Hence relation (16) for $j = i$ implies (18). It follows that the validity of (16) for $j \leqslant i$ implies the validity of (16) for $j = i+1$, and thus, for $j = n$, we obtain

$$P(x) \cap S(y) \neq 0. \tag{19}$$

Now suppose that (19) is true. There exists a word $z \in P(x) \cap S(y)$, that is, we have the chain x, z, y, with $x \in P(z)$ and $z \in S(y)$. Therefore, $y \in R(x)$.

Lemma 3. If, in any language $\{\Gamma, P, \Phi\}$, the relation $y \in R(x)$ implies (19), the language is homogeneous.

PROOF. Let x and y be such that $P(y) \cap S(x) \neq 0$. There exists a word $z \in P(y) \cap S(x)$, and we have the chain x, z, y between x and y. Hence $y \in R(x)$. In view of the hypothesis, this implies relation (19), and the language is homogeneous.

Theorem 10. If $\{\Gamma, P, \Phi\}$ is homogeneous, $K(x) = R(x)$ for each $x \in \Gamma$, that is, the classes coincide with the mixed cells.

PROOF. Let $x \in K(y)$. It follows that, if $P(x) \cap S(y) \neq 0$, then $P(y) \cap S(x) \neq 0$. This implies the existence of a word z such that the sequence x, z, y is a chain. Hence $x \in R(y)$.

Let us now suppose that $x \in R(y)$. Since the language is homogeneous, we have, in view of Lemma 2, $P(y) \cap S(x) \neq 0$. Thus $x \in K(y)$.

REMARK. The hypothesis of homogeneity is used only to establish that $x \in R(y)$ implies $x \in K(y)$. The inclusion $K(y) \subseteq R(y)$ is true for each $x \in \Gamma$ and for each language.

Corollary 3. If $\{\Gamma, P, \Phi\}$ is homogeneous, the classes $K(x)$ define a partition K of Γ and we have $K' = P'$.

PROOF. In view of Theorem 8, the language is adequate. We may apply Theorem 4 and obtain $R' = P'$. In view of Theorem 10 and since the mixed cells define a partition of Γ, it follows that the classes $K(x)$ define a partition K of Γ and $K = R$; hence $K' = P'$.

Theorem 11. The language $\{\Gamma, P, \Phi\}$ is homogeneous if and only if $M(x) = N(x)$ for each $x \in \Gamma$, where $M(x)$ and $N(x)$ are given by relations (68) of Chapter 1.

PROOF. Let us first consider $\{\Gamma, P, \Phi\}$ homogeneous and let $u \in M(x)$. There exists a word $y \in P(x)$ such that $u \in S(y)$. Hence $P(x) \cap S(u) \neq 0$. In view of the homogeneity, it follows that $P(u) \cap S(x) \neq 0$.

Then let $z \in P(u) \cap S(x)$. We have $u \in P(z)$ and $z \in S(x)$. Thus $u \in N(x)$, and $M(x) \subseteq N(x)$.

Now let $u \in N(x)$. There exists a word $y \in S(x)$ such that $u \in P(y)$. Hence $S(x) \cap P(u) \neq 0$. In view of the homogeneity, we deduce that $S(u) \cap P(x) \neq 0$. Then let $z \in S(u) \cap P(x)$. We have $u \in S(z)$ and $z \in P(x)$. Hence $u \in M(x)$. Thus, $N(x) \subseteq M(x)$. We have also proved that the homogeneity of the language implies $M(x) = N(x)$ for each $x \in \Gamma$.

Let us now suppose that $M(x) = N(x)$ for each $x \in \Gamma$. If $P(x) \cap S(y) \neq 0$, let $z \in P(x) \cap S(y)$. We have $x \in P(z)$ and $z \in S(y)$. Hence $x \in N(y)$ and $x \in M(y)$. This means that there exists a word $u \in P(y)$ such that $x \in S(u)$. Hence $u \in S(x) \cap P(y)$. We have also proved that $P(x) \cap S(y) \neq 0$ implies $S(x) \cap P(y) \neq 0$, and thus the language is homogeneous.

Corollary 4.   If $\{\Gamma, P, \Phi\}$ is homogeneous, then $K(x) = M(x) = N(x)$ for each $x \in \Gamma$.

PROOF.   It follows immediately from Theorem 5 and 11.

Proposition 4.   If $N(x) \subseteq M(x)$ for each $x \in \Gamma$, the language is homogeneous.

PROOF.   Let $P(x) \cap S(y) \neq 0$ and $z \in P(x) \cap S(y)$; hence, $x \in P(z)$ and $z \in S(y)$. It follows that $x \in N(y)$. But $N(y) \subseteq M(y)$. Thus $x \in M(y)$ and there exists $u \in P(y)$ such that $x \in S(u)$. Therefore, $P(y) \cap S(x) \neq 0$, and the language is homogeneous.

In the same way we obtain a further proposition.

Proposition 5.   If $M(x) \subseteq N(x)$ for each $x \in \Gamma$, the language is homogeneous.

Theorem 5 and propositions 4 and 5 imply a corollary.

Corollary 5.   If $M(x) = K(x)$ for each $x \in \Gamma$, the language is homogeneous. If $N(x) = K(x)$ for each $x \in \Gamma$, the language is homogeneous.

3. Various Types of Homogeneous Languages

A language is said to be *completely homogeneous* if, for each $x \in \Gamma$, we have $S(x) \subseteq P(x)$.

Proposition 6. If P is the improper partition, then $\{\Gamma, P, \Phi\}$ is completely homogeneous.

PROOF. Obvious.

Proposition 7. If $\{\Gamma, P, \Phi\}$ is such that S is the unit partition of Γ, then $\{\Gamma, P, \Phi\}$ is completely homogeneous.
    A word $x \in \Gamma$ is said to be *completely homogeneous* if $S(x) \subseteq P(x)$.

Proposition 8. In any language $\{\Gamma, P, \Phi\}$, each completely homogeneous word is homogeneous.

PROOF. Let x be completely homogeneous and let $y \in S(x)$, $z \in P(x)$. Since $S(x) \subseteq P(x)$, we have $y \in P(x)$; hence $P(y) = P(x)$ and $S(z) \cap P(y) = S(z) \cap P(x) \supseteq \{z\} \neq 0$. Therefore, x is homogeneous.

Proposition 9. If $\{\Gamma, P, \Phi\}$ is completely homogeneous, it is homogeneous.

PROOF. It suffices to remark that each word is completely homogeneous, and therefore homogeneous. Then apply Theorem 7.

Proposition 10. Each completely homogeneous word is adequate.

PROOF. Obvious.
    A language is said to be *perfect* if for each $x \in \Gamma$ we have $P(x) \subseteq S(x)$. In view of Theorem 4, Chapter I, we have a further proposition.

Proposition 11. A language is perfect if and only if each marked P-structure is perfect.
    The following two propositions are obvious.

Proposition 12. If P is the unit partition of Γ, then $\{\Gamma, P, \Phi\}$ is perfect.

Proposition 13. If $\{\Gamma, P, \Phi\}$ is such that S is the improper partition of Γ, then $\{\Gamma, P, \Phi\}$ is perfect.
    A word x is said to be *perfect* if $P(x) \subseteq S(x)$.

Proposition 14. In any language $\{\Gamma, P, \Phi\}$, each perfect word is homogeneous.

PROOF. Let x be perfect and let $y \in S(x)$, $z \in P(x)$. Since $P(x) \subseteq S(x)$, we have $z \in S(x)$. Hence $S(z) = S(x)$ and $S(z) \cap P(y) = S(x) \cap P(y) \supseteq \{y\} \neq 0$. Therefore, x is homogeneous.

Proposition 15. Each perfect language is a homogeneous language.

PROOF. It suffices to remark that each word is perfect, and therefore homogeneous. Then apply Theorem 7.

A language $\{\Gamma, P, \Phi\}$ is said to be *simple* if it is homogeneous and if $P(x) \cap S(x) = \{x\}$ for each $x \in \Gamma$. Thus, by definition, any simple language is homogeneous. The converse is not true, as is shown by Proposition 16.

Proposition 16. There exists a homogeneous language which is not simple.

PROOF. Let $\{\Gamma, P, \Phi\}$ be a language such that $S(x) \subseteq P(x)$ for each $x \in \Gamma$, whereas S is not the unit partition of Γ. (An example of such a language is $\{\Gamma, S, \Phi\}$, where $\Gamma = \{a, b\}$ and $\Phi = \{a, b\}$.) This language is completely homogeneous and, in view of Proposition 9, it is homogeneous. On the other hand, $P(x) \cap S(x) = S(x)$ and, since $S \neq E$, there exists a word x_1 such that $S(x_1) \neq \{x_1\}$.

A word x is said to be *simple* if for $y \in P(x)$ and $z \in S(x)$ the set $S(y) \cap P(z)$ contains exactly one word.

A language is said to be *locally simple* if all its words are simple.

Theorem 12. A language is simple if and only if it is locally simple.

PROOF. Let $\{\Gamma, P, \Phi\}$ be simple and let $x \in \Gamma$. Since any simple language is homogeneous and in view of Theorem 7, it follows that x is a homogeneous word. Hence for $y \in P(x)$ and $z \in S(x)$ we have $S(y) \cap P(z) \neq 0$. To prove that $S(y) \cap P(z)$ contains exactly one word, we shall reason by contradiction. Let us admit that there exist two different words x' and x'' such that $x' \in S(y) \cap P(z)$ and $x'' \in S(y) \cap P(z)$. It follows that $P(x') = P(x'') = P(z)$ and $S(x') = S(x'') = S(y)$. Hence $P(x') \cap S(x') = P(x'') \cap S(x'') = P(z) \cap S(y)$; therefore, $x'' \in P(x') \cap S(x')$. Since $x' \in P(x') \cap S(x')$, it follows that $P(x') \cap S(x')$ contains more than one word, in contradiction to the assumption that the considered language is simple. Thus, $\{\Gamma, P, \Phi\}$ is locally simple.

Let us now suppose that $\{\Gamma, P, \Phi\}$ is locally simple.

Since any simple word is homogeneous, it follows that $\{\Gamma, P, \Phi\}$ is locally homogeneous and thus, by virtue of Theorem 7, $\Gamma, P, \Phi\}$ is homogeneous. To prove that $P(x) \cap S(x) = \{x\}$ for each $x \in \Gamma$, it suffices to take, in the definition of the notion of a simple word, $y = z = x$ and to remark that $x \in S(x) \cap P(x)$. Therefore, $\{\Gamma, P, \Phi\}$ is simple.

Since any simple language is homogeneous and any homogeneous language is adequate, it follows that any simple language is adequate. The "local variant" of this fact is not true, as it is shown by Theorem 13.

Theorem 13. There exist a language $\{\Gamma, P, \Phi\}$ and a word $x \in \Gamma$ such that x is simple, but not adequate.

PROOF. Let us consider the language used in the proof of Proposition 1. As shown in this proof, no word of this language is adequate. On the other hand, we have $S(a) = \{a, c\}$, $P(a) = \{a\}$, $P(c) = \{c, d\}$. Hence $P(c) \cap S(a) = \{c\} \neq 0$ and $P(a) \cap S(a) = \{a\} \neq 0$. Therefore, a is a simple word.

It is easy to see that there exist simple languages which are neither completely homogeneous nor perfect, whereas there exist completely homogeneous and perfect languages which are not simple. Moreover, we have two stronger propositions, as follows.

Proposition 17. There exists a perfect and completely homogeneous language in which no word is simple.

PROOF. Let $\Gamma = \{a, b\}$, $P(a) = \{a, b\}$, $\Phi = \{a, b\}$. We have $S(a) = \{a, b\}$. Hence $P = S$ and the language is perfect and completely homogeneous; but neither a nor b is simple, since $P(a) \cap S(a) = P(b) \cap S(b) = \{a, b\} \neq \{a\}$ and $\neq \{b\}$.

Proposition 18. There exists a simple language in which each word is neither perfect nor completely homogeneous.

PROOF. Let $\Gamma = \{a, b, c, d\}$, $P(a) = \{a, c\}$, $P(b) = \{b, d\}$, $\Phi = \{ac, bc, ad, bd\}$. We have $S(a) = \{a, b\}$, $S(c) = \{c, d\}$. Hence, for any $x \in \Gamma$ we have neither $P(x) \subseteq S(x)$ nor $S(x) \subseteq P(x)$.

Proposition 19. Any amorphic language is simple.

PROOF. A language is amorphic if and only if $P = E$. Thus, in view of Propositions 12 and 15, any amorphic language is homogeneous.

On the other hand, in any amorphic language we have, for each $x \in \Gamma$, $S(x) \cap P(x) = S(x) \cap \{x\} = \{x\}$. Hence any amorphic language is simple.

A word x is said to be *amorphic* if $P(x) = \{x\}$.

Proposition 20. There exists a simple language in which no word is amorphic.

PROOF. Let us consider the same language as in the proof of Proposition 18. In view of that proposition and since each amorphic word is perfect, it follows that the considered language is simple, but no word is amorphic.

A language is said to be *purely paradigmatic* if $S = E$. A word x is said to be *purely paradigmatic* if $S(x) = \{x\}$.

Proposition 21. Any purely paradigmatic language is completely homogeneous.

PROOF. The proof follows immediately from Proposition 7.

Proposition 22. Any purely paradigmatic language is simple.

PROOF. In view of Propositions 9 and 21, if $\{\Gamma, P, \Phi\}$ is purely paradigmatic, it is homogeneous. On the other hand, since we always have $x \in P(x) \cap S(x)$ and since the language is purely paradigmatic, it follows that $P(x) = \{x\}$. Hence $P(x) \cap S(x) = \{x\}$ for any $x \in \Gamma$. Therefore, $\{\Gamma, P, \Phi\}$ is simple.

It is to be remarked that the "local variant" of Propositions 19 and 22 is not true. Indeed, we have another proposition.

Proposition 23. There exist a language $\{\Gamma, P, \Phi\}$ and two words $x \in \Gamma$ and $y \in \Gamma$ such that x and y are not simple, but x is purely paradigmatic, whereas y is perfect.

PROOF. Let $\Gamma = \{a, b, c, d\}$, $P(a) = \{a, b, c\}$, $P(d) = \{d\}$, $\Phi = \{ab, ac, ad\}$. We have $S(a) = \{a\}, S(b) = \{b, c, d\}$. The word a is purely paradigmatic, but it is not simple, since $P(a) \cap S(b) = \{b, c\}$. The word d is perfect, but it is not simple, since $S(d) \cap P(b) = \{b, c\}$.

4. Completely Adequate Languages

In some languages there exists a stronger property than that of adequacy: For any two words x and y such that x E-dominates y we have $y \in P'(x)$. A language $\{\Gamma, P, \Phi\}$ in which such a condition is fulfilled will be called a *completely adequate language*.

Proposition 24. Any completely adequate language is adequate.

PROOF. It is enough to remark that, if $y \in S(x)$, then x E-dominates y.

Proposition 25. There exists an amorphic and purely paradigmatic language which is not completely adequate.

PROOF. Let $\Gamma = \{a, b, c\}$, $P = E$, $\Phi = \{ab, cb, cc\}$. It is easy to see that $S = E$ and a E-dominates c. If the language were completely adequate, we would have $c \in E'(a)$. But $E' = S$ and, by hypothesis, $S = E$. Thus $E' = E$. It follows that $c \in E'(a)$ implies $c \in E(a)$. Therefore $c = a$. This contradiction shows that the considered language is not completely adequate.

Proposition 26. There exists a completely adequate language which is not homogeneous.

PROOF. Let us consider the language used in the proof of Theorem 9. By Theorem 9, this language is not homogeneous. We shall show that it is completely adequate. It is easy to see that x E-dominates y only in the following cases: $x = b$, $y = d$; $x = a$, $y = b$; $x = d$, $y = b$; $x = c$, $y = d$; $x = c$, $y = b$; $x = a$; $y = d$. We have already proved (in the proof of Theorem 9) that $P(b)$ and $P(d)$ are P-equivalent. In fact, for any two words x and y, $P(x)$ and $P(y)$ are P-equivalent, since for any string of length exactly equal to 2 the corresponding P-structure is marked. In particular, $P(x)$ and $P(y)$ are P-equivalent in each of the six above cases in which x E-dominates y.

Proposition 27. There exists a homogeneous language which is neither amorphic nor completely adequate.

PROOF. Let $\Gamma = \{a, b, c, d, e, f\}$, $\Phi = \{ab, ac, de, fe, ff\}$, and $P = S$. The last equality shows that the considered language is perfect. Hence, by virtue of Proposition 15, it is homogeneous. We have $S(x) = \{x\}$ for $x \neq b$ and $x \neq c$ and $S(b) = \{b, c\}$. Thus, $P(b) = \{b, c\} \neq \{b\}$ and the language is not amorphic. To see that this language is not completely adequate, let us remark that, on one hand, d E-dominates f and, on the other hand, $P(d)$ and $P(f)$ are not P-equivalent, since $P(d) = \{d\}$, $P(f) = \{f\}$, the P-structure $P(f)P(f)$ is marked, whereas the P-structure $P(d)P(f)$ is not.

A word x is called *completely adequate from the left* (*from the right*) if for each y such that x E-dominates y (y E-dominates x) we have $y \in P'(x)$. A word x is called *completely adequate* if it is completely adequate from both the left and the right. It is easy to see that each word completely adequate from the left and each word completely adequate from the right are adequate. A language is said to be *locally completely adequate* (*from the right*) if each word is completely adequate (from the right).

Let us consider a word x such that there is no word y whose morphologic homonymy is less than the morphologic homonymy of x (in the sense of Chapter I, Section 2). This assertion means that there is no word y which E-dominates x and such that x does not E-dominate y. We shall say that such a word x is an *initial word*. Another presentation of this notion was given in Section 4, Chapter I. Denote by $G(a)$ the set of words b such that a E-dominates b. By definition, $G(a)$ is the *elementary grammatical category* generated by a; the same notion was introduced, in another way, in Section 4, Chapter I, where its linguistic significance was also explained. We recall that, with the customary interpretation adopted in a natural language, $G(a)$ is the set of all words whose set of grammatical values contains those of a. For instance, in printed French *beau* is an initial word; $G(beau)$ contains exactly those adjectives whose set of values contains those of *beau*: singular, masculine.

An initial word x is said to be *strongly adequate* if $G(x) \subseteq P'(x)$. If each initial word is strongly adequate, the considered language will be called a *strongly adequate language*.

It is obvious that the set $G(x)$ may be defined for any word x, initial or not; the linguistic significance just explained is true also if x is not an initial word. Even if x is not an initial word, $G(x)$ contains only words whose set of grammatical values contains those of x, and all such words. For instance, in printed French *mince* is not an initial word; however, $G(mince)$ contains only adjectives admitting the values singular, masculine, feminine, and all such adjectives [*beau* does not belong to $G(mince)$]. Let us then extend the property of strong adequacy to any word; a word x – initial or not – is said to be *strongly adequate* if $G(x) \subseteq P'(x)$. Consequently, a language will be called *locally strongly adequate* if each of its words – initial or not – is strongly adequate.

A family F is said to be *initial* if there is an initial word a such that $F = S(a)$. It is easy to see that each word belonging to an initial family is an initial word.

Lemma 4. In any language, and for any $x \in \Gamma$, there exists an initial family F such that each word of F E-dominates the word x.

PROOF. If $S(x)$ is an initial family, we may take $F = S(x)$. If not, there is a word x_1 which does not belong to $S(x)$ and which E-dominates x. If $S(x_1)$ is an initial family, we may take $F = S(x_1)$. If not, we find a word x_2 which is not in $S(x_1)$ and which E-dominates x_1. Continuing in this way, we obtain a sequence of words $x_1, x_2, \ldots, x_n, \ldots$ such that x_n E-dominates x_{n-1} but is not E-dominated by x_{n-1}. We shall prove that the sequence $\{x_n\}$ is finite; in this case, if x_m is the last term of the sequence, we may take $F = S(x_m)$. Thus Lemma 4 is proved. In this aim, it is enough to prove that the terms of $\{x_n\}$ are pairwise distinct. We reason by contradiction. If we would have two positive integers p and s, $p < s$, such that $x_p = x_s$, then, since the relation of E-domination is transitive, x_p would E-dominate x_r for any positive integer $r \leqslant s$; in particular, x_p would E-dominate x_{p+1}. On the other hand, we know that x_{p+1} E-dominates x_p. It follows that $x_{p+1} \in S(x_p)$, in contradiction to the definition of the sequence x_n.

Theorem 14. A language is locally strongly adequate if and only if it is strongly adequate.

PROOF. Let us assume that $\{\Gamma, P, \Phi\}$ is strongly adequate and let $x \in \Gamma$. If x is initial, we have, by hypothesis, $G(x) \subseteq P'(x)$. If x is not initial, then, in view of Lemma 4, there is an initial word y such that y E-dominates x. In view of the hypothesis, we have $G(y) \subseteq P'(y)$. On the other hand, since y E-dominates x, we have $G(x) \subseteq G(y)$. Hence $G(x) \subseteq P'(y)$ and $x \in P'(y)$. This implies $P'(x) = P'(y)$ and $G(x) \subseteq P'(x)$. Therefore x is strongly adequate, and the considered language is locally strongly adequate.

It is immediate that the converse is also true; each locally strongly adequate language is a strongly adequate language.

Proposition 28. A word x is strongly adequate if and only if it is completely adequate from the left.

PROOF. Obvious.

Proposition 29. Given a language L, the following three assertions are pairwise equivalent:

    (1) L is locally completely adequate;

    (2) L is locally strongly adequate;

    (3) L is locally completely adequate from the right.

PROOF. Let us prove that $(1) \Rightarrow (2)$. If $y \in G(x)$, then x E-dominates y and, in view of (1), $y \in P'(x)$. Let us now prove that $(2) \Rightarrow (1)$. If x E-dominates y, then $y \in G(x)$ and, in view of (2), $y \in P'(x)$. If y E-dominates x, then $x \in G(y)$ and, in view of (2), $x \in P'(y)$; the last relation implies that $y \in P'(x)$. Since it is obvious that $(1) \Rightarrow (3)$, it remains to prove that $(3) \Rightarrow (1)$. Let us admit (3). If x is E-dominated by y, then, since x is completely adequate from the right, we have $y \in P'(x)$. If x E-dominates z, then, since z is completely adequate from the right, we have $x \in P'(z)$. Hence $z \in P'(x)$. Thus, we have (1).

The local variant of Proposition 29 is not true, as is shown by the next two propositions.

Proposition 30. There exist a language $\{\Gamma, P, \Phi\}$ and a word $b \in \Gamma$ which is completely adequate from the right, but not strongly adequate.

PROOF. Let $\Gamma = \{a, b, c\}$, $P(a) = \{a, b\}$, $P(c) = \{c\}$, $\Phi = \{ab, ac, cc\}$. Since there is no word $x \neq b$ such that x E-dominates b, it follows that b is completely adequate from the right. On the other hand, since b E-dominates c, $P'(b) = P(b)$ and since c does not belong to $P(b)$, it follows that b is not strongly adequate.

Proposition 31. There exist a language $\{\Gamma, P, \Phi\}$ and a word $c \in \Gamma$ which is strongly adequate, without being completely adequate.

PROOF. Let us consider the language used in the proof of Proposition 30. Since $G(c) = \{c\}$, c is strongly adequate. Since b E-dominates c, but b does not belong to $P'(c)$ $(= P(c) = \{c\})$, we deduce that c is not completely adequate.

Theorem 15. A language is completely adequate if and only if it is strongly adequate.

PROOF. If a language is completely adequate, it is locally completely adequate from the left and, in view of Proposition 28, it is locally strongly adequate. Thus, by Theorem 14, the language is strongly adequate. Conversely, if a language is strongly adequate, then, in view of Theorem 14, it is locally strongly adequate and, by Proposition 29, it is locally completely adequate. Hence it is completely adequate.

REMARK. In the proof of Lemma 4, as in the proof of Theorem 14, essential use is made of the fact that the vocabulary Γ is finite. This general assumption was used only in very few situations. Theorem 15 also makes use, in an essential manner, of this assumption. As we shall see in the following, Theorem 15 ceases to be true if this assumption is removed.

Theorem 16. Let Γ be a countable infinite set. There exists a strongly adequate language over Γ, which is not completely adequate.

PROOF. Let $\Gamma = \{x_1, x_2, \ldots, x_n, \ldots\}$ with $x_i \neq x_j$ when $i \neq j$, and let $P = E$. By definition, the set Φ will contain all strings of the form $x_1 x_1 \ldots,$ $x_1 x_p$, where, denoting by n the number of occurrences of x_1, we have $n \geq 1$ and $p \leq n + 1$. We shall prove that $\{\Gamma, P, \Phi\}$ fulfills the required conditions.

Let $x_n \in \Gamma$. If $n = 1$, there is no positive integer $p \neq 1$ such that x_n E-dominates x_p. Indeed, in the marked string $x_1 x_1$ any replacement of the first term by x_p (with $p > 1$) yields an unmarked string.

Let us now suppose that $n > 1$. In this case, any marked string containing x_n is of the form $x_1 x_1 \ldots x_1 x_n$, where x_1 is repeated as least $n - 1$ times. For any $p \leq n$, the string

$$\underbrace{x_1 x_1 \cdots x_1 x_p}_{n-1 \text{ times}}$$

is marked. Hence x_n E-dominates x_p for each $p \leq n$. Let us now consider an integer $r > n$. The string

$$\underbrace{x_1 x_1 \cdots x_1 x_r}_{n-1 \text{ times}}$$

is unmarked. Therefore x_n E-dominates x_r for no integer $r > n$. It follows that, for $i < j$, x_j, E-dominates x_i, but x_i does not E-dominate x_j. Therefore, for each $x \in \Gamma$, we have $S(x) = \{x\}$, whereas no word x is initial. The condition of strong adequacy is thus satisfied in a trivial manner.

The language considered is not completely adequate. Indeed, if $i < j$, then $P(x_i)$ and $P(x_j)$ are not P-equivalent, since $P = E = S$ and, as we have just shown, x_j E-dominates x_i. Theorem 16 is proved.

Let us denote by $L(x)$ the set of all words y which E-dominate x and by $i(x)$ the number of initial families contained in $L(x)$. The linguistic significance of these objects follows from the fact that $i(x)$ measures the morphologic homonymy of x. Indeed, each initial family contained in $L(x)$ generates an elementary grammatical category containing x and, conversely: Each elementary grammatical category containing x is generated by an initial family contained in $L(x)$. Let us consider, for instance, the French adjectives *différent* and *heureux*. We have $L(différent) = S(différent)$, $L(heureux) = S(différent) \cup S(différents)$. (We are considering printed French, hence *différent* $\neq$ *différents*). It follows that $i(différent) = 1$ and $i(heureux) = 2$. These values agree with our intuition. The adjective *différent* has distinct forms in the masculine singular and masculine plural, whereas the corresponding forms of *heureux* are identical. Another, more significant situation, is that of Rumanian adjectives *frumos, subţire, vechi,* and *gri*. We have $L(frumos) = S(frumos)$, $L(subţire) = S(frumos) \cup S(frumoasă)$, $L(vechi) = S(frumos) \cup S(frumosi) \cup S(frumoase)$, $L(gri) = S(frumos) \cup S(frumoşi) \cup S(frumoasă) \cup S(frumoase)$. Hence $i(frumos) = 1$, $i(subţire) = 2$, $i(vechi) = 3$, and $i(gri) = 4$.

We shall now introduce a notion which is somewhat dual to that of locally strong adequacy. A word x is said to be *perfectly adequate* if $L(x) \subseteq P'(x)$. A language is said to be *locally perfectly adequate* if all its words are perfectly adequate.

Proposition 32. A locally perfectly adequate language is adequate, but there is an adequate language which is not locally perfectly adequate.

PROOF. The first assertion follows immediately from the inclusion $S(x) \subseteq L(x)$; the second assertion is proved by the following example: $\Gamma = \{a, b, c, d\}$, $P(a) = \{a\}$, $P(b) = \{b, c\}$, $P(d) = \{d\}$, $\Phi = \{ab, ac, ad, dd\}$. We have $S = P = P'$. Hence $S(x) = P'(x)$ for each $x \in \Gamma$, and the language is adequate. On the other hand, $L(d) = \{b, c, d\}$ and $P'(d) = \{d\}$. Hence d is not perfectly adequate.

A word x is said to be *final* if there is no word $y \neq x$, such that x E-dominates y, but y does not E-dominate x. The linguistic significance of this notion is that of a word with maximum morphologic homonymy, such as *ferox* in Latin or *souris* in French. We remark that there exist words which are both initial and final; the English adjectives in the positive form, such as *great*, are such words.

A language is said to be *perfectly adequate* if all its final words are perfectly adequate.

A family F is said to be *final* if there is a final word a such that $F = S(a)$. It is easy to see that each word belonging to a final family is a final word.

Lemma 4'. In any language and for any $x \in \Gamma$ there exists a final family F such that x E-dominates each word of F.

PROOF. We may adopt the idea of the proof of Lemma 4, by replacing "initial" by "final" and by changing the sense of all E-dominations.

Theorem 14'. A language is locally perfectly adequate if and only if it is perfectly adequate.

PROOF. We may adopt the idea of the proof of Theorem 14 by replacing "initial" by "final" and by changing the sense of all E-dominations. Instead of Lemma 4, we shall use Lemma 4'.

Proposition 28'. A word x is perfectly adequate if and only if it is completely adequate from the right.

PROOF. Obvious.

Proposition 29'. A language is completely adequate if and only if it is locally perfectly adequate.

PROOF. Let $\{\Gamma, P, \Phi\}$ be completely adequate. If $y \in L(x)$, then y E-dominates x. Hence $y \in P'(x)$, $L(x) \subseteq P'(x)$, and the language is locally perfectly adequate. Conversely, let $\{\Gamma, P, \Phi\}$ be locally perfectly adequate. If x E-dominates y, then $x \in L(y)$. Hence $x \in P'(y)$, and the language is completely adequate.

The local variant of Proposition 29' is not true. Indeed, we have Proposition 31'.

Proposition 31'. There exist a language $\{\Gamma, P, \Phi\}$ and a word $b \in \Gamma$ which is perfectly adequate, without being completely adequate.

PROOF. Let us consider the language used in the proof of Propositions 30 and 31. Since $L(b) = \{b\}$, b is perfectly adequate. On the other hand, since b E-dominates c, but c does not belong to $P'(b)$, it follows that b is not completely adequate.

Theorem 15′. A language is completely adequate if and only if it is perfectly adequate.

PROOF. This proof follows immediately from Theorem 14′ and Proposition 29′.

REMARK. In the proof of Lemma 4′ and, consequently, in the proofs of Theorems 14′ and 15′, essential use is made of the fact that Γ is finite. As is shown by the next theorem, Theorem 15′ ceases to be true if this assumption is removed.

Theorem 16′. Let Γ be a countable infinite set. There exists a perfectly adequate language over Γ which is not completely adequate.

PROOF. Let $\Gamma = \{x_1, \ldots, x_n, \ldots\}$ with $x_i \neq x_j$ when $i \neq j$, and let $P = E$. By definition, the set Φ will contain all strings of the form $x_1 x_1 \ldots x_1 x_p$, where, denoting by n the number of occurrences of x_1, we have $n \geq 1$ and $p \geq n + 1$. We shall prove that $\{\Gamma, P, \Phi\}$ fulfills the required conditions. Indeed, it is easy to see that x_m E-dominates x_{m+1} for each integer $m > 1$, whereas x_1 E-dominates no word x_i with $i > 1$. Hence x_1 is the only final word. But $L(x_1) = \{x_1\}$. Therefore $L(x_1) \subseteq P(x_1)$, and the considered language is perfectly adequate. On the other hand, if $i < j$, then x_j does not E-dominate x_i. Therefore, $P(x_i)$ and $P(x_j)$ are not P-equivalent. It follows that $P(x_i) = P'(x_i) = \{x_i\}$ for each positive integer i; but x_i E-dominates x_j for each $j > i$, although x_j does not belong to $P'(x_i)$ for $j \neq i$. Hence the considered language is not completely adequate.

Theorems 14, 14′, 15, 15′ and Propositions 28, 28′, 29, 29′ yield a further theorem.

Theorem 17. Given a language $L = \{\Gamma, P, \Phi\}$, the following conditions are pairwise equivalent:
  (1) L is completely adequate;
  (2) L is locally completely adequate from the left;
  (3) L is locally completely adequate from the right;
  (4) L is locally completely adequate;
  (5) L is strongly adequate;
  (6) L is locally strongly adequate;
  (7) L is perfectly adequate;
  (8) L is locally perfectly adequate.

5. Other Types of Adequate Languages

A language is said to be *well adequate* if for any pair of words x, y, such that x E-dominates y, we have that $P(x)$ P-dominates $P(y)$. The word x is said to be *well adequate from the left* (*right*) if for any word y such that x E-dominates y (y E-dominates x) $P(x)$ P-dominates $P(y)$ [$P(y)$ P-dominates $P(x)$]. A language is called *locally well adequate from the left* (*right*) if all its words are well adequate from the left (right). A language is said to be *locally well adequate* if it is locally well adequate from both the left and the right.

Proposition 33. Given a language $L = \{\Gamma, P, \Phi\}$, the following conditions are pairwise equivalent:

(1) L is well adequate;

(2) L is locally well adequate;

(3) L is locally well adequate from the left;

(4) L is locally well adequate from the right.

PROOF. Since the implications $(1) \Rightarrow (2)$, $(2) \Rightarrow (1)$, $(2) \Rightarrow (3)$, and $(2) \Rightarrow (4)$ are obvious, it remains to prove the implications $(3) \Rightarrow (1)$ and $(4) \Rightarrow (1)$. Let us suppose that L fulfills (3) and let x and y be two words such that x E-dominates y. Since x is well adequate from the left, it follows that $P(x)$ P-dominates $P(y)$. Hence (1) is satisfied. Let us now suppose that L fulfills (4) and let x and y be two words such that x E-dominates y. Since y is well adequate from the right, it follows that $P(x)$ P-dominates $P(y)$ and (1) is satisfied.

The local variant of Proposition 33 is not true, as shown by Proposition 34.

Proposition 34. There exist a language $\{\Gamma, P, \Phi\}$ and a word $c \in \Gamma$ such that c is well adequate from the left, but not from the right.

PROOF. Let $\Gamma = \{a, b, c\}$, $\Phi = \{ab, ac, cc\}$, $P(a) = \{a, b\}$, $P(c) = \{c\}$. Though b E-dominates c, $P(b)$ does not P-dominate $P(c)$, since $P(b)P(b)$ is a marked P-structure, whereas $P(c)P(b)$ is an unmarked P-structure. Thus c is not well adequate from the right. On the other hand, since there is no word $x \neq c$ which is E-dominated by c, it follows that c is well adequate from the left.

Proposition 35. Any completely adequate language is well adequate; any well adequate language is adequate.

PROOF. The first assertion is obvious. To establish the second assertion, let us remark that, if $x \in S(y)$, then x E-dominates y and y E-dominates x. Hence, since the language is well adequate, $P(x)$ P-dominates $P(y)$ and $P(y)$ P-dominates $P(x)$.

Proposition 36. There exists a well adequate language which is not completely adequate.

PROOF. Let $\Gamma = \{a, b, c, d\}$, $\Phi = \{ab, ac, ca, cc, cdd\}$, $P(a) = \{a, b\}$, $P(c) = \{c\}$, and $P(d) = \{d\}$. Given two distinct words x and y, x E-dominates y if and only if $x = b$ and $y = c$. Since $P(b)$ P-dominates $P(c)$, the language is well adequate. On the other hand, since $P(c)P(d)P(d)$ is a marked P-structure, whereas $P(b)P(d)P(d)$ is an unmarked one, it follows that $P(c)$ does not P-dominate $P(b)$. Hence the considered language is not completely adequate.

Proposition 37. There exists an adequate language which is not well adequate.

PROOF. Let $\Gamma = \{a, b, c\}$, $\Phi = \{ab, ac, cc\}$, $P(a) = \{a, b\}$, $P(c) = \{c\}$. Since $S(x) = \{x\}$ for each $x \in \Gamma$, the language is adequate. On the other hand, since b E-dominates c, but $P(b)$ does not P-dominate $P(c)$ (see the proof of Proposition 34), it follows that the considered language is not well adequate.

Proposition 38. There exists a well adequate language which is not homogeneous.

PROOF. Let us consider the language used in the proof of Theorem 9. Since all P-structures of length equal to 2 are marked and since the length of each marked string is equal to 2, it follows that this language is well adequate. On the other hand, in view of Theorem 9, this language is not homogeneous.

Proposition 39. There exists a homogeneous language which is not well adequate.

PROOF.   Let us consider the language used in the proof of Proposition 37. We have $P(a) \cap S(b) = \{b\}$, $P(b) \cap S(a) = \{a\}$, and $P(x) \cap S(y) = 0$ in all other cases. Hence, the language is homogeneous. On the other hand, in view of Proposition 37, this language is not well adequate.

A language is said to be *inversely adequate* if, for any words x and y such that x E-dominates y, $P(y)$ P-dominates $P(x)$. It is easy to see that each inversely adequate language is an adequate language.

6. Various Types of Linguistic Isomorphism

Let us consider two languages $L_1 = \{\Gamma_1, P_1, \Phi_1\}$ and $L_2 = \{\Gamma_2, P_2, \Phi_2\}$. We shall introduce some types of isomorphism between L_1 and L_2 as follows.

L_1 and L_2 are *paradigmatically isomorphic* (*P-isomorphic*) when there is a 1 : 1 mapping f of Γ_1 onto Γ_2, such that $y \in P_1(x)(x \in \Gamma_1, y \in \Gamma_1)$ if and only if $f(y) \in P_2(f(x))$ [in other words, $P_2(f(x)) = f(P_1(x))$].

L_1 and L_2 are *syntagmatically isomorphic* (*Φ-isomorphic*) when there is a 1 : 1 mapping g of Γ_1 onto Γ_2 such that $a_1 a_2 \cdots a_n \in \Phi_1$ ($a_i \in \Gamma_1$ when $1 \leq i \leq n$) if and only if $g(a_1)g(a_2) \cdots g(a_n) \in \Phi_2$.

L_1 and L_2 are *distributionally isomorphic* (*S-isomorphic*) when there is a 1 : 1 mapping h of Γ_1 onto Γ_2, such that $y \in S_1(x)(x \in \Gamma_1, y \in \Gamma_1)$ if and only if $h(y) \in S_2(h(x))$ [in other words, $S_2(h(x)) = h(S_1(x))$, where S_1 and S_2 are the partitions into families in L_1, L_2, respectively.

Given a string $u = a_1 \cdots a_n$ and a mapping $f : \Gamma_1 \rightarrow \Gamma_2$, we put $f(u) = f(a_1) \cdots f(a_n)$.

Proposition 40.   If L_1 and L_2 are syntagmatically isomorphic, they are distributionally isomorphic.

PROOF.   We shall show that $y \in S_1(x)$ ($x \in \Gamma_1, y \in \Gamma_1$), if and only if $g(y) \in S_2(g(x))$. Let $y \in S_1(x)$. This means that, for any two strings u and v, we have either

$$uxv \in \Phi_1, \qquad uyv \in \Phi_1, \tag{20}$$

or

$$uxv \notin \Phi_1, \qquad uyv \notin \Phi_1. \tag{21}$$

In view of the Φ-isomorphism, (20) implies

$$g(u)g(x)g(v) \in \Phi_2, \qquad g(u)g(y)g(v) \in \Phi_2, \qquad (20')$$

whereas (21) implies

$$g(u)g(x)g(v) \notin \Phi_2, \qquad g(u)g(y)g(v) \notin \Phi_2. \qquad (21')$$

Since u and v are arbitrary strings over Γ_1, $g(u)$ and $g(v)$ are arbitrary strings over Γ_2. Hence $g(y) \in S_2(g(x))$. Conversely, if the last relation is true, then, for any strings u, v over Γ_1, we have either (20') or (21'). Therefore, since L_1 and L_2 are Φ-isomorphic, we have either (20) or (21). Thus $y \in S_1(x)$.

Proposition 41. There exist two languages which are distributionally isomorphic, but not syntagmatically isomorphic.

PROOF.   Let $\Gamma_1 = \Gamma_2 = \{a, b\}$, $P_1 = P_2 = E$, $\Phi_1 = \{ab, ba\}$, $\Phi_2 = \{abb, baa\}$. It is easy to see that $S_1 = S_2 = E$. Hence $\{\Gamma_1, P_1, \Phi_1\}$ and $\{\Gamma_2, P_2, \Phi_2\}$ are S-isomorphic; but these languages are not Φ-isomorphic, since any string of Φ_1 is of length equal to 2 and any string of Φ_2 is of length equal to 3.

We shall also define another type of isomorphism, as follows. Two languages L_1 and L_2 are *PS-isomorphic* when there is a 1 : 1 mapping φ of Γ_1 onto Γ_2, such that $y \in P_1(x)(x \in \Gamma_1, y \in \Gamma_1)$ if and only if $\varphi(y) \in P_2(\varphi(x))$ and $y \in S_1(x)(x \in \Gamma_1, y \in \Gamma_1)$ if and only if $\varphi(y) \in S_2(\varphi(x))$.

The simplest example of two PS-isomorphic languages $\{\Gamma_1, P_1, \Phi_1\}$ and $\{\Gamma_2, P_2, \Phi_2\}$ is obtained when these languages are P-isomorphic, while $P_1 = S_1$ and $P_2 = S_2$. Another example is Proposition 42.

Proposition 42. There exist two PS-isomorphic languages $\{\Gamma_1, P_1, \Phi_1\}$ and $\{\Gamma_2 P_2, \Phi_2\}$, such that $P_1 \neq S_1$ and $P_2 \neq S_2$.

PROOF.   Let $\Gamma_1 = \{a, b, c\}$, $P_1(a) = \{a, b\}$, $\Phi_1 = \{ab, ac\}$, $\Gamma_2 = \{x, y, z\}$, $P_2(x) = \{x, z\}$, $\Phi_2 = \{xz, yz\}$. Define $\varphi : \Gamma_1 \to \Gamma_2$ as follows: $\varphi(a) = z$, $\varphi(b) = x$, $\varphi(c) = y$. We have $P_2(\varphi(a)) = \varphi(P_1(a))$, $P_2(\varphi(c)) = \varphi(P_2(c))$ and, since $S_1(b) = \{b, c\}$ and $S_2(x) = \{x, y\}$, it follows that $S_2(\varphi(a)) = \varphi(S_1(a))$, $S_2(\varphi(b)) = \varphi(S_1(b))$. Hence, the considered languages are PS-isomorphic, although $P_1 \neq S_1$ and $P_2 \neq S_2$.

It is obvious that, if L_1 and L_2 are PS-isomorphic, they are both P-isomorphic and S-isomorphic. The converse is not true, as shown in the next proposition.

Proposition 43. There exist two P-isomorphic and S-isomorphic languages which are not PS-isomorphic.

PROOF. Let $\Gamma_1 = \Gamma_2 = \{a, b, c, d\}$, $P_1(b) = \{b, c, d\} = P_2(b)$, $\Phi_1 = \{ab, ac, ad\}$, $\Phi_2 = \{ad, bd, cd\}$. By taking as f the identical mapping of Γ_1, it follows that L_1 and L_2 are P-isomorphic. Since $S_1 = P_1$ and $S_2(a) = \{a, b, c\}$, by taking a $1:1$ mapping h of Γ_1 onto Γ_2, such that $h(a) = d$, we get $S_2(h(x)) = h(S_1(x))$ for each $x \in \Gamma_1$. Hence L_1 and L_2 are S-isomorphic. On the other hand, L_1 and L_2 are not PS-isomorphic. Indeed, if a $1:1$ mapping φ of Γ_1 onto Γ_2 were to exist, such that $P_2(\varphi(x)) = \varphi(P_1(x))$ and $S_2(\varphi(x)) = \varphi(S_1(x))$ for any $x \in \Gamma_1$, we would have, on one hand, $\varphi(a) = a$ [since $P_1(a) = P_2(a) = \{a\}$], and, on the other hand, $\varphi(a) = d$ [since $S_1(x) = \{x\}$ only when $x = a$ and $S_2(x) = \{x\}$ only when $x = d$]. This contradiction shows that such a mapping φ does not exist. Hence L_1 and L_2 are not PS-isomorphic.

Proposition 44. If L_1 is amorphic, while L_1 and L_2 are P-isomorphic, then L_2 is also amorphic.

PROOF. Let $f : \Gamma_1 \to \Gamma_2$ be such that $P_2(f(x)) = f(P_1(x))$ for each $x \in \Gamma_1$. Since L_1 is amorphic, we have $P_1(x) = \{x\}$. Hence $P_2(f(x)) = f(x)$ for each $x \in \Gamma_1$. Therefore, L_2 is amorphic.

Proposition 45. If L_1 is purely paradigmatic, while L_1 and L_2 are S-isomorphic, then L_2 is also purely paradigmatic.

PROOF. Let $h : \Gamma_1 \to \Gamma_2$ be such that $S_2(h(x)) = h(S_1(x))$ for each $x \in \Gamma_1$. Since L_1 is purely paradigmatic, we have $S_1(x) = \{x\}$. Hence $S_2(h(x)) = h(x)$ for each $x \in \Gamma_1$ and therefore L_2 is purely paradigmatic.

Theorem 18. If L_1 is homogeneous, while L_1 and L_2 are PS-isomorphic, then L_2 is also homogeneous.

PROOF. By hypothesis, there exists a $1:1$ mapping φ of Γ_1 onto Γ_2, such that $P_2(\varphi(x)) = \varphi(P_1(x))$ and $S_2(\varphi(x)) = \varphi(S_1(x))$ for any $x \in \Gamma_1$. If $S_2(\varphi(x)) \cap P_2(\varphi(y)) \neq 0$, then, since φ is $1:1$, we have $\varphi(S_1(x)) \cap \varphi(P_1(y)) = \varphi(S_1(x)) \cap P_1(y)) \neq 0$. Hence $S_1(x) \cap P_1(y) \neq 0$. In view of the homogeneity of L_1, it follows that $S_1(y) \cap P_1(x) \neq 0$. Thus $\varphi(S_1(y) \cap P_1(x)) \neq 0$. But, again using the fact that φ is $1:1$, we have $\varphi(S_1(y) \cap P_1(x)) = \varphi(S_1(y)) \cap \varphi(P_1(x)) = S_2(\varphi(y)) \cap P_2(\varphi(x)) \neq 0$. Therefore L_2 is homogeneous.

Proposition 46. There exist two P-isomorphic and S-isomorphic languages L_1 and L_2 such that L_1 is homogeneous, but L_2 is not.

PROOF. Let us consider the languages used in the proof of Proposition 43. In view of that proposition, these two languages are P-isomorphic and S-isomorphic. Since $P_1 = S_1$, L_1 is homogeneous. On the other hand, since $P_2(a) \cap S_2(d) = 0$, whereas $P_2(d) \cap S_2(a) = \{b, c\}$, it follows that L_2 is not homogeneous.

The proof of Proposition 46 yields another.

Proposition 47. There exist two P-isomorphic and S-isomorphic languages L_1 and L_2 such that L_1 is both completely homogeneous and perfect, whereas L_2 is not homogeneous.

Proposition 48. If L_1 is simple, while L_1 and L_2 are PS-isomorphic, then L_2 is also simple.

PROOF. Since L_1 is simple, it is homogeneous. Hence, in view of Theorem 18, L_2 is homogeneous. It remains to prove that, for any $x \in \Gamma_1$, we have $P_2(\varphi(x)) \cap S_2(\varphi(x)) = \{\varphi(x)\}$. Since φ is $1:1$ and L_1 is simple, we have $P_2(\varphi(x)) \cap S_2(\varphi(x)) = \varphi(P_1(x)) \cap \varphi(S_1(x)) = \varphi(P_1(x) \cap S_1(x)) = \varphi(x)$. Hence L_2 is simple.

Proposition 49. There exist two P-isomorphic and S-isomorphic languages L_1 and L_2 such that L_1 is simple but L_2 is not.

PROOF. Let $\Gamma_1 = \{a, b, c, d, e, l\}$, $P_1(a) = \{a, b, c\}$, $P_1(d) = \{d, e, l\}$, $\Phi_1 = \{ab, db, ae, de, ac, al, dc, dl\}$, $\Gamma_2 = \{x, y, z, u, v, w\}$, $P_2(x) = \{x, y, z\}$, $P_2(u) = \{u, v, w\}$, $\Phi_2 = \{xz, yz, xu, yu, xv, xw, yv, yw\}$. It is easy to see that $S_1(a) = \{a, d\}$, $S_1(b) = \{b, e\}$, $S_1(c) = \{c, l\}$, $S_2(x) = \{x, y\}$, $S_2(z) = \{z, u\}$, $S_2(v) = \{v, w\}$. If $f(a) = x$, $f(b) = y$, $f(c) = z$, $f(d) = u$, $f(e) = v$, $f(l) = w$, then $P_2(f(m)) = f(P_1(m))$ for any $m \in \Gamma_1$. Hence L_1 and L_2 are P-isomorphic. If $h(a) = x$, $h(b) = z$, $h(c) = v$, $h(d) = y$, $h(e) = u$, $h(l) = w$, then $S_2(h(m)) = h(S_1(m))$ for any $m \in \Gamma_1$. Hence L_1 and L_2 are S-isomorphic. On the other hand, it is easy to see that $S_1(m) \cap P_1(n)$ contains exactly one word for any $m \in \Gamma_1, n \in \Gamma_1$. Therefore L_1 is simple, whereas $S_2(x) \cap P_2(x) = \{x, y\}$. Hence L_2 is not simple.

Theorem 19. There exist two PS-isomorphic languages L_1 and L_2 such that L_1 is adequate, while L_2 is not.

PROOF. Let $\Gamma_1 = \Gamma_2 = \{a, b, c, d\}$, $P_1(a) = P_2(a) = \{a, b\}$, $P_1(c) = P_2(c) = \{c, d\}$, $\Phi_1 = \{aa, bb, cc, ab, ba, ac, ca, bc, cb, a, b, c, d\}$, $\Phi_2 = \{ad, bd, cd\}$. We have $S_1(a) = S_2(a) = \{a, b, c\}$, $S_1(d) = S_2(d) = \{d\}$. Hence φ may be taken as the identical mapping of Γ_1, and we have $S_2(\varphi(x)) = \varphi(S_1(x))$, $P_2(\varphi(x)) = \varphi(P_1(x))$; L_1 and L_2 are PS-isomorphic. Since all P_1-structures of length not greater than 2 are marked, it follows that $P_1'(a) = \Gamma_1$. Hence L_1 is adequate. On the other hand, since $P_2(a)P_2(c)$ is a marked P_2-structure, while $P_2(a)P_2(a)$ is an unmarked one, it follows that $P_2'(a) = P_2(a) = \{a, b\}$. Hence $S_2(a)$ is not contained in $P_2'(a)$ and L_2 is not adequate.

Theorem 20. There exist two PS-isomorphic languages L_1 and L_2 such that L_1 is completely adequate, while L_2 is not adequate.

PROOF. The required languages L_1 and L_2 are precisely those used in the proof of Theorem 19. Indeed, since P_1' is the improper partition of Γ_1, it follows that L_1 is completely adequate.

Proposition 50. There exist two PS-isomorphic languages L_1 and L_2 such that L_1 is well adequate, while L_2 is not adequate.

PROOF. The proof of Theorem 20 also yields Proposition 50.

REMARK. Theorems 19 and 20 and Proposition 50 make the introduction of the following definitions natural.
   A language is said to be absolutely adequate (absolutely completely adequate, absolutely well adequate) if all its PS-isomorphic images are adequate (completely adequate, well adequate).
   A language is said to be absolutely inadequate (absolutely noncompletely adequate, absolutely nonwell adequate), if all its PS-isomorphic images are inadequate (noncompletely adequate, nonwell adequate). It would be interesting to see if such languages exist.
   It is immediate that any absolutely adequate (absolutely completely adequate, absolutely well adequate) language is adequate (completely adequate, well adequate); any absolutely inadequate (absolutely noncompletely adequate, absolutely nonwell adequate) language is inadequate (noncompletely adequate, nonwell adequate).
   Theorem 18 yields a further proposition.

Proposition 51. Any homogeneous language is absolutely adequate.

It would be interesting to find a necessary and sufficient condition that an adequate language be absolutely adequate. (Does there exist an absolutely adequate language which is not homogeneous?)

Propositions 46, 47, and 49 make the following definitions natural.

A language is said to be absolutely homogeneous (absolutely completely homogeneous, absolutely perfect, absolutely simple) if all its both P- and S-isomorphic images are homogeneous (completely homogeneous, perfect, simple).

A language is said to be absolutely nonhomogeneous (absolutely noncompletely homogeneous, absolutely nonperfect, absolutely nonsimple) if all its both P- and S-isomorphic images are nonhomogeneous (noncompletely homogeneous, nonperfect, nonsimple).

Propositions 12, 19, and 44 yield Proposition 52.

Proposition 52. Any amorphic language is absolutely perfect and absolutely simple (hence absolutely homogeneous).

Propositions 9, 21, and 45 yield Proposition 53.

Proposition 53. Any purely paradigmatic language is absolutely homogeneous and absolutely completely homogeneous.

It would be interesting to find necessary and sufficient conditions that a language be absolutely homogeneous (absolutely completely homogeneous, absolutely perfect, absolutely simple). The same problem arises for the absolutely nonhomogeneous (absolutely noncompletely homogeneous, absolutely nonperfect, absolutely nonsimple) languages.

A language for which $P = E$ and $S \neq E$ is an absolutely noncompletely homogeneous language. If $P \neq E$ and $S = E$, we obtain an absolutely nonperfect language.

We may define a new type of isomorphism, stronger than the PS-isomorphism. Two languages $L_1 = \{\Gamma_1, P_1, \Phi_1\}$ and $L_2 = \{\Gamma_2, P_2, \Phi_2\}$ will be called $P\Phi$-isomorphic if there exists a 1 : 1 mapping ψ of Γ_1 onto Γ_2, such that $P_2(\psi(x)) = \psi(P_1(x))$ for each $x \in \Gamma_1$ and such that the string $\psi(x_1)\psi(x_2)\cdots\psi(x_n)$ belongs to Φ_2 if and only if the string $x_1 x_2 \cdots x_n$ belongs to $\Phi_1 (x_i \in \Gamma_1$ when $1 \leq i \leq n)$.

Proposition 40 and the proof of Proposition 41 yield a further statement.

Proposition 54. If L_1 and L_2 are $P\Phi$-isomorphic, they are PS-isomorphic; but there exist two PS-isomorphic languages which are not $P\Phi$-isomorphic.

The $P\Phi$-isomorphism is sufficiently strong so that it preserves any property concerning a language and whose definition involves only the objects Γ, P, and Φ. In particular, we have Proposition 55.

Proposition 55. If L_1 and L_2 are $P\Phi$-isomorphic and L_1 is adequate (completely adequate, well adequate), then L_2 is also adequate (completely adequate, well adequate).

We may define a type of isomorphism which is weaker than the $P\Phi$-isomorphism, but stronger than the PS-isomorphism. Two languages $L_1 = \{\Gamma_1, P_1, \Phi_1\}$ and $L_2 = \{\Gamma_2, P_2, \Gamma_2\}$ will be called *PP'S-isomorphic* if there exists a $1 : 1$ mapping γ of Γ_1 onto Γ_2, such that $P_2(\gamma(x)) = \gamma(P_1(x))$, $P_2'(\gamma(x)) = \gamma(P_1'(x))$ and $S_2(\gamma(x)) = \gamma(S_1(x))$ for any $x \in \Gamma_1$.

Theorem 21. There exist two *PP'S*-isomorphic languages which are not $P\Phi$-isomorphic.

PROOF. Let $\Gamma_1 = \Gamma_2 = \{a, b, c\}$, $P_1 = P_2 = E$, $\Phi_1 = \{ab, ac, aa\}$, $\Phi_2 = \{aab, aac, aaa\}$. Define γ as the identical mapping of Γ_1. Since $S_1(a) = S_2(a) = \{a\}$ and $S_1(b) = S_2(b) = \{b, c\}$, we have $S_1 = S_2$. But $P_1' = E' = S_1$ and $P_2' = E' = S_2$. Hence $P_1' = P_2'$, and the three equalities defining the *PP'S*-isomorphism are obviously fulfilled. On the other hand, the considered languages are not Φ-isomorphic, since the length of any string of L_1 is equal to 2, whereas the length of any string of L_2 is equal to 3.

Since the definition of an adequate language uses the partitions P' and S exclusively, it is natural to define a new type of isomorphism as follows: Two languages L_1 and L_2 will be called *P'S-isomorphic* if there exists a $1 : 1$ mapping ω of Γ_1 onto Γ_2, such that $P_2'(\omega(x)) = \omega(P_1'(x))$ and $S_2(\omega(x)) = \omega(S_1(x))$. It is obvious that two *PP'S*-isomorphic languages are *P'S*-isomorphic, but the converse is not true, as is shown by Proposition 56.

Proposition 56. There exist two *P'S*-isomorphic languages which are not *PP'S*-isomorphic.

PROOF. Let $\Gamma_1, \Gamma_2, P_1, \Phi_1$, and Φ_2 be defined as in the proof of Theorem 21 and let $P_2(a) = \{a\}$, $P_2(b) = \{b, c\}$. Since $P_2(a)$ and $P_2(b)$ are not P-equivalent, we have $P_2 = P_2'$. On the other hand, $P_2' = S_2$, $P_1' = S_1$, and $S_1 = S_2$. Hence $P_1' = P_2'$. Taking for ω the identical mapping of Γ_1, it is easy to see that L_1 and L_2 are *P'S*-isomorphic. But L_1 and

L_2 are not P-isomorphic, since P_1 is the unit partition of Γ_1, whereas $P_2 \neq E$.

The following proposition is almost obvious.

Proposition 57. If L_1 and L_2 are two $P'S$-isomorphic languages and L_1 is adequate, then L_2 is also adequate.

PROOF. Since $S_1(x) \subseteq P_1'(x)$, we have $\omega(S_1(x)) \subseteq \omega(P_1'(x))$. Since $S_2(\omega(x)) = \omega(S_1(x))$ and $P_2'(\omega(x)) = \omega(P_1'(x))$, it follows that $S_2(\omega(x)) \subseteq P_2'(\omega(x))$. Since x is arbitrary in Γ_1, $\omega(x)$ is arbitrary in Γ_2 and Proposition 57 is proved.

Theorem 22. There exist two $PP'S$-isomorphic languages L_1 and L_2, such that L_1 is completely adequate, while L_2 is not.

PROOF. Let Γ_1, Γ_2, P_1, P_2, and Φ_2 be defined as in the proof of Theorem 21 and let $\Phi_1 = \{b, c, ab, ac, aa\}$. Given $x \in \Gamma_1$ and $y \in \Gamma_1$, x E-dominates y in L_1 if and only if either $x = b$, $y = c$, or $x = c$, $y = b$. Since $P_1(b)$ and $P_1(c)$ are P-equivalent, it follows that L_1 is completely adequate. On the other hand, c E-dominates a in L_2, but $P_2(c)$ and $P_2(a)$ are not P-equivalent, since c does not belong to $S_2(a)$. Finally, since $P_1 = P_2$, $P_1' = P_2'$, and $S_1 = S_2$, L_1 and L_2 are $PP'S$-isomorphic.

Continuing this investigation, one can define a new type of isomorphism, which preserves the property of being completely adequate. Similar problems arise for the well adequate languages and for the inversely adequate languages.

7. Some Characteristics of Finite-State Languages

Using some partitions of T and their derivatives, we shall give several characteristics of finite-state languages. We recall that a language $\{\Gamma, \Phi\}$ is a finite-state language if the number of T-distributional classes with respect to Φ is finite. The notions and results of Section 12, Chapter I, will be used. It is to be remarked that a finite-state language involves no paradigmatic structure, that is, no partition of Γ. In exchange, the study of finite-state languages requires a systematic investigation of some partitions of the free semigroup T generated by Γ. These partitions were studied in Section 12, Chapter I. For simplicity, we shall denote by the same letter an equivalence relation in T and the corresponding partition of T in equivalence classes.

Theorem 23. Let $L = \{\Gamma, \Phi\}$ be a language over Γ. The following propositions are pairwise equivalent:

(1) L is a finite-state language;

(2) There exists a congruence relation P in T, such that L is a union of P-equivalence classes, whereas the derivative of P is a finite partition;

(3) Given a congruence relation P in T, such that L is a union of P-equivalence classes, the derivative of P is a finite partition.

PROOF. Let us first show that $(1) \Rightarrow (2)$. Since L is a finite-state language, the sets $\mu(x)$ define a finite partition of T, each $\mu(x)$ being a T-distributional class. In view of Theorem 6, Chapter I, μ is a congruence relation in T. In view of Proposition 17, Chapter I, and of Corollary 2′, Chapter I, the partition in T-distributional classes is its proper derivative. Since for any $x \in \Phi$ and $y \in \mu(x)$ we have $y \in \Phi$, it follows that Φ is a union of T-distributional classes and (2) is proved by taking $P = \mu$.

We shall now prove that $(1) \Rightarrow (3)$. To this aim, we shall show that (1) implies $P' = \mu$; since (1) is equivalent to the finiteness of the partition μ, the implication considered will be proved.

Let x and y be such that $x \in T$, $y \in T$, and xPy. Since P is invariant from the right, we have $xwPyw$ for any $w \in T$. This implies, in view of the invariance from the left, that $zxwPzyw$ for any $z \in T$. Since L is the union of some P-equivalence classes and since $zxw \in L$, it follows that $zyw \in L$. We have thus proved that xPy and $zxw \in L$ imply $zyw \in L$. On the other hand, since P is symmetric, it follows that xPy and $zyw \in L$ imply $zxw \in L$. Therefore, xPy implies $x\mu y$ and the partition P is finer than μ. Since, in any case, the unit partition E of T is finer than P and regularly finer than μ (see Proposition 17, Chapter I), it follows that E is regularly finer than P. In view of Lemma 6, Chapter I, and again using Proposition 17, Chapter I, we find that $E' = P' = \mu$.

Let us assume (2). As we have just proved, $P' = \mu$. Hence μ is a finite partition and (1) is true. Thus, $(2) \Rightarrow (1)$.

Let us assume (3). Since μ is a congruence relation in T (see Theorem 6, Chapter I) and L is the union of some μ-equivalence classes, we may take in (2) $P = \mu$. Hence $(3) \Rightarrow (2)$, and Theorem 23 is proved.

The following theorem is well-known in automata theory and uses some notions and results of Section 12, Chapter I.

Theorem of Myhill and Rabin-Scott. The following assertions are pairwise equivalent:
   (1) $L = \{\Gamma, \Phi\}$ is a finite-state language;
   (4) The number of δ-equivalence classes is finite;
   (5) The number of λ-equivalence classes is finite.

All known proofs of this theorem use notions and facts concerning the generation of a finite-state language and therefore is beyond the object of the present book. (See [29, 32].) Since assertions (1), (4), and (5) involve only the distributional structure of the language L, it would be very interesting to find a direct proof of the above theorem, that is, a proof which uses no notion and no fact concerning the generation of L by a finite-state machine.

With the aid of the above theorem of Myhill and Rabin-Scott and using the notions and results concerning the derivative from the right (from the left) of a partition of T, we may obtain some new characterizations of finite state languages. We give here, without proof, a theorem of [29], p. 123.

Theorem 24. Let $L = \{\Gamma, \Phi\}$. The following assertions are pairwise equivalent:
   (1) L is a finite-state language;
   (6) There exists an invariant from the right equivalence relation r in T, such that Φ is the union of some r-equivalence classes, while the derivative from the right of the partition r is a finite partition of T;
   (7) [is obtained from (6), by changing "right" to "left"];
   (8) Given an invariant from the right equivalence relation r in T, such that Φ is the union of some r-equivalence classes, the derivative from the right of the partition r is a finite partition of T;
   (9) [is obtained from (8), by changing "right" to "left"].

Other interesting characterizations of finite-state languages, which do not involve the manner of their generation, are given by Chomsky and Miller [7], by Rabin and Scott [32], and by Kleene [21]. These studies are continued in [1, 8, 9, 10]. We shall give without proof, a result of Kleene, Myhill, and Rabin and Scott [32].

Let us denote by $cl(A)$ the union $A^0 \cup A^1 \cup \cdots \cup A^n \cup \cdots$, where A is a subset of the free semigroup T generated by Γ, A^0 contains only the zero string, and $A^n = A \cdot A \cdots A$, with A being repeated n times. Then, we have a further theorem

Theorem of Kleene, Myhill and Rabin-Scott. The class of finite-state languages over Γ is the smallest class τ of languages (sets of strings) over Γ, such that the following three conditions are fulfilled:

(1) if A is a finite language over Γ, then $A \in \tau$;

(2) if $A \in \tau$ and $B \in \tau$, then $A \cup B \in \tau$ and $AB \in \tau$;

(3) if $A \in \tau$, then $cl(A) \in \tau$.

It would be interesting to find, for this theorem, a proof which does not involve automata structure.

In conclusion, we shall give some nontrivial examples of finite-state languages and an example of language which is not a finite-state language. In this aim, we shall consider some languages introduced by Curry [11].

Let $\Gamma_1 = \{a, b\}$ and $\Phi_1 = \{a, ab, abb, \ldots, ab^n, \ldots\}$, where $b^n = b \cdot b \ldots b$, b being repeated n times. The language $\{\Gamma_1, \Phi_1\}$ is a model of the system of positive integers. It may be defined inductively, as follows: $a \in \Phi_1$; if $x \in \Phi_1$, then $xb \in \Phi_1$ (x being a string over Γ_1). It is easy to see that $\{\Gamma_1, \Phi_1\}$ is a finite-state language. Indeed, on one hand, all marked strings belong to the same T-distributional class; on the other hand, all semimarked strings also belong to the same T-distributional class. Since the parasitic strings form a single T-distributional class, it follows that we have only three T-distributional classes with respect to Φ_1. Hence $\{\Gamma_1, \Phi_1\}$ is a finite-state language.

Let $\Gamma_2 = \{a, b, c\}$ and $\Phi_2 = \{ab^n caq^m\}_{n,m \in N}$, where N is the set of nonnegative integers. If c is interpreted as the equality relation, each string of Φ_2 may be interpreted as an assertion, which is true if and only if $n = m$. One can prove that $\{\Gamma_2, \Phi_2\}$ is also a finite-state language [30].

Let $\Phi_3 = \{ab^n cab^n\}_{n \in N}$. This is the set of theorems. It is not a finite-state language since, for $m \neq n$, the strings b^m and b^n belong to different T-distributional classes. Hence we have infinitely many T-distributional classes with respect to Φ_3. Another proof of this fact is given in [30].

Some characterizations of finite-state languages which involve the manner of their generation are given by Chomsky [8, 9].

8. Some Applications to Natural Languages

We intend to discuss the various types of artificial languages studied above, in connection with some situations in natural languages. In the following, Γ will be the vocabulary of a natural language L, $P(x)$ (for $x \in \Gamma$) will be the set of all flectional forms of x, and Φ will be the set of well-formed sentences in L. Sometimes, Φ will be only a subset of well-formed sentences (this fact will be mentioned explicitly).

It is necessary first to anticipate an idea which will be explored in Chapter III: In any language, for every word x, the set $P'(x)$ is considered the set of all words belonging to the same part of speech as x. According to this interpretation of the derivative partition P', an adequate language is a language where the following implication is true: If two words x and y are in identical distribution, then x and y belong to the same part of speech. We do not know a natural language which is not adequate. Some examples which seem to contradict this assertion are based on the traditional point of view concerning the parts of speech. For instance, the Rumanian words *un* and *acest* are in identical distribution, although, according to the traditional grammar, *un* is an indefinite article, whereas *acest* is a demonstrative adjective.

If the property of adequacy is general enough to belong to every natural language, the property of homogeneity is too restrictive to be fulfilled by a natural language. But in every natural language there are some homogeneous words, and we may obtain very large homogeneous portions of natural languages if we ignore some words and restrict the set of marked strings.

We recall first that each amorphic word is a homogeneous word. The so-called *singularia tantum* (nouns without plural form) and *pluralia tantum* (nouns without singular form) are, in both English and French, amorphic words, hence homogeneous words. Such examples are the words *water, iron, air, sun, south, physics, politics, news* in English, *moeurs* in French. Other French amorphic words are such nouns as *bras, noix, nez, souris,* whose singular and plural forms coincide.

It is interesting to remark that almost all nonamorphic nouns are, both in English and French, nonhomogeneous. The English word *book* is not homogeneous, since $sun \in S(book)$, $books \in P(book)$, and $P(sun) \cap S(books) = 0$. Passing to French, the only marked strings considered will be those of the form noun + qualifying adjective or qualifying adjective + noun. The French word *mouches* is not homogeneous, since $moeurs \in S(mouches)$, $mouche \in P(mouches)$, and $P(moeurs) \cap S(mouche) = 0$. It is easy to see that the existence of singularia tantum and of pluralia tantum is precisely the reason for nonhomogeneity of almost all English and French nouns. If we ignore the singularia tantum and the pluralia tantum, almost all English nouns and all French nouns become homogeneous. Let us prove this assertion. The English word *book* becomes a homogeneous word. Indeed, we have $P(book) = \{book, books\}$, whereas every word belonging to $S(book)$ is a singular noun form. Thus, if $y \in S(book)$, the plural form y' of y belongs to $S(books)$. Hence, if $z \in P(book)$, then $S(z) \cap P(y) \neq 0$.

Under the same assumption of ignoring the singularia and pluralia tantum, all French nouns are homogeneous. (We deal throughout with printed French.) If $x = maison$, then $P(maison) = \{maison, maisons\}$ and $S(maison)$ contains only feminine singular noun forms, without homonymy of number. If $y \in P(maison)$ and $z \in S(maison)$, then $S(y) \cap P(z)$ contains either the word z (when $y = x$), or the plural form of z (when $y = maisons$). Hence $S(y) \cap P(z) \neq 0$. Therefore, *maison* is a homogeneous word. In the same way, we can prove that *maisons*, *garçon*, and *garçons* are homogeneous words. The other types of French nouns, such as *souris*, are amorphic, and hence homogeneous.

A quite different situation arises in Rumanian and in Latin, when the only marked strings considered are those of the form noun + qualifying adjective or qualifying adjective + noun. Here, the existence of non-homogeneous nouns is due to the specific structure of grammatical gender. Let us consider the Rumanian noun *scaune*. We have $c\breve{a}r\c{t}i \in S(scaune)$, $scaun \in P(scaune)$, and $P(c\breve{a}r\c{t}i) \cap S(scaun) = 0$. Hence the word *scaune* is not homogeneous. In the same way we may prove that all plural forms of neuter or feminine nouns and all singular forms of neuter or masculine nouns are nonhomogeneous words. This non-homogeneity is due to the coincidence, in the singular, between masculine and neuter noun forms, and in the plural, between feminine and neuter noun forms. If we decompose every paradigm of a neuter noun into two paradigms, one containing all singular forms, the other containing all plural forms, the above proof of nonhomogeneity fails and the neuter nouns, such as *scaun* and *scaune*, become homogeneous; but the nonhomogeneity of several words persists, owing to the existence of singularia and pluralia tantum. Indeed, we have $aur \in S(pom)$, $pomi \in P(pom)$, and $P(aur) \cap S(pomi) = 0$, since *aur* is singulara tantum. Therefore "pom" is nonhomogeneous. We also have $icre \in S(c\breve{a}r\c{t}i)$, $carte \in P(c\breve{a}r\c{t}i)$, and $P(icre) \cap S(carte) = 0$, since *icre* is plurale tantum. Therefore *c\breve{a}r\c{t}i* is nonhomogeneous. A removal of this nonhomogeneity is obtained if we decompose every noun paradigm into two disjoint new paradigms, one singular, the other plural.

The only Rumanian nouns whose homogeneity is assured even without decomposing the noun paradigms are such words as *ochi, arici, învăţătoare*, *nume*, which present homonymy between singular and plural forms.

It is scarcely probable that a natural language could be entirely homogeneous. There are degrees of nonhomogeneity and Revzin shows [33, 34, pp. 88–89] that Russian is more nonhomogeneous than Polish and Polish more than Czech. In general, the nonhomogeneity of nouns in Slavic languages is very great [33]. The Russian nouns are non-homogeneous, as is proved by the example $P(stul) \cap S(lampy) = \{stulja\}$, $S(stul) \cap P(lampy) = 0$ [33]. This nonhomogeneity is because (Kulagina [22], p. 214) the plural forms of Russian adjectives are the same for all genders; this implies that all Russian plural noun forms of a determined case belong to the same distributional class, whereas the Russian singular noun forms of a determined case are distributed in several families, each family containing only noun forms of a determined gender. The nonhomogeneity of Czech nouns is proved by the example $P(st\mathring{u}l) \cap S(tu\check{z}ky) = \{stoly\}$, $P(tu\check{z}ky) \cap S(st\mathring{u}l) = 0$. Other examples in Czech may be found in [18] and [31]. Extensive remarks concerning various distinctions between the Slavic languages are made in [34], pp. 88–89 and in [33] using nonhomogeneous words.

It is easy to see that all homogeneous words we have considered above are simple words. Indeed, the condition $S(x) \cap P(x) = \{x\}$ is always fulfilled when x is an English, French, or Rumanian noun and if we ignore stylistic or parallel variants. But there are other paradigms, for instance, verb paradigms, which do not always fulfill this condition. In Rumanian, we have *mergeai* $\in S(mergi) \cap P(mergi)$. Hence most verb forms are not simple. In [34], p. 87, is given the example of the nonsimple German words *sagt* and *sprach*. Indeed, we have *sagte* $\in P(sagt) \cap S(sagt)$ and *spricht* $\in S(sprach) \cap P(sprach)$. An interesting example of nonsimplicity occurs in Estonian [33, 34, p. 86].

Although, as shown by Propositions 24 and 27, the property of complete adequacy is effectively stronger than adequacy, it is hard to find an adequate word in a natural language which is not completely adequate; since the words of a natural language are adequate, it follows that a natural language is completely adequate.

There are some situations which seem to contradict the complete adequacy of natural languages. Such a situation concerns the relation between nouns and pronouns. It is known that a noun x may be replaced by a corresponding pronoun y. Hence it seems that x *E*-dominates y, although the noun and the pronoun are different parts of speech. But in fact, a noun may be replaced by a pronoun only in certain contexts, and thus a noun does not E-dominate a pronoun. For instance, let us consider the well-formed Russian strings *čolovek rabotaet* and *harošii čolovek*. The replacement of *čolovek* by *on* in the first string yields a well-formed string, but the same replacement in the second string does not yield a well-formed one. Consider then the well-formed French strings *Jean mange* and *c'est pour Jean ce livre*. The replacement of *Jean* by *il* in the first string yields a well-formed string; the same replacement in the second string does not yield a well-formed one.

A similar situation arises when a noun and a corresponding pronoun present different types of morphologic homonymy. For instance, the Rumanian noun form *numele* is both a singular and a plural form, whereas the corresponding pronouns (*el* and *ele*) are different. Thus, if we consider the well-formed Rumanian strings *numele este frumos* and *numele sînt frumoase,* we remark that the replacement of *numele* by *el* in the first string yields a well-formed Rumanian string. The same replacement in the second string does not yield a well-formed one. This situation will be studied from another point of view in the following chapter.

Very significant from the standpoint of natural languages is Theorem 17, which asserts, among other things, that a language is completely adequate if and only if it is strongly adequate. It is not hard to see what constitutes the strong adequacy of a natural language. We have already seen that the elementary grammatical category $G(x)$ generated by an initial word x contains exactly those words y such that every grammatical value of x is also a grammatical value of y. But these "grammatical values" are nothing more than the morphemes, in the sense of glossematic acceptance of this term. (See, in this respect, the fundamental works of Hjelmslev [15–17]). An elementary grammatical category is the projection, in the plane of expression, of a certain saturated combination of morphemes (such a combination is called sometimes a *grammatem*). It is natural to expect that all words which are projections of the same type of morphemic combination belong to the same part of speech.

It should be remarked, however, that contrary to appearances, one can have some noncompletely adequate portions of a natural language. Indeed, the complete adequacy of a word involves a complex net of relations concerning the entire respective language. If we diminish this complexity, the complete adequacy may be removed. Consider, for instance, the following portion of French: $\Gamma = \{je,\ chante,\ chantais,\ parler,\ marcher,\ vite\}$, $P(je) = \{je\}$, $P(chante) = \{chante,\ chantais\}$, $P(parler) = \{parler\}$, $P(marcher) = \{marcher\}$, $P(vite) = \{vite\}$, $\Phi = \{je\ chante,\ je\ chantais,\ parler\ vite,\ marcher\ vite,\ marcher\ marcher\}$.

It is easily seen that this language is $P\Phi$-isomorphic to the language used in the proof of Proposition 27. Hence, by virtue of Propositions 27 and 55, it follows that this portion of French is not completely adequate. A similar noncompletely adequate portion may be detected in Rumanian, if we take $\Gamma = \{eu, merg, mergeam, omul, repede, alearg\u{a}\}$, $P(x) = \{x\}$ if $x \in \Gamma$ and $x \neq merg, mergeam, P(merg) = \{merg, mergeam\}$, $\Phi = \{eu\ merg, eu\ mergeam, omul\ alearg\u{a}, repede\ alearg\u{a}, repede\ repede\}$.

The adequacy may also be removed when we consider only a portion of a natural language. Consider, for instance, the following portion of Latin: $\Gamma = \{vis, domus, res, rei\}$, $P(vis) = \{vis\}$, $P(domus) = \{domus\}$, $P(res) = \{res, rei\}$, $\Phi = \{vis\ domus, res\ domus, vis\ rei, res\ rei\}$. It is easy to see that this language is $P\Phi$-isomorphic to the language used in the proof of Proposition 1. Hence, by virtue of Propositions 1 and 55, it follows that this portion of Latin contains no adequate word. A similar nonadequate portion may be detected in Rumanian, by taking $\Gamma = \{casa, p\u{a}m\^{i}ntului, omul, omului\}$, $P(casa) = \{casa\}$, $P(p\u{a}m\^{i}ntului) = \{p\u{a}m\^{i}ntului\}$, $P(omul) = \{omul, omului\}$, $\Phi = \{casa\ p\u{a}m\^{i}ntului, omul\ p\u{a}m\^{i}ntului, casa\ omului, omul\ omului\}$. Since such small portions permit us to isolate some phenomena and to study them in a pure form, the types of formal languages studied in this chapter may be of considerable utility.

Since, in view of Proposition 35, every completely adequate language is well adequate, it follows that any natural language is well adequate. But it is not hard to find small well adequate portions of a natural language, which are not completely adequate. Consider for instance the following fragment of Latin: $\Gamma = \{rei, rerum, diei, civis\}$, $P(rei) = \{rei, rerum\}$, $P(diei) = \{diei\}$, $P(civis) = \{civis\}$, $\Phi = \{rei\ rerum, rei\ diei, diei\ rei, diei\ diei, diei\ civis\ civis\}$. This fragment, which may be useful in the study of the genitive case, is $P\Phi$-isomorphic to the language used in the proof of Proposition 36. Hence, in view of Propositions 36 and 55, it is well adequate, but not completely adequate.

If, from the Latin fragment just considered, we retain the subfragment $\Gamma = \{rei, rerum, diei\}$, $P(rei) = \{rei, rerum\}$, $P(diei) = \{diei\}$, $\Phi = \{rei\ rerum, rei\ diei, diei\ diei\}$, we get a $P\Phi$-isomorphic image of the language used in the proof of Proposition 37. Hence, in view of Propositions 37 and 55, it follows that this Latin subfragment is adequate, but not well adequate.

Very significant from the standpoint of a natural language are the finite-state languages. Every finite fragment of a natural language is a finite-state language. Indeed, we have a theorem.

Theorem 25. If Φ is a finite set of strings over Γ, then $\{\Gamma, \Phi\}$ is a finite-state language.

PROOF. Since Φ is finite, it follows that there are only finitely many semimarked strings with respect to Φ. Therefore, there are only finitely many T-distributional classes with respect to Φ, each of which contains at least one marked or semimarked string. Since all parasitic strings with respect to Φ belong, obviously, to the same T-distributional class, it follows that $\{\Gamma, \Phi\}$ is a finite-state language.

Chomsky discussed ([6], Section 2) some possibilities of describing a natural language with the aid of an infinite sequence of finite-state grammars. Its description involves finite-state Markov processes. On the other hand, Ceitin proposed a notion of convergence of a sequence of models to a given object [5]. Let $\Phi_1, \Phi_2, \ldots, \Phi_n, \ldots$ be a sequence of languages over Γ and let Φ be a language over Γ. We shall say that $\{\Phi_n\}(1 \leqslant n < \infty)$ converges to Φ if the following two conditions are fulfilled:

(1) $\Phi = \bigcup_{1 \leqslant n < \infty} \Phi_n$;

(2) given a string $x \in \Phi$, there exists a positive integer n_x such that, if $n > n_x$, then $x \in \Phi_n$.

We shall say that Φ_n is an n-approximation of Φ.

Theorem 26. Given a language Φ over Γ, there exists a sequence $\{\Phi_n\}(1 \leqslant n < \infty)$ of finite-state languages over Γ, which converges to Φ.

PROOF. We may define Φ_n as the set of those strings of Φ whose length is not greater than n. It follows that Φ_n is a finite language. Hence, in view of Theorem 25 it is a finite-state language. Conditions (1) and (2) are obviously fulfilled.

Starting with a finite fragment of a natural language, we easily get infinite fragments which are finite-state languages. One method is use of the so-called coordination rapports, formed by simple concatenation or by such words as *and*. The coordination rapports preserve the finite-state language structure. The exact meaning of this assertion is given by the next two theorems.

Proposition 58. If $\{\Gamma, \Phi_1\}$ and $\{\Gamma, \Phi_2\}$ are finite-state languages, then $\{\Gamma, \Phi_1\Phi_2\}$ is a finite-state language.

PROOF.   It follows immediately from the theorem of Kleene, Myhill, and Rabin–Scott (Section 2; see also [21, 32]).

Theorem 27.   Let $\{\Gamma, \Phi\}$ be a finite-state language and let a be a fixed word in Γ. Denote by Φ_1 the smallest subset of T satisfying the following properties:
   (1) $\Phi \subseteq \Phi_1$;
   (2) if $x \in \Phi_1$ and $y \in \Phi_1$, then $xay \in \Phi_1$.
   Then $\{\Gamma, \Phi_1\}$ is a finite-state language.

PROOF.   It is easy to see that Φ_1 contains exactly those strings having the form $x_1 a x_2 \ldots x_{i-1} a x_i \ldots, x_{n-1} a x_n$, where $n \geqslant 1$ and $x_i \in \Phi$ when $1 \leqslant i \leqslant n$. It follows that Φ_1 is a T-distributional class with respect to Φ_1. As far as the semimarked strings with respect to Φ_1 are concerned, they form at most three T-distributional classes, as follows: The first class contains all semimarked strings which have a as the first term but not as last term. The second class contains all semimarked strings which have a as last term but not as first term. The third class contains all semimarked strings which have a as both first and last term. Since all parasitic strings belong to the same T-distributional class, the number of T-distributional classes with respect to Φ_1 is at most equal to 5, and so Φ_1 is a finite-state language.

REMARKS.   Theorem 27 was proved in another way, ([29], p. 203). It is interesting to remark that even if Φ is finite, but nonempty, the corresponding set Φ_1 is always an infinite language.
   Starting with a finite fragment Φ of English and using the conjunction $a = and$, the corresponding fragment Φ_1 of English, obtained by Theorem 27, is a finite-state language. A similar result holds when we consider a finite collection of conjunctions such as *and* and *or* in English, *i* and *ili* in Russian, *und* and *oder* in German, *et* and *ou* in French. Indeed, it is not difficult to prove the following generalization of Theorem 27.

Theorem 27'.   Let $\{\Gamma, \Phi\}$ be a finite-state language and let $a_1, a_2, \ldots, a_p$ be p distinct fixed words in Γ. Denote by Φ_1 the smallest subset of T satisfying the following properties:
   (1) $\Phi \subseteq \Phi_1$;
   (2) if $x \in \Phi_1$ and $y \in \Phi_1$, then $xa_1y \in \Phi_1$, $xa_2y \in \Phi_1, \ldots, xa_py \in \Phi_1$.
   Then $\{\Gamma, \Phi_1\}$ is a finite-state language.
   Other syntactic constructions, such as conditional subordination,

do not preserve the finite-state language structure. The exact meaning of this assertion is given by Theorem 28.

Theorem 28. Let $\{\Gamma, \Phi\}$ be a finite-state language and let a and b be two distinct fixed words in Γ. Denote by Φ_2 the smallest subset of T satisfying the following properties:

(1) $\Phi \subseteq \Phi_2$;

(2) if $x \in \Phi_2$ and $y \in \Phi_2$, then $axby \in \Phi_2$. Then $\{\Gamma, \Phi_2\}$ is not a finite-state language.

PROOF. It is easy to see that Φ_2 contains all strings which have the form $a^n x (by)^n$, where x and y are arbitrary elements in Φ and n is any nonnegative integer. Let us admit that $\{\Gamma, \Phi_2\}$ is a finite-state language. Then there exists an infinite sequence $P_1 < P_2 < \cdots < P_s < \cdots$ of positive integers, such that the strings $(by)^{P_1}, (by)^{P_2}, \ldots, (by)^{P_s}, \ldots$ belong to the same T-distributional class with respect to Φ_2. It follows that all strings of the form $a^{P_1} x (by)^{P_s} (s = 1, 2, \ldots)$ belong to Φ_2; this is a contradiction and so Theorem 28 is proved.

REMARKS. Theorem 28 was given in [29], pp. 204–205. It must be remarked that Φ_2 is always infinite, even if Φ is a finite (nonempty) language. If Φ is a finite fragment of English and if $a = if$ and $b = then$, then Φ_2 is the infinite fragment of English obtained from Φ by conditional subordination.

Other related questions are discussed in [1] and [29].

Of great interest from the standpoint of a natural language is the fact that all Boolean operations preserve the finite-state language structure. Indeed, we have a further theorem.

Theorem 29. The class τ of the finite-state languages over a fixed vocabulary Γ is a Boolean algebra.

PROOF. Let $\Phi \subseteq T$. It is obvious that the T-distributional classes with respect to Φ are identical to the T-distributional classes with respect to $T - \Phi$. This implies that for any finite-state language Φ, the complementary language $T - \Phi$ is also a finite-state language.

Consider now two finite-state languages Φ_1 and Φ_2. We shall show that $\Phi_1 \cap \Phi_2$ is a finite-state language. Denote by $C_1, C_2, \ldots, C_{n_1}$ the T-distributional classes with respect to Φ_1 and by $C'_1, C'_2, \ldots, C'_{n_2}$ the T-distributional classes with respect to Φ_2. Let $x \in C_i \cap C'_j$ and $y \in C_i \cap C'_j$ ($1 \leqslant i \leqslant n_1$, $1 \leqslant j \leqslant n_2$). Given two strings u and v such that $uxv \in \Phi_1 \cap \Phi_2$, we have $uyv \in \Phi_1$ (since x and y belong to C_i) and $uyv \in \Phi_2$ (since x and y belong to C'_j). Hence $uyv \in \Phi_1 \cap \Phi_2$. Conversely, it is easily seen that $uyv \in \Phi_1 \cap \Phi_2$ implies $uxv \in \Phi_1 \cap \Phi_2$. It follows that each intersection set $C_i \cap C_j'$ is contained in a T-distributional class with respect to $\Phi_1 \cap \Phi_2$. Since the number of these intersection sets is at most equal to $n_1 n_2$ (and thus finite), we see that $\Phi_1 \cap \Phi_2$ is a finite-state language.

Since $\Phi_1 - \Phi_2 = \Phi_1 \cap (T - \Phi_2)$ and $\Phi_1 \cup \Phi_2 = T - [(T - \Phi_1) \cap (T - \Phi_2)]$, it follows that τ is a Boolean algebra.

REMARK. Theorem 29 was proved in another way [32].

Passing to various types of linguistic isomorphism, we can remark that we have already used the $P\Phi$-isomorphism in the illustration of complete or noncomplete adequate languages and of well or non-well adequate languages. The importance of various types of linguistic isomorphism is given by such results as Proposition 44, Theorem 18, Propositions 45, 48, 55, and 57, which permit us to detect the type of a language when we know its type of isomorphic image. For instance, most English noun paradigms are P-isomorphic to the corresponding French noun paradigms; if $\Gamma_1 = \{book, books, teacher, teachers\}$, $\Gamma_2 = \{livre, livres, professeur, professeurs\}$, $P_1(book) = \{book, books\}$, $P_1(teachers) = \{teacher, teachers\}$, $P_2(livre) = \{livre, livres\}$, $P_2(professeur) = \{professeur, professeurs\}$, and $f : \Gamma_1 \to \Gamma_2$ is such that for $x \in \Gamma_1$, $f(x)$ is the French translation of x, then $P_2(f(x)) = f(P_1(x))$ for each $x \in \Gamma_1$.

Other illustrations of the various types of linguistic isomorphism will be discussed in the next two chapters.

9. Bibliographic Remarks

The traditional linguistic typology, discussed in many papers (see, for instance, [2, 3, 12, 13, 24, 35] and, especially, [36]) may be correlated with the above considerations, although they are based on the morphemic structure of words. For instance, homogeneity and strong adequacy are, in some ways, approximations of the so-called agglutinative languages (such as Hungarian) whereas the amorphic languages are approximations of the corresponding amorphic languages in the traditional linguistic typology.

The notions of adequate language and that of homogeneous language were introduced by Uspenskii [37]. Theorems 1, 4, 8, and 10 are given, without proof, in [37]. The notion of simple language was introduced by Kulagina [22]. Corollary 3 is a generalization of a theorem of [22], where the same result is given for simple languages. Theorems 1, 4, 8 and 10 are proved, in another way, by Revzin [34]. Some of the results contained in this chapter were previously proved [26–28]. For French illustrations of various questions discussed above the work of Braffort may be used [4]; for Hungarian illustrations, those of Kiefer [19, 20]. Finite-state languages are the first step in the so-called Chomsky hierarchy; see, in this respect, the very clear synthetic expositions of Gross [14] and Kurki-Suonio [23]. Some notions and results of the first two chapters are discussed, using the algebra of binary relations, by Lenskoi [25].

REFERENCES

1. Y. Bar-Hillel and E. Shamir, Finite state languages: formal representations and adequacy problems. *Bull. Res. Council Israel, Sec. F,* **8,** 155–166 (1960).
2. C. E. Bazell, "Linguistic Typology." London, 1958.
3. E. Benveniste, La classification des langues. *Conf. Inst. linguistique Paris* **11,** 1954.
4. P. Braffort, Éléments de linguistique mathématique. "Enseignement préparatoire aux techniques de la documentation automatique." Euratom Bruxelles, 1960, pp. 51–85.
5. G. S. Ceitin, Construction of mathematical language models (in Russian). *Dok. na Conf. Obrabotke Inform.* Moscow, 1961.
6. N. Chomsky, Three models for the description of language. *IRE Trans. Inform. Theory* 2 (3), 113–124 (1956).
7. N. Chomsky and G. A. Miller, Finite-state languages, *Inform. Control* **1,** (1), 91–112 (1958).
8. N. Chomsky, On certain formal properties of grammars. *Inform. Control* **2,** 137–167 (1959).
9. N. Chomsky, Formal properties of grammars, *in* "Handbook of Mathematical Psychology," Vol. II (R. D. Luce, R. R. Bush, and E. Galanter, eds.), Wiley, New York, pp. 323–418 (1963).
10. K. Čulik, Some notes on finite-state languages and events represented by finite automata using labelled graphs. *Časopis pro pestovani mat.* **86,** 43–55 (1961).
11. H. B. Curry, Some logical aspects of grammatical structure, *in* "Structure of Language and Its Mathematical Aspects." *Proc. Symp. Appl. Math.* **12,** 56–68 (1961).
12. J. H. Greenberg, The nature and uses of linguistic typologies. *Intern. J. Am. Linguistics* **23,** (27), (1957).
13. J. H. Greenberg, A quantitative approach to the morphological typology of languages. *Intern. J. Am. Linguistics* **26,** (3), (1960).
14. M. Gross, Linguistique mathématique et langages de programmation. *Rev. Française Traitement l'Inform. [Chiffres]* **6,** 231–253 (1963).
15. L. Hjelmslev, "Principes de grammaire générale." Copenhagen, 1928.
16. L. Hjelmslev, Essai d'une théorie des morphèmes. Actes du IVe Congrès international des linguistes, Copenhagen, 1938, pp. 140–151.
17. L. Hjelmslev, "Prolegomena to a theory of language." Baltimore, 1953.
18. A. Jaurisová and M. Jauris, Užiti teorie množin v jazykovědě. *Slovo a slovesnost* **21,** (1960).
19. F. Kiefer, A halmazelmelet egy nyelvészeti alkalmasásához. "Altalános Nyelvészeti Tanulmányok" (Zs. Telegdi, ed.). *Akadémiai Kiadó,* Budapest, 1963.
20. F. Kiefer, Halmazelméleti és matematikai logikai modellek a nyelvtudományban, *in* "A matematikai nyelvészet és a gépi forditás kérdései" (L. Kalmár and Zs. Telegdi, eds.). *Akadémiai Kiadó,* Budapest, 1964.

21. S. C. Kleene, "Representation of Events in Nerve Nets and Finite Automata Studies (C. E. Shannon and J. McCarthy, eds.). Princeton Univ. Press, Princeton, N. J., 1956.

22. O. S. Kulagina, On one method of defining grammatical notions on the basis of set theory (in Russian). *Probl. Kibernetiki* **1**, 203–214 (1958).

23. R. Kurki-Suonio, On some sets of formal grammars. *Ann. Acad. Sci. Fennicae, Ser. A, S. Math. No. 349*, 1–32 (1964).

24. P. S. Kuznecov, "The morphologic classification of languages" (in Russian). Izd. Moskovskogo gosud. universiteta, 1954.

25. D. N. Lenskoi, On some applications of the algebra of binary relations in linguistics (in Russian). *Uch. Zap. Kabardinsk. Gos. Univ., Ser. Fiz.-Mat. No.16*, Nal'cik, 1962.

26. S. Marcus, Asupra unui model logic al părţii de vorbire. *Studii Cercetări Mat.* **13** (1), 37–62 (1962).

27. S. Marcus, Typologie des langues et modèles logiques. *Acta Math. Acad. Sci. Hung.* **14** (3–4), 269–281 (1963).

28. S. Marcus, Langues complètement adéquates et langues régulières. *Z. Math. Logik Grund. Math.* **10** (1), 7–13 (1964).

29. S. Marcus, "Gramatici şi automate finite." Editura Academiei R. P. R., Bucureşti, 1964.

30. S. Marcus, Sur un modèle de H. B. Curry pour le langage mathématique. *Compt. Rend.* **258** (7), 1954–1956 (1964).

31. L. Nebesky and P. Sgall, *Algebraická lingvistika*, în "Cesty moderní jazykovědy, Jazykověda a automatizace." Československá společnost pro šíření politických a vědeckých znalostí. Orbis, Praha, 1964, pp. 72–102.

32. M. O. Rabin and D. Scott, Finite automata and their decision problems. *IBM J. Res. Develop.* **3** (2), 114–125 (1959).

33. I. I. Revzin, On some notions from the so-called set theoretic conception of language (in Russian). *Vopr. Jazykoznanija* **1960** (6), 88–94.

34. I. I. Revzin, "Language Models" (in Russian). Izd. Akad. Nauk SSSR, Moskow, 1962.

35. H. Spang-Hansen, "Probability and structural classification in language description." Copenhagen, 1959.

36. B. A. Uspenskiï, "The Principles of the Structural Typology" (in Russian). Izd. Moskovskogo gosud. universiteta, 1962.

37. V. A. Uspenskiï, On defining the part of speech in the set-theoretic system of language (in Russian). *Byull. Obed. Probl. Mašinnogo Perevoda No. 5*, 22–26 (1957).

NOTE ADDED IN PROOF

A class of languages more general than finite state languages, which admit an intrinsic characterization, was introduced by V. Amar and G. Putzolu (On a family of linear grammars, *Inform. Control* **7**, 283–291 (1964); Generalizations of regular events, *Inform. Control* **8**, 56–63 (1965)). New aspects of linguistic typology are studied by B. A. Uspenskii ("Structural typology of languages" (in Russian), Izd. Nauka, Moskow, 1965). Some problems concerning the *P*-isomorphism, the *S*-isomorphism and the *PS*-isomorphism are solved by B. Zelinka (Sur le *P*-isomorphisme et le *S*-isomorphisme des langues homogènes, to appear in *Sbornik Vysoké školy strojní a textilní v Liberci*; Sur le *PS*-isomorphisme des langues, to appear in *Z. Math. Logik Grund. Math.*).

Chapter III

Parts of Speech and Syntactic Types

1. Introduction

The notion of part of speech is fundamental to linguistics and many authors have tried to give a rigorous description of it. Such great linguists as Bröndal, Hjelmslev [22], Kurylowicz [28], and Harris [17] have explored this problem and the contemporary models of the part of speech use essentially the results of their investigations. Applied linguists are very interested in an adequate decomposition of the vocabulary into parts of speech (see, for instance, the paper of Ruvinskii [43]). The difficulties in this area arise from the very complex character of this notion, which is a mixture of semantic, morphologic, and syntactic factors. The proportion in which each of these factors occurs in the structure of the parts of speech depends on the language considered. For instance, the parts of speech in English are dominated by syntactic factors, whereas in Slavic languages, in Latin, and in Rumanian, the morphologic (paradigmatic) aspects of the parts of speech are essential. This is perhaps one of the reasons for the great variety of logical models proposed for the notion of parts of speech. We shall present in this chapter two points of view concerning the logical description of the parts of speech. The first point of view, having its starting point in the preceding chapters, has been developed by Kulagina [27], Uspenskii [46], Revzin [40, 41], and Marcus [33] and concerns especially flectional languages. The second has its origin in mathematical logic, in the work of Lesniewski [32] and Ajdukiewicz [1]; it has been developed by Bar-Hillel [3], Lambek [29–31], Bar-Hillel et al. [6], and Chomsky [11] and concerns especially the syntactic aspects of the parts of speech.

2. Parts of Speech as Cells of the Derivative Partition P'

Let us consider a language $\{\Gamma, P, \Phi\}$ and let us interpret Γ as the vocabulary of a natural language L, $P(x)$ (for $x \in \Gamma$) as the set of all inflected forms of x, and Φ as the set of all well-formed sentences in L. Such an interpretation does not correspond to the real situation in a natural language, since the condition that P be a partition of Γ is not fulfilled. For instance, the English word *excuse* belongs to $P(excuses)$, but also to $P(excused)$. We may avoid this difficulty by considering the union $P(excuse) \cup P(excused)$ as a single cell of P, but such an interpretation ignores the linguistic nature of the word *excuse* which is both a noun and a verb. In other languages, such as Rumanian, Russian, or Latin, the existence of two distinct sets $P(x_1)$ and $P(x_2)$ with a nonvoid intersection is less frequent than in English. We shall ignore, in the following, this possibility; two homonymous forms such as *free* (adjective) and *free* (verb) will be considered distinct and their corresponding P-cells disjoint.

It should be remarked that the partial homonymy of two words is possible even if these words belong to the same part of speech. Consider, for instance, the Rumanian words *cap* (chief) with the plural form *capi, cap* (head) with the plural form *capete,* and *cap* (cape) with the plural form *capuri.* Each of these words is a noun and we have three mutually distinct P-cells: $P(capi)$, $P(capete)$, $P(capuri)$ such that $cap \in P(capi) \cap P(capete) \cap P(capuri)$. But such a situation will remain outside the model presented further on.

With the interpretation considered above, the cells of the derivative partition P' will be adopted as a model of first approximation of the parts of speech in L. The adequacy of this model depends upon the nature of L; in this respect, we shall consider the linguistic typology investigated in the preceding chapter. In any case, it must be remarked that in such a model two distinct parts of speech are always disjoint. Although this condition is not fulfilled in a natural language, we may find large enough portions where the absence of homonymy makes it possible that two distinct parts of speech are always disjoint.

We begin by discussing a short fragment of French, which will enable us to explain the model adopted.

Let us put $\Gamma = P(un) \cup P(professeur) \cup P(maison) \cup P(grand) \cup P(petit) \cup P(vieux) \cup P(écrit) \cup P(arrive)$ [where $P(un) = \{un, une, le, la, les, des\}$, $P(professeur) = \{professeur, professeurs\}$, $P(maison) = \{maison, maisons\}$, $P(grand) = \{grand, grande, grands, grandes\}$, $P(petit) = \{petit, petits, petite, petites\}$, $P(vieux) = \{vieux, vieille, vieilles\}$, $P(écrit) = \{écrit, écrivent, écrivait, écrivaient, écrira, écriront\}$, $P(arrive) = \{arrive, arrivent, arrivait, arrivaient, arrivera, arriveront\}$] and $\Phi_1 = \{un$ *professeur arrive, le professeur arrive, un professeur arrivait, le professeur arrivait, un professeur arrivera, le professeur arrivera, une maison arrive, la maison arrive, une maison arrivait, la maison arrivait, une maison arrivera, la maison arrivera, un grand professeur arrive, un petit professeur arrive, un vieux professeur arrive, le grand professeur arrive, le petit professeur arrive, le vieux professeur arrive, un grand professeur arrivait, un petit professeur arrivait, un vieux professeur arrivait, le grand professeur arrivait, le petit professeur arrivait, le vieux professeur arrivait, un grand professeur arrivera, un petit professeur arrivera, un vieux professeur arrivera, le grand professeur arrivera, le petit professeur arrivera, le vieux professeur arrivera, une grande maison arrive, une petite maison arrive, une vieille maison arrive, la grande maison arrive, la petite maison arrive, la vieille maison arrive, une grande maison arrivait, une petite maison arrivait, une vieille maison arrivait, la grande maison arrivait, la petite maison arrivait, la vieille maison arrivait, une grande maison arrivera, une petite maison arrivera, une vieille maison arrivera, la grande maison arrivera, la petite maison arrivera, la vieille maison arrivera}.*

Let us denote by Φ_2 the set of strings obtained from the strings of Φ_1 by replacing the various forms of the verb *arrive* by the corresponding forms of the verb *écrit*. Let us denote by Φ_3 and by Φ_4 the sets of strings obtained from the strings of Φ_1 and Φ_2 respectively, by replacing every form of singular by the corresponding form of plural (*un* and *une* by *des*, *le* and *la* by *les*, *professeur* by *professeurs*, *grand* by *grands*, *arrive* by *arrivent*, etc.) Finally, put $\Phi = \Phi_1 \cup \Phi_2 \cup \Phi_3 \cup \Phi_4$. It is easy to see that Φ contains only such strings as are grammatically correct French sentences over the vocabulary Γ. A sentence such as *une maison arrive*, which seems to be incorrect, is doubtful from a semantic standpoint, but perfectly correct from a grammatical one. Conversely, we may have a grammatically incorrect sentence, which is semantically clear. The Rumanian sentence *oamenii este deştepţi* fulfills these conditions.

3. Grammaticality

In fact, the problem of grammaticality is more complex and many authors have tried to reduce this notion to a simpler one (see, for instance, Revzin [42]). Other authors, such as Chomsky [8], have introduced the concept of *degree of grammaticalness* [10, 11]. Instead of partitioning the free semigroup T generated by Γ into the two subsets Φ (well-formed sentences) and $T - \Phi$ (nongrammatical strings), one defines a set Φ^* of perfectly well-formed sentences and all strings in T are partially ordered in terms of degree of grammaticalness. Strings not in Φ^* can still often be understood, in terms of the structural descriptions assigned to these strings. A string x of $T - \Phi^*$ can be understood by imposing on it an interpretation, guided by its analogies to sentences of Φ^*; x is called a *deviant sentence*, and the measure of this deviation from grammatical regularities gives the degree of grammaticalness of x. A detailed discussion of these and other related questions may be found in some papers by Ziff [49, 50], Katz [26], Jakobson [24], Hill [19], and Putnam [39]. But the most rigorous attempt to give a precise description of the various degrees of grammaticalness has been made by Miller and Chomsky ([37], pp. 443–449). We shall not broach here the details of these points of view, since the notion of grammaticalness will not be used in this chapter. But it should be remarked that some authors do not agree with the above interpretation of the marked strings. For instance, Gross ([16], p. 35) considers the French sentence *le loup mange le problème* is not grammatically correct, since one of the rules of the French grammar says that an abstract word cannot be a direct object of a verb such as *mange*. Hence, for Gross, the French sentences *une maison arrive* and *une maison écrit* are probably grammatically noncorrect sentences, in contrast to our above assumption.

4. Linguistic Explanation of the Model of Part of Speech

Let us now return to the fragment of French considered. It is easy to see that for each $a \in \Gamma$ the P-cell $P(a)$ contains only flectional forms of a. For some words a, $P(a)$ does not contain all flectional forms of a, but only those which occur in the sentences of Φ.

There is a general simple property fulfilled in every natural language: If two words a and b belong to the same paradigm [that is: if $b \in P(a)$], they belong to the same part of speech. According to this rule, a rigorous definition of the parts of speech should regard every part of speech as the union of some P-cells. The problem is now the following: Given two words a and b, under which conditions may we consider that $P(a)$ and $P(b)$ are contained in the same part of speech? The answer given by Kulagina [27] says: if and only if $P(a)$ and $P(b)$ are P-equivalent, that is, if and only if $b \in P'(a)$. (See, for these notions and notations, Section 1.5.).

Let us verify, on the above fragment of French, the legitimacy of this convention. We shall show that *maison* $\in P'(professeur)$, *petit* $\in P'(grand)$, *vieux* $\in P'(grand)$, and *écrit* $\in P'(arrive)$.

Let us put $\mathscr{P}_{11} = P(un)$, $\mathscr{P}_{12} = P(un) \ P(grand)$, $\mathscr{P}_{13} = P(un) \ P(petit)$, $\mathscr{P}_{14} = P(un) \ P(vieux)$, $\mathscr{P}_{21} = P(arrive)$, and $\mathscr{P}_{22} = P(écrit)$. It is easy to see that every marked P-structure containing the P-cell $P(professeur)$ has one of the forms $\mathscr{P}_{1i} \ P(professeur) \ \mathscr{P}_{2j}$, where $1 \le i \le 4$ and $1 \le j \le 2$. We shall show that the P-structures obtained from $\mathscr{P}_{1i} \ P(maison) \ \mathscr{P}_{2j}$ ($1 \le i \le 4$, $1 \le j \le 2$) are all marked. We have: *une* $\in P(un)$, *maison* $\in P(maison)$, *arrive* $\in P(arrive)$, and *une maison arrive* is a marked string. Hence $\mathscr{P}_{11} \ P(maison) \ \mathscr{P}_{21}$ is marked; *grande* $\in P(grand)$ and *une grande maison arrive* is a marked string. Thus $\mathscr{P}_{12} \ P(maison) \ \mathscr{P}_{11}$ is marked; *petite* $\in P(petit)$ and *une petite maison arrive* is a marked string. Hence $\mathscr{P}_{13} \ P(maison) \ \mathscr{P}_{11}$ is marked; *vieille* $\in P(vieux)$ and *une vieille maison arrive* is a marked string. Thus $\mathscr{P}_{14} P(maison) \ \mathscr{P}_{11}$ is marked; since all the above strings remain marked when *arrive* is replaced by *écrit*, it follows that $\mathscr{P}_{1i} P(maison)\mathscr{P}_{22}$ is a marked P-structure for every i such that $1 \le i \le 4$. Since all marked P-structures containing $P(maison)$ are of the form $\mathscr{P}_{1i}P(maison) \ \mathscr{P}_{2j}$ ($1 \le i \le 4$, $1 \le j \le 2$), it follows that $P(professeur)$ and $P(maison)$ are P-equivalent. It follows immediately that $P'(professeur) = P(professeur) \cup P(maison)$.

Let us put $\mathscr{P}_{31} = P(professeur) \ P(arrive)$, $\mathscr{P}_{32} = P(professeur) \ P(écrit)$, $\mathscr{P}_{33} = P(maison) \ P(arrive)$, $\mathscr{P}_{34} = P(maison) \ P(écrit)$. It is easy to see that every marked P-structure containing the P-cell $P(grand)$ has one of the forms $\mathscr{P}_{11} \ P(grand) \ \mathscr{P}_{3i}$ ($1 \le i \le 4$). Since $\mathscr{P}_{11} \ P(petit) \ \mathscr{P}_{3i}$ is a marked P-structure for every i such that $1 \le i \le 4$ and since every marked P-structure containing $P(petit)$ has one of these forms, it follows that $P(petit)$ and $P(grand)$ are P-equivalent. Similarly, we may see that $P(vieux)$ and $P(grand)$ are P-equivalent. It follows immediately that $P'(grand) = P(grand) \cup P(petit) \cup P(vieux)$.

Let us put $\mathscr{P}_{41} = P(un)P(grand)P(professeur)$, $\mathscr{P}_{42} = P(un)P(petit)$ $P(professeur)$, $\mathscr{P}_{43} = P(un)P(vieux)P(professeur)$, $\mathscr{P}_{44} = P(un)P(grand)$ $P(maison)$, $\mathscr{P}_{45} = P(un)P(petit)P(maison)$, $\mathscr{P}_{46} = P(un)P(vieux)P(maison)$. It is easy to see that every marked P-structure containing the P-cell $P(arrive)$ has one of the forms $\mathscr{P}_{4i}P(arrive)$ ($1 \le i \le 6$). Since $\mathscr{P}_{4i}P(écrit)$

is a marked P-structure for $1 \leq i \leq 6$ and since every marked P-structure containing $P(\acute{e}crit)$ has one of these forms, it follows that $P(arrive)$ and $P(\acute{e}crit)$ are P-equivalent. It is easy to see that $P'(arrive) = P(arrive) \cup P(\acute{e}crit)$.

$P'(un)$ [$= P(un)$] is the part of speech called *article*; $P'(grand)$ is the part of speech called *adjective*; $P'(professeur)$ is the part of speech called *noun*; $P'(arrive)$ is the part of speech called *verb*.

It is now clear that the parts of speech have no absolute character; they depend upon the set Φ of marked strings (that is, they depend upon the syntax of the language) and upon the partition P(that is, upon the morphology of the language). The parts of speech of a natural language are a function of P and Φ, since we never take into account all possible sentences and paradigms of a natural language. In every concrete problem we consider a fragment complex enough to give a good approximation of the natural language and simple enough to permit a systematic and detailed investigation.

Let us consider another example, concerning Rumanian. If we intend to define only two parts of speech, the noun and the adjective, we may use the following language $\{\Gamma, P, \Phi\}$. $\Gamma = P(cas\breve{a}) \cup P(pom) \cup P(film) \cup P(frumos) \cup P(mare) \cup P(nou)$, where $P(cas\breve{a}) = \{cas\breve{a}, casei, casa, casele, caselor, case\}$, $P(pom) = \{pom, pomului, pomul, pomi, pomilor, pomii\}$, $P(film) = \{film, filme, filmului, filmele, filmelor, filmul\}$, $P(frumos) = \{frumos, frumoas\breve{a}, frumoşi, frumoase\}$, $P(mare) = \{mare, mari\}$, $P(nou) = \{nou, nou\breve{a}, noi\}$. The set Φ will contain, by definition, all well-formed Rumanian strings of length equal to 2, on the vocabulary Γ. [Any string of the form aa ($a \in \Gamma$) will be considered unmarked.]

We may show that $P'(cas\breve{a}) = P(cas\breve{a}) \cup P(pom) \cup P(film)$ and $P'(frumos) = P(frumos) \cup P(mare) \cup P(nou)$ [$P'(cas\breve{a})$ will define the noun, whereas $P'(frumos)$ will define the adjective]. Let us first show that $P(cas\breve{a})$ and $P(pom)$ are P-equivalent. The P-structure $P(cas\breve{a})$ $P(frumos)$ is marked, since *cas\breve{a} frumoas\breve{a}* is a well-formed string. The P-structure $P(pom)P(cas\breve{a})$ is marked, since *pomul casei* is a well-formed string. But every marked P-structure containing the P-cell $P(cas\breve{a})$ has one of the forms $P(x)$ $P(cas\breve{a})$ and $P(cas\breve{a})$ $P(x)$, where $x \in P(frumos) \cup P(mare) \cup P(nou) \cup P(cas\breve{a}) \cup P(pom) \cup P(film)$. On the other hand, each of the P-structures $P(x)P(pom)$ and $P(pom)P(x)$ is marked. Conversely, each marked P-structure containing the P-cell $P(pom)$ has one of the forms $P(x)P(pom)$, $P(pom)P(x)$; therefore, $P(cas\breve{a})$ and $P(pom)$ are P-equivalent.

In a similar manner one can prove that $P(casă)$ and $P(film)$ are P-equivalent; $P(frumos)$, $P(mare)$, and $P(nou)$ are also P-equivalent. Let us show that $P(casă)$ and $P(frumos)$ are not P-equivalent. Indeed, if we consider the marked P-structure $P(casă)P(frumos)$ and if we replace $P(casă)$ by $P(frumos)$, we obtain the unmarked P-structure $P(frumos)P(frumos)$.

It should be remarked that $P'(casă)$ contains nouns of different genders, whereas $P'(frumos)$ contains adjectives of different types from the standpoint of their morphologic homonymy.

To make the structure of the parts of speech clearer and more flexible, we shall sometimes consider the part of speech of a word a not the union of all P-cells P-equivalent to $P(a)$, but the set of all P-cells P-equivalent to $P(a)$. We shall use these two acceptations alternatively, without specification.

We may now explain the profound reason for the above definition of parts of speech. Let us consider a language $L = \{\Gamma, P, \Phi\}$. To this language we may associate another one, namely, the language $P(L) = \{\Gamma_1, P_1, \Phi_1\}$, where Γ_1 is the set of all P-cells in L, P_1 is the partition of Γ_1 into P-equivalence classes (with respect to L), and Φ_1 is the set of all marked P-structures (with respect to L). The language $P(L)$ will be called the P-abstraction of L. This level of abstraction is precisely the level at which the logical structure of the parts of speech may be understood, since they are nothing more than the distributional classes in $P(L)$. Indeed, the P'-cells of L are precisely the distributional classes of $P(L)$. In this manner, all results concerning distributional classes may be used in the investigation of the parts of speech.

Given a language $L = \{\Gamma, P, \Phi\}$, we may consider the P-abstraction of its P-abstraction. If $P(L) = \{\Gamma_1, P_1, \Phi_1\}$, then $P(P(L)) = \{\Gamma_2, P_2, \Phi_2\}$, where Γ_2 is the set of P_1-cells [with respect to $P(L)$], P_2 is the partition of Γ_2 into P_1-equivalence classes [with respect to $P(L)$], and Φ_2 is the set of marked P_1-structures [with respect to $P(L)$]. It is easy to see that every P_1-cell in $P(L)$ is a P'-cell in L and, conversely, every P'-cell in L is a P_1-cell in $P(L)$. Further, every P_2-cell in $P(P(L))$ is a P_1'-cell in $P(L)$. Hence it is a P''-cell in L. Conversely, every P''-cell in L is a P'_1-cell in $P(L)$. Hence it is a P_2-cell in $P(P(L))$. In view of Corollary 2, Chapter I, we have, in $L, P' = P''$. Therefore two distinct P_1-cells are never equivalent in $P(L)$. Since Γ_2 is precisely the set of P'-equivalence classes in L, it follows that P_2 is the unit partition of Γ_2. The paradigmatic structure of $P(P(L))$ is thus trivial. It may be ignored, and we get $P(P(L)) = \{\Gamma_2, \Phi_2\}$, that is $P(P(L))$ is a language whose words are the parts of speech in L, whereas the marked strings are those sequences of parts of speech which are possible in L.

In some sense, the P-abstraction of the P-abstraction of a language is its maximum degree of abstraction. Indeed, if we intend to form the language $P(P(P(L))) = \{\Gamma_3, P_3, \Phi_3\}$, we find that $\Gamma_3 = \Gamma_2$ (since P_2 is the unit partition of Γ_2), $\Phi_3 = \Phi_2$, and $P_3 = P_2$; thus $P(P(P(L))) = P(P(L))$.

Given a part of speech $\mathscr{P}$, it is interesting to find a class $\mathscr{C}$ of contexts which fulfills the following conditions: (1) for each word $a \in \mathscr{P}$ there is a context $(x, y) \in \mathscr{C}$, such that $xay \in \Phi$; (2) given a word b which is not in $\mathscr{P}$, there is no context $(u, v) \in \mathscr{C}$ such that $ubv \in \Phi$. The class $\mathscr{C}$ is said to be a *diagnostic class* of $\mathscr{P}$. This notion owes its origin to Harris [17].

It stands to reason that the most interesting diagnostic classes of $\mathscr{P}$ are those containing the minimum number of contexts. If there is a diagnostic class $\mathscr{C}$ of $\mathscr{P}$ containing a single context (x, y), then (x, y) is said to be a *diagnostic context* of $\mathscr{P}$. The existence of diagnostic contexts is possible particularly in a language with a reduced flection, such as English. In other languages, with more complex morphology, most diagnostic classes contain several contexts.

Determining the diagnostic classes is a very important task of structural linguistics, since the diagnostic classes of $\mathscr{P}$ permit us to isolate $\mathscr{P}$ and to study it intrinsically.

5. Parts of Speech in Adequate and in Homogeneous Languages

In the above discussions we have made no assumption as to the nature of the language under consideration. But there is a general hypothesis, due to Uspenskii [46], which says that each natural language is adequate. This is not true for the artificial languages, as shown by Theorem 1, Chapter II. It is important to determine what new informations we may get concerning the parts of speech, if the language considered is adequate.

Let us first recall Theorem 4, Chapter II. If $\{\Gamma, P, \Phi\}$ is adequate, then $R' = P'$. This theorem yields a new way of determining the parts of speech. Given a word $a \in \Gamma$, its part of speech is identical to $R'(a)$. A third possibility of determining the parts of speech in an adequate language is given by Theorem 6, Chapter II. If, in such a language, the classes $K(x)$ define a partition of Γ, then $K' = P'$. Hence the part of speech of a word a is identical to $K'(a)$. In this connection, it is interesting to establish whether the assumption that the classes $K(x)$ form a partition is not redundant. The answer is negative, as it is shown by Proposition 1.

Proposition 1. There exists an adequate language whose classes do not form a partition of Γ.

PROOF. Let us consider the language L used in the proof of Theorem 9, Chapter II. In view of this theorem, L is adequate. On the other hand, using the notation introduced in Section 11, Chapter I, we have $M(a) = S(a) \cup S(b) = \{a, b, d\}$, $N(a) = P(a) = \{a, b\}$, $M(b) = S(a) \cup S(b) = \{a, b, d\}$, $N(b) = P(b) \cup P(d) = \{a, b, c, d\}$. Hence $K(a) = \{a, b, d\}$ and $K(b) = \{a, b, c, d\}$ and the classes do not form a partition of Γ.

It is known (see Theorem 8, Chapter II) that each homogeneous language is adequate. But Corollary 3, Chapter II, asserts that in every homogeneous language the classes form a partition of Γ. Does this last property characterize the homogeneous languages among the adequate languages? The answer is negative, as shown by the following result of Zelinka [48].

Theorem 1. There exists an adequate nonhomogeneous language, whose classes form a partition of Γ.

PROOF. Let $\Gamma = \{a, b_1, b_2, c_1, c_2, d\}$, $P(a) = \{a, b_1, c_1\}$, $P(b_2) = \{b_2, c_2\}$, $P(d) = \{d\}$, $\Phi = \{aa, b_1c_1, b_1c_2, b_2c_1, b_2c_2, d\}$. It is easy to see that $S(a) = \{a\}$, $S(b_1) = \{b_1, b_2\}$, $S(c_1) = \{c_1, c_2\}$, $S(d) = \{d\}$. We have the following marked P-structures: $P(a)P(b_2)$, $P(b_2)P(a)$, $P(a)P(a)$, $P(b_2)P(b_2)$, and $P(d)$. Since $P(a) = P(b_1) = P(c_1)$ and $P(b_2) = P(c_2)$, it follows that, for any $x \in \Gamma$ such that $x \neq d$, $P(x)$ is P-equivalent to $P(a)$, that is, $P'(a) = P'(b_1) = P'(b_2) = P'(c_1) = P'(c_2) = \{a, b_1, b_2, c_1, c_2\}$ and $P'(d) = \{d\}$. We have, for every $x \in \Gamma$, $S(x) \subseteq P'(x)$, and the considered language is adequate. But it is not homogeneous, since $P(a) \cap S(b_2) = \{b_1\} \neq 0$, whereas $P(b_2) \cap S(a) = 0$.

In view of Theorem 5, Chapter I, we have, for any $x \in \Gamma$, $K(x) = M(x) \cup N(x)$. By means of this formula, we get $K(a) = K(b_1) = K(b_2) = K(c_1) = K(c_2) = \{a, b_1, b_2, c_1, c_2,\}$ and $K(d) = \{d\}$. Hence the classes form a partition of Γ.

Theorem 1 and Theorem 6, Chapter II, show that there exist adequate nonhomogeneous languages whose parts of speech may be obtained in three ways: as P'-cells, as R'-cells, and as K'-cells. This fact is very important, since many fragments of natural languages are adequate but not homogeneous (see, in this respect, Section 8, Chapter II).

Thus, let us consider the fragment of the Russian vocabulary consisting of all Russian nouns and adjectives. For every noun a, $P(a)$ will be the set of forms obtained from a by changing the case and/or the number; for every adjective b, $P(b)$ will be the set of forms obtained from b by changing the gender, the number and/or the case. If Γ is the set of all noun forms and adjective forms and Φ is the set of all noun syntagms of the form *adjective + noun*, the language $\{\Gamma, P, \Phi\}$ is adequate, but not homogeneous. (See Kulagina [27], p. 214.)

Concerning the partition into classes, we have a Theorem.

Theorem 2.   There exists a nonadequate language whose classes form a partition of Γ.

PROOF.   Let $\Gamma = \{a, b_1, b_2, c_1, c_2\}$, $P(a) = \{a\}$, $P(b_1) = \{b_1, b_2\}$, $P(c_1) = \{c_1, c_2\}$, $\Phi = \{b_2a, b_2b_1, b_1b_2, ac_1, b_1c_1, c_1a, c_1c_2, ab_2, c_1b_1\}$.   We have $a \in S(b_1)$. On the other hand, by comparing the marked P-structure $P(b_1)P(a)$ and the unmarked P-structure $P(a)P(a)$, we deduce that $P(a)$ and $P(b_1)$ are not P-equivalent. Therefore, the language considered is not adequate. (See Revzin, [41], p. 175.) By means of the formula $K(x) = M(x) \cup N(x)$ (for every $x \in \Gamma$; see Theorem 5, Chapter I) we get $M(a) = \{a, b_1\}$, $N(a) = \{a, b_1, b_2\}$, $M(b_1) = \{a, b_1, b_2\}$, $N(b_1) = \{a, b_1, b_2\}$, $M(b_2) = \{a, b_1, b_2\}$, $N(b_2) = \{b_1, b_2\}$, $M(c_1) = N(c_1) = M(c_2) = N(c_2) = \{c_1, c_2\}$.   Hence $K(a) = K(b_1) = K(b_2) = \{a, b_1, b_2\}$, $K(c_1) = K(c_2) = \{c_1, c_2\}$ and Theorem 2 is completely proved.

The most advantageous conditions concerning the analysis of the parts of speech are offered by the homogeneous languages. Indeed, in view of Theorem 10, Chapter II, in every homogeneous language the classes coincide with the mixed cells, that is $K(x) = R(x)$ for any $x \in \Gamma$. Since we have (in any adequate language) $R'(x) = P'(x)$ for each $x \in \Gamma$, it follows that, in homogeneous language, $K'(x) = R'(x) = P'(x)$ for any $x \in \Gamma$. On the other hand, the classes of a homogeneous language may be easily determined by means of Corollary 4, Chapter II, which asserts that, in such languages, $K(x) = M(x) = N(x)$ for any $x \in \Gamma$.

To illustrate the above situation, let us consider the fragment of French vocabulary consisting of all French nouns and adjectives (see Kulagina [27], p. 213, Braffort [7], pp. 69–71, and Revzin [40]). We shall ignore any homonymic form such as *cas*, *mince*, etc. For any noun a, $P(a)$ will be formed by two elements: the singular and the plural forms. For any adjective b, $P(b)$ will be formed by four elements, namely, the forms of singular masculine, singular feminine, plural masculine, and plural feminine. The set Φ will be formed by all well-formed noun syntagms of the type *adjective + noun* or *noun + adjective*. We have four families of nouns (S_1 = the family of masculine singular noun forms, S_2 = the family of masculine plural noun forms, S_3 = the family of feminine singular noun forms, S_4 = the family of feminine plural noun forms) and four families of adjectives (S_5 = the family of masculine singular adjective forms, S_6 = the family of masculine plural adjective forms, S_7 = the family of feminine singular adjective forms, S_8 = the family of feminine plural adjective forms.

If a is a noun and b is an adjective, then $P(a) \cap S(b) = P(b) \cap S(a) = 0$. If a and b are either both nouns or both adjectives, each of the sets $P(a) \cap S(b)$ and $P(b) \cap S(a)$ contains exactly one element; if a and b are both adjectives, then $P(a) \cap S(b)$ contains the flectional form of a which has the same gender and the same number as b [and similarly for $P(b) \cap S(a)$]. If a and b are both nouns, we distinguish two possibilities. If a and b are of the same gender, then $P(a) \cap S(b)$ contains the flectional form of a which has the same number as b [and similarly for $P(b) \cap S(a)$]. If a and b are of different gender, then $P(a) \cap S(b) = P(b) \cap S(a) = 0$. It follows that in any case the sets $P(a) \cap S(b)$ and $P(b) \cap S(a)$ are either both void or both nonvoid. Hence the considered fragment of French is homogeneous. In view of Corollary 4, Chapter II, we have, for any word a,

$$K(a) = \cup \{S(b); \ b \in P(a)\}.$$

If a is a noun, then $K(a)$ will contain all noun forms of the same gender as a since, in this case, $P(a)$ contains only nouns of the same gender as a. We thus get two classes of nouns: one formed by masculine nouns, the other by feminine nouns. If a is an adjective, then $K(a)$ will contain all adjective forms, since, in this case, $P(a)$ contains adjectives of both genders and both numbers.

In view of Theorem 10, Chapter II, we may get the parts of speech by taking the derivative partition K'. If a and b are two nouns of different genders and if c is an adjective, the K-structures $K(a)K(c)$ and $K(b)K(c)$ are both marked, whereas the K-structures $K(c)K(a)$ and $K(c)K(b)$ are also both marked [since $K(c)$ contains adjectives of both genders]. It follows that $K(a)$ and $K(b)$ are K-equivalent. Therefore $K'(a) \supseteq K(a) \cup K(b)$, that is, $K'(a)$ contains all nouns. If a is a noun and c is an adjective, then $K(a)$ contains all nouns. If a is a noun and c is an adjective, then $K(a)$ and $K(c)$ are not K-equivalent, since the K-structure $K(a)K(c)$ is marked, whereas the K-structure $K(c)K(c)$ is not. It follows that $K'(a) = K(a) \cup K(b)$. For any adjective c, $K'(c) = K(c) =$ the set of all adjectives. Therefore, the parts of speech obtained by means of the above model coincide with the traditional ones. But for other choices of Γ and Φ some differences may arise, especially concerning pronouns, articles, numerals, adverbs, and some types of adjectives. For instance, the Rumanian words *un* and *acest* belong to the same P'-cell for most choices of Φ, although, in the customary Rumanian grammars, *un* is considered an article, whereas *acest* is considered a demonstrative adjective. Another example: If the expression *il est très mort* is not considered a well-formed French sentence, *mort* does not belong to the same P'-cell as *beau*.

Given two languages $L_1 = \{\Gamma_1, P_1, \Phi_1\}$ and $L_2 = \{\Gamma_2, P_2, \Phi_2\}$, we shall say that they are P'-isomorphic, if there is a $1:1$ mapping φ of Γ_1 onto Γ_2, such that $y \in P_1'(x)$ in L_1 if and only if $\varphi(y) \in P_2'(\varphi(x))$ in L_2. Since the parts of speech of a language are precisely its P'-cells, it follows that the P'-isomorphism preserves the parts of speech.

In Section 6, Chapter II, were defined various types of linguistic isomorphism. It is immediately apparent that two $P\Phi$-isomorphic languages, two $PP'S$-isomorphic languages, and two $P'S$-isomorphic languages are P'-isomorphic, but the converse is not true. It may be also seen that the P'-isomorphism is not comparable to the PS-isomorphism.

6. Syntactic Types

The starting point in the problem of syntactic types is described clearly by Lambek ([31], p. 166), using the following analogy: In classical physics it was possible to decide whether an equation was "grammatically correct" by comparing the dimensions of the two sides of the equation. One may ask whether it is similarly possible to assign grammatical types to the words of a natural language in such a way that the grammatical correctness of a sentence can be determined by computation with these types. Such possibilities already exist in certain artificial languages (for example, propositional calculus), where there are rules which distinguish between well-formed and non well-formed formulas.

Let us first consider one simple example (see Bar-Hillel [3] or [5], p. 62). The English string *poor John sleeps* would be analyzed, according to a customary method, in the following way: *poor* is an adjective (A), *John* is a noun (N), *sleep* is a verb (V), *-s* is a morpheme added to a verb to form a verbal phrase (*Vv*). Since *poor John* is a noun phrase and *sleeps* is a verb, we may say that *AN* (the juxtaposition means concatenation) gives a *N* and *V(Vv)* gives a *V*. According to the notation to be proposed and explained in the following, *John* will belong to the type *n*, *poor* to *n* / *n*, *sleeps* to *n* \ *s*, where *n* is to be interpreted, approximately, as the category of namelike strings, *n* / *n* as the category of those strings that with an *n* to their right form a string belonging to the same category *n*, and *n* \ *s* as the category of those strings that with an *n* to their left form a string belonging to the category of sentences. That the string *poor John sleeps* is a sentence can now be tested mechanically, without recourse to any syntactic statements, by using something like ordinary multiplication of fractions on the index sequence corresponding to the given string (*n* / *n*)*n*(*n* \ *s*). In the subsequence (*n* / *n*)*n* we may simplify to the right and obtain *n*; the whole sequence becomes *n*(*n* \ *s*); we may simplify to the left and we get the type *s*, that is, *poor John sleeps* is a well-formed English sentence (sometimes we shall say *sentence* instead of *well-formed sentence*).

Let us now proceed to sketch the general method following Lambek [29]. We consider a vocabulary *V*. We begin by assigning certain primitive types to some words and some strings on *V*. From these primitive types compound types are built up by three formal operations: *multiplication, left division,* and *right division,* denoted by simple juxtaposition, by \ and by /, respectively. We write $X \to x$ to indicate that the string *X* has type *x*. The defined compound types have the following significance: If $X \to x$ and $Y \to y$, then $XY \to xy$; if $XY \to z$ and $Y \to y$, then $X \to z$ / *y* (read *z over y*); if $XY \to z$ and $X \to x$, then $Y \to x$ \ *z* (read *x under z*). In other words, an expression of type *x* / *y*, when followed by an expression of type *y*, produces an expression of type *x*, as does an expression of type *y* \ *x* when preceded by an expression of type *y*.

If any expression of type *x* is also of type *y*, we shall write $x \to y$. The definition of left division and of right division implies that

$$(x \;/\; y)y \to x \quad \text{and} \quad y(y \setminus x) \to x. \tag{I}$$

Among the primitive types there always exists the type *s* ascribed to all sentences (that is, marked strings) and only to sentences. Now, if we could say whether a given string α is a marked one, then we could compute the types ascribed to the terms of α and we verify whether the compound type is precisely *s*.

Sometimes, when we are dealing with fragments of natural languages, we consider only two primitive types: s, the type of sentences, and n, the type of names; but in more complex situations we must consider a greater number of primitive types. For instance, we sometimes introduce the primitive type i, of intransitive infinitive. For the sake of simplicity, we here restrict type s so it is ascribed only to complete declarative sentences (that is, we rule out requests and questions, as well as most replies, which are usually incomplete). By a *name* we understand primarily a proper name, but we shall also assign type n to all expressions which can occur in any context in which all proper names can occur. Thus type n is ascribed to the so-called class nouns *milk, rice,...,* which can occur without an article, and to compound expressions such as *poor John* or *fresh milk*. We do not need to assign type n to the so-called count nouns *king, chair,...,* which require an article, nor to the pronoun *he*, as it cannot replace *John* in *poor John works*.

To better understand the linguistic significance of the above syntactic types, we shall illustrate the assignment of types to English words by considering a number of sample sentences (Lambek [29], p. 156–157). Each word type is indicated in parenthesis.

$$John\,(n)\,works\,(n \setminus s). \tag{1}$$

This remains a sentence if *John* is replaced by any other name. Hence *works* is type $n \setminus s$.

$$[poor\,(n \diagup n)\,John\,(n)]\,works\,(n \setminus s). \tag{2}$$

Here *poor John* takes the place of the name in (1); in fact *poor John* can occur in any context in which all names can occur; hence it is type n. Moreover, so are *poor Tom, poor Jane,...,* thus *poor* is type $n \diagup n$.

$$[John\,(n)\,works\,(n \setminus s)]\,here\,(s \setminus s). \tag{3}$$

The word *here* transforms (1), or any other sentence, into a new sentence; hence it is type $s \setminus s$.

$$John\,(n)\,[never\,((n \setminus s) \diagup (n \setminus s))\,works\,(n \setminus s)]. \tag{4}$$

Since *John* can be replaced by any name, *never works* is type $n \setminus s$; therefore, *never* is $(n \setminus s) \diagup (n \setminus s)$.

$$[John\,(n)\,works\,(n \setminus s)]\,[for\,((s \setminus s) \diagup n)\,Jane\,(n)]. \tag{5}$$

This indicates that *for Jane* should be the same type as *here* in (3), namely, $s \setminus s$, and, since *Jane* can be replaced by any other name, *for* is type $(s \setminus s) / n$.

$$[John\ (n)\ works\ (n \setminus s)]\ [and\ ((s \setminus s) / s)\ \{Jane\ (n)\ rests\ (n \setminus s)\}] \qquad (6)$$

This illustrates how *and* can join two arbitrary sentences to form a new sentence; its type is therefore $(s \setminus s) / s$.

$$John\ (n)\ [likes\ ((n \setminus s) / n)\ Jane\ (n)]. \qquad (7)$$

Here *likes Jane* is the same type as *works* in (1); hence *likes* is type $(n \setminus s) / n$.

Example (7) raises an important question. Let us group the sentence

$$[John\ (n)\ likes\ (n \setminus (s / n))]\ Jane\ (n). \qquad (7')$$

Here *John likes* is type s / n. Hence *likes* must be the new type $n \setminus (s / n)$. We would regard the two types of *likes* in (7) and (7') in some sense equivalent. Abstracting from this particular situation, we write symbolically

$$(x \setminus y) / z \rightleftarrows x \setminus (y / z). \qquad (\text{II})$$

We may write $x \setminus y / z$ for either side of this equivalence. Further examples of this convention are afforded by the types of *never*, *for*, and *and* (see Table 1). To avoid multiplication of parentheses, we may also abbreviate $(x / y) / z$ as $x / y / z$ and, symmetrically, $z \setminus (y \setminus x)$ as $z \setminus y \setminus x$. However, parentheses must not be omitted in such compounds as $x / (y / z)$, $(z \setminus y) \setminus x$, $(x / y) \setminus z$, and $z / (y \setminus x)$.

TABLE 1

	Word	Type	Part of speech
(1)	Works	$n \setminus s$	Intransitive verb
(2)	Poor	n / n	Adjective
(3)	Here	$s \setminus s$	Adverb
(4)	Never	$n \setminus s / (n \setminus s)$	Adverb
(5)	For	$s \setminus s / n$	Preposition
(6)	And	$s \setminus s / s$	Conjunction
(7)	Likes	$n \setminus s / n$	Transitive verb

The syntactic types correspond approximately to the traditional parts of speech. Thus, in (1) *works* is an intransitive verb, in (2) *poor* is an adjective, in (3) *here* is an adverb, in (4) *never* is an adverb, in (5) *for* is a preposition, in (6) *and* is a conjunction, in (7) *likes* is a transitive verb.

In this manner we can build up a list of types for a gradually increasing portion of the English vocabulary. To distinguish between different forms such as *works* and *work*, usually represented by a single dictionary entry, it is necessary to allow for more than two primitive types. Thus we might assign the type n^* to all plural nouns, such as *men*, or *chairs*. In contrast to examples (1), (2), (5), and (7) we then have *men* (n^*) *work* $(n^* \setminus s)$, *poor* (n^* / n^*) *men* (n^*) *work* $(n^* \setminus s)$, *John* (n) *works* $(n \setminus s)$ *for* $(s \setminus s / n^*)$ *men* (n^*), *John* (n) *likes* $(n \setminus s / n^*)$ *girls* (n^*), *men* (n^*) *like* $(n^* \setminus s / n)$ *Jane* (n). This assignment distinguishes between the forms *work* and *works, like* and *likes*, but it introduces a multiplicity of types for *poor, for, like,* and *likes*.

A more thorough analysis of the English verb phrase would compel us to introduce further primitive types for the infinitive and the two kinds of participles of intransitive verb. That analysis will be made in the next section.

Suppose we have before us a string of words whose types are given. Then we can compute the type of the entire expression, provided its so-called phrase structure has been made visible by some device (such as brackets). Consider for example *John* (n) [*likes* $(n \setminus s / n)$ {*fresh* (n / n) *milk* (n)}]. The corresponding computation can be written as $n((n \setminus s / n)((n / n)n)) \rightarrow n((n \setminus s / n)n) \rightarrow n(n \setminus s) \rightarrow s$.

In formal languages, this process offers an effective test of whether a given string of symbols is a well-formed formula. For in these languages, each word (usually consisting of a single sign) has just one preassigned type, and the use of brackets is obligatory.

Suppose we now wish to compute the type of a string of English words, which are taken from a given type list. We cannot proceed quite as directly as in the formal systems, for two reasons. First, brackets do not usually occur in English texts (unless we regard punctuation as an attempt to indicate grouping). Two ways of inserting brackets into an expression may lead to essentially different syntactic resolutions. Second, English words usually possess more than one type. For instance, the adverbial expression *today* is type s / s or $s \setminus s$, depending on whether it precedes or follows the modified sentence. The word *sound* may be a noun, an adjective, or a verb, either transitive or intransitive, depending on the context.

A mechanical procedure for analyzing English sentences would consist of four steps:

(1) Insert brackets in all admissible ways.

(2) To each word, assign all types permitted by a given type list.

(3) For each grouping and type assignment, compute the type of the total expression.

(4) Select that method of grouping and that type assignment which yields the desired type s.

To realize step (3), we must introduce some new rules of computation. For instance, example (4) suggests the rule $s \setminus s \rightarrow (n \setminus s) \setminus (n \setminus s)$.

Other rules are suggested by the following discussion concerning English pronouns.

$$He\,(s \diagup (n \setminus s))\,works\,(n \setminus s), \quad he\,(s \diagup (n \setminus s))\,likes\,(n \setminus s \diagup n)$$
$$Jane\,(n). \quad (8)$$

Since *he* transforms such expressions as *works* or *likes Jane* of type $n \setminus s$ into sentences, we assign to it type $s \diagup (n \setminus s)$. At any rate, assignment of type $s \diagup (n \setminus s)$ to *he* is valid, irrespective of whether we regard pronouns as names. In fact, by the same argument, the name *John* also is type $s \diagup (n \setminus s)$. To discuss this point, let us analyze the sentence

$$He\,(s \diagup (n \setminus s))\,likes\,(n \setminus s \diagup n)\,him\,((s \diagup n) \setminus s). \quad (9)$$

The sequence of types $(s \diagup (n \setminus s))\,(n \setminus s \diagup n)\,((s \diagup n) \setminus s)$ cannot be simplified any further by rules (I) and (II), and we introduce two new rules:

$$(x \diagup y)(y \diagup z) \rightarrow x \diagup z, \quad (x \setminus y)(y \setminus z) \rightarrow x \setminus z. \quad (III)$$

We may then assign type $(s \diagup n \setminus s))\,(n \setminus s \diagup n) \rightarrow s \diagup n$ to *he likes* and type $(n \setminus s \diagup n)((s \diagup n) \setminus s) \rightarrow n \setminus s$ to *likes him*, permitting two equivalent resolutions: [*he likes*] $(s \diagup n)\,him\,((s \diagup n) \setminus s)$: *he* $(s \diagup (n \setminus s))$ [*likes him*] $(n \setminus s)$. Rules (III) also allow alternative, although equivalent, resolutions of expressions considered earlier; for example, sentence (5) can now also be grouped *John* [*works* {*for Jane*}], where the predicate has type $((n \setminus s)((s \setminus s \diagup n)n) \rightarrow (n \setminus s)\,(s \setminus s) \rightarrow n \setminus s$.

We saw, in the discussion of (8), that the name *John* is the same type as the pronoun *him*. We symbolize the situation by writing $n \rightarrow s \diagup (n \setminus s)$, $n \rightarrow (s \diagup n) \setminus s$, and, more generally,

$$x \rightarrow y \diagup (x \setminus y), \quad x \rightarrow (y \diagup x) \setminus x. \quad (IV)$$

These new rules may actually be required for computations. Suppose that from sample sentences such as *books by him bore*, we arrived at the type $n^* \setminus n^* / n'$ for *by*, where n' is short for $(s / n) \setminus s$. The phrase *books by John* then requires the computation $n^*(n^* \setminus n^* / n')n$ $\rightarrow (n^* / n')n \rightarrow (n^* / n')n' \rightarrow n^*$, which utilizes rules (I), (IV), and (I) in that order.

All the considerations of Section 6 are, essentially, those of Lambek [29].

7. Analysis of the English Verb Phrase

In this Section we shall use the method of syntactic types to examine the structure of the English verb phrase. All these considerations are due to Lambek [30].

We shall consider a fragment of English containing the names *John* and *Jane*, the verbs *must, work, call, have, be,* the adverb *today,* the conjunctions *but* and *while* and a few other words of the same types. We also admit inflected forms such as *works, worked,* or *working.* We shall attempt to decide which sequences of these words are sentences and which are not. However, we may as well admit that some sentences will escape our net, because certain constructions, for example, the gerund, will not be considered here.

We adopt the following primitive types: s (complete declarative sentence), n (name), i (infinitive of intransitive verb), p (present participle of intransitive verb), q (past participle of intransitive verb). We shall regard the assignment of types to certain English words to have been successful provided (1) every sentence consisting of these words is type s and (2) only sentences are type s. It is hoped that the assignments of the present Section will conform with (2), but we cannot satisfy (1) as long as we omit some possible constructions from consideration, for example, *While calling Jane, John is working today.*

A number of key sentences will illustrate our choice of types: *John* (n) *works* $(n \setminus s)$; *John* (n) *must* $(n \setminus s / i)$ *work* (i); *John* (n) *is* $(n \setminus s / p)$ *working* (p); *John* (n) *has* $(n \setminus s / q)$ *worked* (q). The choice of type for *must, is,* and *has* is determined by the desire to assure that *must work, is working,* and *has worked* are all the same type $n \setminus s$ as *works.*

Consider the sentences: *John* (n) *must* $(n \setminus s / i)$ *be* (i / p) *working* (p); *John* (n) *must* $(n \setminus s / i)$ *have* (i / q) *worked* (q); *John* (n) *has*

$(n \setminus s \diagup q)$ *been* $(q \diagup p)$ *working* (p). Here, *be working* and *have worked* should be the same type i as *work*, whereas *been working* should be the same type q as *worked*.

Finally, we consider a number of sentences containing different forms of the transitive verb *call*: *John* (n) *calls* $(n \setminus s \diagup n)$ *Jane* (n); *John* (n) *(must* $(n \setminus s \diagup i)$ *call* $(i \diagup n)$ *Jane* (n); *John* (n) *is* $(n \setminus s \diagup p)$ *calling* $(p \diagup n)$ *Jane* (n); *John* (n) *has* $(n \setminus s \diagup q)$ *called* $(q \diagup n)$ *Jane* (n); *Jane* (n) *is* $(n \setminus s \diagup (q \diagup n))$ *called* $(q \diagup n)$ (by John). The resulting types are embodied in Table 2.

TABLE 2

	Modal auxiliary	Intransitive	Transitive	Auxiliary	Progressive auxiliary	Positive auxiliary
Infinitive		Work i	Call $i \diagup n$	Have $i \diagup q$	Be $i \diagup p$	Be $i \diagup (q \diagup n)$
Present Participle		Working p	Calling $p \diagup n$			Being $p \diagup (q \diagup n)$
Past participle		Worked q	Called $q \diagup n$		Been $q \diagup p$	Been $q \diagup (q \diagup n)$
Third person singular	Must $n \setminus s \diagup i$	Works $n \setminus s$	Calls $n \setminus s \diagup n$	Has $n \setminus s \diagup q$	Is $n \setminus s \diagup p$	Is $n \setminus s \diagup (q \diagup n)$

To illustrate calculations based on Table 2, let us consider the string *John* (n) *must* $(n \setminus s \diagup i)$ *have* $(i \diagup q)$ *been* $(q \diagup p)$ *calling* $(p \diagup n)$ Jane (n). We have $n(n \setminus s \diagup i) \rightarrow s \diagup i$, $(i \diagup q)(q \diagup p) \rightarrow i \diagup p$, $(p \diagup n)n \rightarrow p$, $(i \diagup p)p \rightarrow i$, $(s \diagup i)i \rightarrow s$. Hence the considered string is a sentence. The string *John* (n) *is* $(n \setminus s \diagup p)$ *being* $(p \diagup (q \diagup n))$ *called* $(q \diagup n)$ is also a sentence, since we have $n(n \setminus s \diagup p) \rightarrow s \diagup p$, $p \diagup (q \diagup n)(q \diagup n) \rightarrow p$, and $(s \diagup p)p \rightarrow s$.

Table 2 is not complete. Principal omissions are the following: doubly transitive verbs such as *give*, or *appoint*; verbs which relate nouns and adjectives, as in *the lunch tastes good*; first person forms such as *am*; plural forms of the verb such as *are*.

Table 2 is more extensive than it looks, since many entries are merely representative samples. Thus *work* represents all intransitive verbs, *calls* represents all transitive verbs, and *must* represents all modal auxiliaries such as *will, shall, can, may, would, should, could, might.* Furthermore, the passive auxiliary *be* may often be replaced by *get*, and the progressive auxiliary *be* seems to represent a large class of verbs, including at first sight *start, begin, keep, continue, stop* and *finish.*

Some of the forms appearing in the table can also be different types. Thus *call* may be a noun, and *have* and *be* may also appear as main verbs, as in *John must have lunch* and *John must be good.*

The gaps in the first column of Table 2 are because *must* has no infinitive and the conceivable forms *musting* (p / i) and *musted* (q / i) do not exist. The gaps in the second and third columns of Table 2 exist because the auxiliary *have* has no present and no past participle and the active auxiliary *be* has no present participle. This is not quite correct if we consider *having* in *having worked, John rested* as a participle. However, the main verb *have* and the passive auxiliary *be* (as well as the main verb *be*) has a present participle, as is attested by the sentences: *John is having lunch; John has had lunch; John is being called.* The corresponding types are *having* (p / n), *had* (q / n), *being* ($p / (q / n)$).

One can interpret Table 2 as a kind of multiplication table, as shown in Table 3. The entries of Table 3 are in fact obtained by multiplication according to rules (I) and (III). For example, $(p / i)i \rightarrow p$ by (I), and $(q / i)(i / p) \rightarrow q / p$ by (III).

TABLE 3

	i / i	i	i / n	i / q	i / p	$i / (q / n)$
i / i	i / i	i	i / n	i / q	i / p	$i / (q / n)$
p / i	p / i	p	p / n	p / q	p / p	$p / (q / n)$
q / i	q / i	q	q / n	q / q	q / p	$q / (q / n)$
$n \backslash s / i$	$n \backslash s / i$	$n \backslash s$	$n \backslash s / n$	$n \backslash s / q$	$n \backslash s / p$	$n \backslash s / (q / n)$

Suppose we assign to *calling* and *been* the full types $(p / i)i$ and $(q / i)(i / p)$ of Table 3, rather than the contracted types p and q / p. Then *calling* is treated as though it consisted of two parts which carry the types p / i and i in this order (compare with *to call*). Similarly, *works* would be treated like the composite *does work*. If we assign compound types to verb forms in this manner, we are led to a new way of looking at adverbs. Although the old assignment suggests [*John* (*n*) *works* (*n* \ *s*)] *today* (*s* \ *s*), where *n*(*n* \ *s*) → *s*, *s*(*s* \ *s*) → *s*, the new assignment allows the more intimate construction *John* (*n*) [*works* ((*n* \ *s* / *i*)*i*) *today* (*i* \ *i*)], where *i*(*i* \ *i*) → *i*, (*n* \ *s* / *i*)*i* → *n* \ *s*. Therefore, ((*n* \ *s* / *i*)*i*)(*i* \ *i*) → *n* \ *s* and *n*(*n* \ *s*) → *s*. The new assignment also permits us to distinguish between the types of coordinate and subordinate conjunctions, as in the sentences [*John works*] (*s*) *and* (*s* \ *s* / *s*) [*Jane sleeps*] (*s*) and *John* (*n*) *works* ((*n* \ *s* / *i*)*i*) *while* (*i* \ *i* / *s*) [*Jane sleeps*] (*s*).

8. The Associative Syntactic Calculus

Consider a vocabulary Γ and a set of elements called *primitive types*. Let us suppose that, to certain strings over Γ, there have been assigned certain primitive types. Let us define a set $\mathscr{T}$ of elements called *types*, defined as follows: All primitive types are types; if *x* and *y* are types, then *xy*, *x* \ *y*, and *x* / *y* are also types (the considered operations have already been explained in Section 6). The following theorem is now valid.

Theorem 3.   We have the following rules:
 (1) $x \to x$;
 (2) $(xy)z \to x(yz)$;
 (2′) $x(yz) \to (xy)z$;
 (3) if $xy \to z$, then $x \to z / y$;
 (3′) if $xy \to z$, then $y \to x \setminus z$;
 (4) if $x \to z / y$, then $xy \to z$;
 (4′) if $y \to x \setminus z$, then $xy \to z$;
 (5) if $x \to y$ and $y \to z$, then $x \to z$.

PROOF.   Rules (1) and (5) hold trivially. To prove (2) and (2′), let *A* be a string of type *x*, *B* a string of type *y*, and *C* a string of type *z*. Then (*AB*)*C* is type (*xy*)*z*. On the other hand, *BC* is of type *yz*. Hence *A*(*BC*) is of type *x*(*yz*). Since (*AB*)*C* and *A*(*BC*) are the same string, (2) and (2′) follow. Rules (3′) and (4′) are symmetric duals of (3) and (4). Therefore, it suffices to prove the latter.

Assume $xy \to z$ and let the string *A* be type *x*. Then for any string *B* of type y, AB is type z; hence A is type $z \diagup y$. Thus $x \to z \diagup y$. Conversely, assume $x \to z \diagup y$ and let A, B, be types x, y, respectively; then AB is type z. Thus $xy \to z$ and Theorem 3 is proved.

In view of rules (2) and (2'), the syntactic calculus developed here is called the *associative syntactic calculus*. It may be viewed abstractly as a formal language or as a deductive system ([29], p. 163). Another set of rules which are valid in the associative syntactic calculus are given by Theorem 4.

Theorem 4.

(6) $x \to (xy) \diagup y$;

(6') $y \to x \diagdown (xy)$;

(7) $(z \diagup y)y \to z$;

(7') $x(x \diagdown z) \to z$;

(8) $y \to (z \diagup y) \diagdown z$;

(8') $x \to z \diagup (x \diagdown z)$;

(9) $(x \diagdown y) \diagup z \rightleftarrows x \diagdown (y \diagup z)$;

(10) $(x \diagup y)z \rightleftarrows x(zy)$;

(10') $z \diagdown (y \diagdown x) \rightleftarrows (yz) \diagdown x$;

(11)   if $x \to x'$ and $y \to y'$, then $xy \to x'y'$;

(12)   if $x \to x'$ and $y \to y'$, then $x \diagup y' \to x' \diagup y$;

(12')   if $x \to x'$ and $y \to y'$, then $y \diagdown x \to y' \diagdown x'$;

(13) $(z \diagup y)(y \diagup x) \to z \diagup x$;

(13') $(y \diagdown x)(x \diagdown z) \to y \diagdown z$;

(14) $z \diagup y \to (z \diagup x) \diagup (y \diagup x)$;

(14') $x \diagdown z \to (y \diagdown x) \diagdown (y \diagdown z)$.

PROOF. (6) follows from $xy \to xy$ by (3); (6') follows from $xy \to xy$ by (3'); (7) follows from $z \diagup y \to z \diagup y$ by (4); (7') follows from $x \diagdown z \to x \diagdown z$ by (4'); (8) follows from (7) by (3') and (8') follows from (7') by (3).

Let us prove the first implication of (9). Denote by t the expression $(x \diagdown y) \diagup z$. We then have, in view of (4), $tz \to x \diagdown y$. This implies, in view of (4'), $x(tz) \to y$. Since, in view of (2), we have $(xt)z \to x(tz)$, it follows, by (5), that $(xt)z \to y$. We may apply (3) and obtain $xt \to y \diagup z$. Finally, in view of (3'), it follows that $t \to x \diagdown (y \diagup z)$.

To prove the second implication of (9), let us put $u = x \diagdown (y \diagup z)$. In view of (4'), we have $xu \to y \diagup z$ and, by (4), we obtain $(xu)z \to y$. Since (2') implies $x(uz) \to (xu)z$, it follows, by (5), that $x(uz) \to y$. In view of (3'), we have $uz \to x \diagdown y$. Hence, by (3), $u \to (x \diagdown y) \diagup z$.

Let us prove (10). Denote by t the expression $(x \diagup y) \diagup z$ and by u

the expression $x \diagup (zy)$. In view of (4), $tz \to x \diagup y$ and, further, $(tz)y \to x$. By $(2')$, $t(zy) \to (tz)y$. Hence, by (5), $t(zy) \to x$. Finally, in view of (3), $t \to x \diagup (zy)$. To prove the other implication of (10), we remark that, in view of (4), $u(zy) \to x$. Since, by (2), we have $(uz)y \to u(zy)$; it follows, by (5), that $(uz)y \to x$. This implies, in view of (3), $uz \to x \diagup y$ and, further, $u \to (x \diagup y) \diagup z$.

$(10')$ may be proved in the same way as (10), but by using $(3')$ and $(4')$ instead of (3) and (4), respectively.

Let us prove (11). Since $x'y \to x'y$, we have, in view of (3), $x' \to (x'y) \diagup y$ and, since $x \to x'$, it follows, by (5), that $x \to (x'y) \diagup y$. This implies, in view of (4), $xy \to x'y$. On the other hand, from $x'y' \to x'y'$ it follows, in view of $(3')$, that $y' \to x' \diagdown (x'y')$. Since $y \to y'$, we deduce, by (5), that $y \to x' \diagdown (x'y')$ and, by $(4')$ we obtain $x'y \to x'y'$. Since we also have $xy \to x'y$, it follows, in view of (5), that $xy \to x'y'$.

Let us prove (12). We have, by (1), $x \diagup y' \to x \diagup y'$. Hence, in view of (4), $(x \diagup y')y' \to x$. This implies, by $(3')$, that $y' \to (x \diagup y') \diagdown x$. Since we also have $y \to y'$, it follows, by (5), that $y \to (x \diagup y') \diagdown x$ and further, by $(4')$, we get $(x \diagup y')y \to x$. This implies, in view of (3), that $x \diagup y' \to x \diagup y$. On the other hand, since, by (1), we have $x \diagup y \to x \diagup y$, it follows, by (4), $(x \diagup y)y \to x$. Hence, in view of (5) and of the fact that $x \to x'$, we get $(x \diagup y)y \to x'$. This implies, in view of (4), that $x \diagup y \to x' \diagup y$. Since we have already proved that $x \diagup y' \to x \diagup y$, it follows, by (5), that $x \diagup y' \to x' \diagup y$.

In a similar way, but using $(4')$ instead of (4), (3) instead of $(3')$, (4) instead of $(4')$, and $(3')$ instead of (3), one can prove $(12')$.

Let us prove (13). Since, in view of (8), we have $y \to (z \diagup y) \diagdown z$, it follows, by (12), that $y \diagup x \to ((z \diagup y) \diagdown z) \diagup x$. On the other hand, in view of (9), we have $((z \diagup y) \diagdown z) \diagup x \to (z \diagup y) \diagdown (z \diagup x)$. Hence, by (5), $y \diagup x \to (z \diagup y) \diagdown (z \diagup x)$. This implies, in view of $(4')$, that $(z \diagup y)(y \diagup x) \to z \diagup x$.

In a similar way, but using $(8')$ instead of (8), $(12')$ instead of (12), and (4) instead of $(4')$, one can prove $(13')$.

Finally, let us remark that (14) follows from (13) by (3) and $(14')$ follows from $(13')$ by $(3')$. Theorem 4 is thus completely proved.

REMARK. Many plausible rules are in fact false. For example, the following are not valid: $(x \diagup y) \diagup z \to x \diagup (y \diagup z)$, $(x \diagup y) \diagdown z \to x \diagup (y \diagdown z)$, $xy \to yx$, $z \to (z \diagup y)y$ ([30], p. 84).

The syntactic rules (7) $(7')$, (9), (13) $(13')$ and (8) $(8')$ coincide with rules (I), (II), (III), and (IV), respectively. Theorems 3 and 4 are due to

Lambek ([29], pp. 163–164), but some details of Theorem 4 are due to Geanău (personal communication). Theorems 3 and 4 have been used by Ionescu to establish the syntactic types of Rumanian [23].

Hiż remarks that Lambek's syntactic calculus is based on the assumption that a modifier of an expression occurs adjacent to the expression it modifies. An expression acts on another expression from the left, or from the right, but always in a juxtaposition. This is a proper grammatical analysis for languages in which concatenation plays a fundamental grammatical role (as it does in English). But there are nonconcatenative languages (Latin). In a Latin sentence, a masculine noun can be modified by an adjective in the masculine form at nearly any point of the sentence, provided that other nouns in the sentence are feminine or neuter ([21], p. 265). These remarks agree with those of Chomsky, who believes that only a small number of basic sentences in a language should be analyzed by Lambek's method and that other sentences may be obtained from them by certain transformations (see the footnote of [30] p. 85). On the other hand, Ionescu claims that Lambek's syntactic calculus is also applicable to languages—such as Rumanian—in which concatenation does not play a fundamental grammatical role, provided the order of words in the sentences is precise [23].

9. Nonassociative Syntactic Calculus

As Lambek remarks ([31], p. 167), unless elaborate precautions are taken, the most natural assignments of types to English words tempt one to admit many pseudo-sentences as grammatical: *John is poor sad*; *John likes poor him*; *Who works and John rests*? However, these pseudo-sentences could be systematically ascribed to one cause, namely, the fact that types had been assigned to unstructured strings of words. Suppose we assign types not to strings, but to phrases, that is, bracketed strings of words (or perhaps morphemes).

Let us consider a set of strings called *atomic phrases* and let us adopt the following recursive definition of *phrases* (juxtaposition denotes concatenation and parentheses denote themselves; brackets on the outside of a complete phrase may be omitted). All atomic phrases are phrases: If A and B are phrases, so is (AB).

Types are introduced by a similar recursive definition. We shall consider a finite set of elements called *primitive types*. All primitive types are types. Three binary operations with types are defined, such that, if x and y are types, so are (xy), $(x \diagup y)$, and $(x \diagdown y)$.

Types are assigned to phrases in accordance with the following rules: If A is type a and B is type b, then (AB) is type (ab); if (AB) is type c for all B of type b, then A is type $(c \diagup b)$; if (AB) is type c for all A of type a, then B is type $(a \diagdown c)$ [31].

Theorem 5. In a nonassociative syntactic calculus we have the following rules [31]:

(1) $x \rightarrow x$;
(3) if $xy \rightarrow z$, then $x \rightarrow z \diagup y$;
(3') if $xy \rightarrow z$, then $y \rightarrow x \diagdown z$;
(4) if $x \rightarrow z \diagup y$, then $xy \rightarrow z$;
(4') if $y \rightarrow x \diagdown z$, then $xy \rightarrow z$;
(5) if $x \rightarrow y$ and $y \rightarrow z$, then $x \rightarrow z$.

The following rules fail to hold:

(2) $(xy)z \rightarrow x(yz)$;
(2') $x(yz) \rightarrow (xy)z$;
(9) $(x \diagdown y) \diagup z \rightleftarrows x \diagdown (y \diagup z)$;
(13) $(x \diagup y)(y \diagup z) \rightarrow x \diagup z$;
(15) $(x \diagup y) \diagup z \rightleftarrows x \diagup (zy)$.

PROOF. (1), (3), (3'), (4), (4'), and (5) may be proved as in Theorem 3. Now let A, B, and C be phrases of types a, b, and c, respectively. The phrase $(AB)C$ is type $(ab)c$, and the phrase $A(BC)$ is type $a(bc)$. But $(AB)C$ and $A(BC)$ are different syntactic constructions; hence (2) and (2') fail to hold. For similar reasons, (9), (13), and (15) [which are consequences of the associative laws (2) and (2')] also fail to hold.

Theorem 5 permits us to present the nonassociative syntactic calculus as a deductive system, as follows. First we consider a set of elements called *variables*. Then we recursively define another set whose elements are called *terms*: All variables are terms; if x and y are terms, so are (xy), $(x \diagdown y)$, and $(x \diagup y)$. We introduce a single *formula*: $x \rightarrow y$ (where x and y are terms) and a single *axiom scheme*: $x \rightarrow x$. Theorem 5 suggests the rules of inferences (3), (3'), (4), (4'), and (5).

The syntactic calculus permits us to transfer some grammatical rules from the grammar to the dictionary. This fact may be illustrated by the sentence *John must work*. A phrase-structure analysis of this sentence is: *John* (*n*) [*must* (*m*) *work* (*i*)], $mi \to v$, $nv \to s$. This analysis presumes that we are given a dictionary with the type assignments $John \to n$, $must \to m$, $work \to i$, and a list containing two grammatical rules: $mi \to v$ and $nv \to s$. By the syntactic calculus, the last two rules become $m \to v \diagup i$ and $v \to n \diagdown s$. Thus, we get the single rule $m \to (n \diagdown s) \diagup i$. We may now revise the dictionary thus: $John \to n$, $must \to (n \diagdown s) \diagup i$, $work \to i$. We may then analyze the same sentence as follows: *John* (*n*) [*must* $((n \diagdown s) \diagup i)$ *work* (*i*)], $((n \diagdown s) \diagup i)i) \to n \diagdown s$, $n(n \diagdown s) \to s$.

Suppose we have replaced all grammatical rules of a language by suitable type assignments in the dictionary. It is then possible to parse a given string of words in mechanical fashion: We turn the string into a phrase X by bracketing and write under each word one of the types assigned to it by the dictionary. Let x be the compound type of the whole phrase. If we have $x \to s$, X is a statement. If $x \to i$, X may be one kind of request, and so on. This process is repeated for all bracketings and type assignments.

It is interesting to know for which languages it is possible to replace all grammatical rules by type assignments in the dictionary. Many formal languages of mathematical logic (see [29], pp. 159–160) admit this possibility. But we shall concern ourselves here with other important languages, those generated by the so-called phrase-structure grammars, due to Chomsky [9]. For our purpose it will be convenient to think of a phrase-structure grammar as follows: The dictionary assigns to each atomic phrase a finite number of primitive types, whereas the grammar consists of a finite number of rules of the form $p_i p_j \to p_k$, where the p_i are primitive types. The set of all sentences in a phrase-structure grammar is called a *phrase-structure language*. These correspond to what is called by Chomsky [9] a type-2 grammar (a type-2 language, respectively). There are some phrase-structure grammars for which the elimination of grammatical rules in favor of dictionary entries can be carried out, without making the dictionary infinite. In this respect, we shall consider the language L_2, defined by Chomsky ([9], p. 151). The sentences of this language are all strings of the form XX^*, where X is a string over the vocabulary $\{A, H\}$, whereas X^* is the mirror image of X. It is easy to see that L_2 is defined by the dictionary: $A \to a$, $s \diagup a$, $(s \diagup a) \diagup s$, $H \to h$, $s \diagup h$, $(s \diagup h) \diagup s$. On the other hand, L_2 is a phrase-structure language (more precisely, L_2 is a type-2 language which is not a finite-state language; see, for instance, [9] and [34], p. 75 and pp. 166–167).

We shall now give some examples taken from English concerning elimination of grammatical rules in favor of dictionary entries [31].

In a previous section it was suggested that the pronoun *he* be given the type $s \diagup (n \diagdown s)$. This means that *he*, when followed by any phrase of type *ns* (for example, *must work*) yields a phrase of type *s*. In other words, the type assignment $he \to s \diagup (n \diagdown s)$ is equivalent to the transformation rule "if $nX \to s$, then *he* $X \to s$." Such a rule may indeed be implied by the totality of rules and type assignments of a phrase-structure grammar, but it is not one of these rules; it would not do to enter $he \to n$ into the dictionary, for then the nonsentence *John must like he* would be type *s*. We have here a transformation rule which can be conveniently replaced by a type assignment in the dictionary.

A similar example is the rule "if $nX \to s$, then *who* $X \to (?)$", where (?) is the type assigned to well-formed questions. This is equivalent to the dictionary entry $who \to (?) \diagup (n \diagdown s)$.

The transformation rule "if $n(must\ i) \to s$, then $(must\ n)i \to (?)$" could be handled by supplementing the original dictionary entry *must* $\to (n \diagdown s) \diagup i$ by the further assignment $must \to ((?) \diagup i) \diagup n$. This would not allow us to derive the sentence *must he work?* Let $\hat{n} = s \diagup (n \diagdown s)$ be the type of *he* considered above; then we want the type assignment $must \to ((?) \diagup i) \diagup \hat{n}$. It is sufficient for the dictionary to carry this last assignment, since $((?) \diagup i) \diagup \hat{n} \to ((?) \diagup i) \diagup n$ is a derivable formula in the syntactic calculus. Instead of proving this rule, let us parse the sentence *must John work?* using *must* $\to ((?) \diagup i) \diagup \hat{n}$ and the provable formula $n \to \hat{n} = s \diagup (n \diagdown s)$. Thus $[must\ ((?) \diagup i) \diagup \hat{n})$ *John* $(n)]$ *work* $(i), (((?) \diagup i) \diagup \hat{n})\hat{n} \to (?) \diagup i, ((?) \diagup i)i \to (?).$

10. Categorial Grammars

Another kind of syntactic calculus has been investigated by Bar-Hillel ([5], pp. 99–115) and Bar-Hillel *et al.* [6]. An improved version was given by Bar-Hillel ([4], [5], pp. 185–218 and, especially, pp. 188–189). The standpoint of these authors is very similar to that of Lambek and is formulated by Bar-Hillel ([5], pp. 187–188). The grammar is meant to be a device by which the syntactic structure, and in particular the sentence analysis of a given string could be determined. This determination must depend exclusively on the shape and order of the elements. This is achieved by assuming that each of the finitely many elements of the given natural language had finitely many syntactic functions, by developing a suitable notation for these syntactic functions (or categories, as they are called [2, 6, 32]), and by designing an algorithm operating on this notation. It is assumed, in such an investigation, that every sentence can be parsed, according to finitely many rules, into two or more contiguous constituents, either of which is already a final constituent or else can itself be parsed into two or more immediate constituents. This parsing is not necessarily supposed to be unique. Syntactically ambiguous sentences allow for two or more different parsings.

Following Ajdukiewicz [1], the combination of constituents is regarded as the result of the operation of one of the constituents (the governor) upon the others. To each word are assigned finitely many fundamental categories. We can also define a set of rules operating upon these categories, so-called cancellation rules.

Let us now give the exact definition of some grammars of the above type. A *bidirectional categorial grammar* is a quintuple $\langle \Gamma, C, \Sigma, R, f \rangle$, where Γ is a finite set of elements (the *vocabulary*), C is the closure of a finite set of fundamental categories, say $\psi_1, \ldots, \psi_n$, under the operations of right and left diagonalization [that is, whenever α and β are categories, (α / β) and $(a \setminus \beta)$ are categories], Σ is a distinguished category of C (the *category of sentences*), R is the set of the two cancellation rules $(\varphi_i / \varphi_j)\varphi_j \to \varphi_i$ and $\varphi_i(\varphi_i \setminus \varphi_j) \to \varphi_j$, and f is a function from Γ to finite subsets of C (the *assignment function*).

We say that a category sequence α *directly cancels to* β, if β results from α, by one application of one of the cancellation rules. We say that α *cancels to* β if β results from α by finitely many applications of these rules; more exactly, if there exist category sequences $\gamma_1, \gamma_2, \ldots, \gamma_n$ such that $\alpha = \gamma_1$, $\beta = \gamma_n$, and γ_i directly cancels to γ_{i+1}, for $i = 1, \ldots, n - 1$.

A string x over Γ is defined as a *sentence* if, and only if, at least one of the category sequences assigned to x by f cancels to Σ. The set of all sentences is then the *language determined by the given bidirectional categorial grammar*. Such a language is called a *bidirectional categorial language*.

The functioning of such a grammar can be clarified by an example (Chomsky [11], p. 412; we shall take $\Sigma = s$). Suppose that our grammar contains the fundamental categories n and s, the vocabulary $\Gamma = \{John, Mary, loves, died, is, old, very\}$ and let us define the function f as follows:

$f(John) = f(Mary) = \{n\}$; $f(died) = \{n \setminus s\}$; $f(loves) = \{(n \setminus s) \diagup n\}$; $f(old) = \{n \diagup n\}$; $f(very) = \{(n \diagup n) \diagup (n \diagup n)\}$; $f(is) = \{(n \setminus s) \diagup (n \diagup n)\}$. Thus intransitive verbs (such as *died*) are regarded as operators that convert nouns appearing to their left to sentences; transitive verbs (*loves*) are regarded as operators that convert nouns appearing to their right to intransitive verbs; adjectives are regarded as operators that convert nouns appearing to their right to nouns; *very* is regarded as an operator that converts an adjective appearing to its right to an adjective; *is* is regarded as an operator that converts an adjective appearing to its right to an intransitive verb. Such strings as the following resolve to *s*. Therefore, they are sentences in the considered bidirectional categorial grammar: *John* (n) *died* $(n \setminus s)$, $n(n \setminus s) \rightarrow s$; *John* (n) *loves* $((n \setminus s) \diagup n)$ *Mary* (n), $((n \setminus s) \diagup n) n \rightarrow n \setminus s$, $n(n \setminus s) \rightarrow s$; *John* (n) *is* $((n \setminus s) \diagup (n \diagup n))$ *very* $((n \diagup n) \diagup (n \diagup n))$ *old* $(n \diagup n)$, $((n \diagup n) \diagup (n \diagup n))$ $(n \diagup n) \rightarrow n \diagup n$, $((n \setminus s) \diagup (n \diagup n))(n \setminus n) \rightarrow n \setminus s$, $n(n \setminus s) \rightarrow s$.

If instead of *C* we consider the closure of a finite set of fundamental categories under the operation of right (left) diagonalization, Γ, Σ, *R*, and *f* remaining unchanged, we obtain the definition of a *right* (*left*) *categorial grammar*. A language determined by a right (left) categorial grammar is a *right* (*left*) *categorial language*. A right categorial grammar (language) and a left categorial grammar (language) are called *unidirectional categorial grammars* (*languages*). Ajdukiewicz considered only this last form, since he was primarily concerned with systems using Polish parenthesis—free notation, in which functors precede arguments.

If in the definition of a left (right) categorial grammar, we replace *C* by a set containing precisely the (finitely many) fundamental categories ψ_i and the categories $(\psi_i \setminus \psi_j)$ and $(\psi_i \setminus (\psi_j \setminus \psi_k))$ [or, alternatively, $(\psi_i \diagup \psi_j)$ and $(\psi_i \diagup (\psi_j \diagup \psi_k))$], we get a *restricted left* (*right*) *categorial grammar*. The language determined by such a grammar is a *restricted left* (*right*) *categorial language*.

We may now define a *restricted unidirectional categorial grammar* as a grammar which is a restricted left categorial grammar or a restricted right categorial grammar. We may also define a *restricted bidirectional categorial grammar* as a quintuple $\langle \Gamma, C^*, \Sigma, R, f \rangle$, where Γ, Σ, *R*, and *f* have the same significance as in the preceding definitions, whereas C^* is the set of all categories of the form ψ_i, $(\psi_i \setminus \psi_j)$, $(\psi_i \setminus (\psi_j \setminus \psi_k))$, $(\psi_i \diagup \psi_j)$, $(\psi_i \diagup (\psi_j \diagup \psi_k))$. The language determined by such a grammar is called a *restricted bidirectional categorial language*.

It follows immediately from the definitions that every unidirectional (restricted unidirectional) categorial language is a bidirectional (restricted bidirectional) categorial language. On the other hand, it is easy to see that every restricted bidirectional categorial language is a bidirectional categorial language. But Bar-Hillel *et al.* have proved the surprising result that the converse of each of the above statements is also true, that is, we have Theorem 6.

Theorem 6. *Every bidirectional categorial language is an unidirectional categorial language and even a restricted unidirectional categorial language* ([6], [5], pp. 106–114, 189).

The proof of this theorem is indirect. It is proved, in fact, that every bidirectional categorial language, every unidirectional categorial language, and every restricted unidirectional categorial language are type-2 languages in the sense of Chomsky [9] and, conversely, every type-2 language is a restricted unidirectional categorial language. Since the proof of the second part of this theorem is very long ([5], pp. 107–114), we shall only give the first part. But first let us give the suitable form of the definition of a type-2 language ([5], pp. 104–105).

A *simple phrase-structure system* is an ordered couple $\langle \Gamma, P \rangle$, where Γ is a finite vocabulary and P is a finite set of productions of the form $X \rightarrow x (x \neq X \in \Gamma$ and x is not the empty string). A string y *directly generates* a string $z (y \Rightarrow z)$ if y has the form $X_0 X_1 X_2 \ldots X_{n-1} X_n$ ($n \geqslant 0$) and z can be given the form $x_0 x_1 x_2 \ldots x_{n-1} x_n$, such that, for all i, either $X_i = x_i$ (in which case X_i is said to be carried over) or $X_i \rightarrow x_i$, in which case X_i is said to be *rewritten*. A string x *generates* y ($x \Rightarrow y$) if there exists a sequence of strings $z_0, z_1, \ldots, z_r$ such that $x = z_0$, $y = z_r$ and $z_{i-1} \Rightarrow z_i$ ($1 \leqslant i \leqslant r$).

A *context-free grammar* (or a *type-2 grammar*) is an ordered quadruple $G = \langle \Gamma, P, T, S \rangle$, where $\langle \Gamma, P \rangle$ is a simple phrase-structure system, T (the *terminal vocabulary*) is a subset of Γ, none of whose elements occur on the left side of a production, and S is a distinguished element of $\Gamma - T$ (the *initial symbol*). A string x is a *sentence of G* if x is a string over T (a *terminal string*) and $S \Rightarrow x$ in the simple phrase-structure system $\langle \Gamma, P \rangle$. We shall denote by $L(G)$ the set of all sentences of G.

A language L over a vocabulary T is a *type-2 language* if there exists a context-free grammar G such that $L = L(G)$. (A context-free grammar can be viewed as a combinatorial system as defined, for example, by Davis [14], with S an axiom and P the set of productions. It is, more specifically, a rather special kind of semi-Thue system, since in a general semi-Thue system the productions have the form $x_1 \rightarrow x_2$, whereas in a simple phrase-structure system the form is $X \rightarrow x$).

Theorem 7. For any bidirectional categorial grammar $H = \langle \Gamma, C, \Sigma, R, f \rangle$ it is possible to construct a context-free grammar G, such that $L(G)$ is precisely the language determined by H.

PROOF. Let $\mathscr{C}_\Gamma$ be the union of all category sets assigned by f to the elements of Γ. Since Γ is finite and $f(X)$ is finite for every $X \in \Gamma$, it follows that $\mathscr{C}_\Gamma$ is a finite set of categories.

Let us now define inductively the set $\overline{\mathscr{C}}_\Gamma$ as follows: If $\varphi \in \mathscr{C}_\Gamma$, then $\varphi \in \overline{\mathscr{C}}_\Gamma$; if $(\varphi \setminus \psi) \in \overline{\mathscr{C}}_\Gamma$, then φ and ψ belong to $\overline{\mathscr{C}}_\Gamma$; if $(\varphi / \psi) \in \overline{\mathscr{C}}_\Gamma$, then φ and ψ belong to $\overline{\mathscr{C}}_\Gamma$. Let $V = \Gamma \cup \overline{\mathscr{C}}_\Gamma$ and let P consist of the following productions: $\varphi \rightarrow (\varphi / \psi)\psi$, if $(\varphi / \psi) \in \overline{\mathscr{C}}_\Gamma$; $\varphi \rightarrow \psi(\psi \setminus \varphi)$ if $(\psi \setminus \varphi) \in \overline{\mathscr{C}}_\Gamma$; $\varphi \rightarrow X$, if $\varphi \in f(X)$ (for every $X \in \Gamma$). P is clearly finite and $G = \langle V, P, \Gamma, \Sigma \rangle$ is the required context-free grammar. (V is the vocabulary, P the set of productions, Γ the terminal vocabulary of G, and Σ the initial symbol of G.) Indeed, $L(G)$ is precisely the language determined by H.

It would be interesting to find a direct proof of Theorem 6, that is, a proof that uses neither Theorem 7 nor its converse. In fact, such a direct proof of Theorem 6 does not use the notions of context-free grammar and type-2 language.

The syntactic calculus developed by Lambek and exposed in the previous sections differs in several respects from the various types of categorial grammars; in particular, Lambek's calculus allows a greater degree of flexibility in category (type) assignment. Thus his rules of resolution assert that a category α is at the same time a category of the form $\beta / (\alpha \setminus \beta)$, so that, in this and other ways, it is possible to increase the complexity and length of the sequence of category symbols associated with a string by application of rules of resolution. It is not known how Lambek's system is related to bidirectional categorial grammars (unidirectional categorial grammars or context-free grammars), although one would expect to find that the relation is quite close; perhaps every type-2 language may be obtained by a Lambek system and, conversely, every language formed by the sentences of a Lambek system is of type 2 (see Chomsky [11], p. 413).

Similar approaches to those described in Section 6–11 are discussed by Hiż [20], Wundheiler and Wundheiler [47], Suszko [44], Curry and Feys [13], and Curry [12]. In the last paper, the syntactic calculus is regarded from the standpoint of functors; thus n / s would mean a functor forming a noun from a sentential argument on its right, whereas $n \setminus s$ would mean a functor forming a sentence from a nominal argument on the left.

A more formalized description of categorial grammars is given by Mitchell [38]. Some generalizations of the above systems are given by Matthews [35, 36]. For the linguistic origin of the syntactic calculus see, among others, Fries [15] and Harwood [18]. A specific approach to the problem of parts of speech may be found in Šaumjan and Soboleva [45].

Lambek begins his paper [29] with the following words written by Otto Jespersen in 1924 [25]: "The definitions (of the parts of speech) are very far from having attained the degree of exactitude found in Euclidean geometry." The models investigated in the present chapter are an attempt to diminish the discrepancy between the traditional concept of part of speech, on one hand, and mathematical rigor, on the other.

REFERENCES

1. K. Ajdukiewicz, Die syntaktische Konnexität. Studia Philosophica **1935** (1), 1–27.
2. Y. Bar-Hillel, On syntactical categories. *J. Symbolic Logic* **15**, 1–16 (1950).
3. Y. Bar-Hillel, A quasi-arithmetical notation for syntactic description. *Language* **29**, 47–58 (1953).
4. Y. Bar-Hillel, Four lectures on algebraic linguistics and machine translation. A revised version of a series of lectures given in July, 1962, before a NATO advanced summer institute of automatic translation of languages, in Venice, Italy.
5. Y. Bar-Hillel, Language and Information: Selected Essays on Their Theory and Application. Addison-Wesley, Reading, Mass. 1964.
6. Y. Bar-Hillel, C. Gaifman, and E. Shamir, On categorial and phrase structure grammars. *Bull. Res. Council Israel, Sec. F,* **9**, 1–16 (1960).
7. P. Braffort, "Éléments de linguistique mathématique." Enseignement préparatoire aux techniques de la documentation automatique. Euratom, CETIS, Bruxelles, 1960, pp. 51–85.
8. N. Chomsky, "The Logical Structure of Linguistic Theory." Microfilm, Massachusetts Institute of Technology Library, 1955.
9. N. Chomsky, On certain formal properties of grammars, *Inform. Control* **2**, 137–167 (1959).
10. N. Chomsky, Some methodological remarks on generative grammar. *Word* **17**, 219–239 (1961).
11. N. Chomsky, Formal properties of grammars, *in* "Handbook of Mathematical Psychology," Vol. II (R. D. Luce, R. R. Bush, and E. Galanter, eds.), Wiley, New York, 1963, pp. 323–418.
12. H. B. Curry, Some logical aspects of grammatical structure, *in* "Structure of Language and Its Mathematical Aspects." *Proc. 12th Symp. Appl. Math.* American Mathematical Society, Providence, R.I. 1961, 56–68.

13. H. B. Curry and R. Feys, "Combinatory Logic." North-Holland, Amsterdam, 1958.
14. M. Davis, "Computability and Unsolvability." McGraw-Hill, New York, 1958.
15. C. C. Fries, "The Structure of English." New York, 1952.
16. M. Gross, "Théorie des langages." Cours lytographié, Paris, 1964.
17. Z. S. Harris, "Structural Linguistics." Univ. Chicago Press, Chicago, 1961.
18. F. W. Harwood, Axiomatic syntax. The construction and evaluation of a syntactic calculus. *Language* **31** (3), 409–413 (1955).
19. A. A. Hill, Grammaticality. *Word* **17** (1), 1–10 (1961).
20. H. Hiż, Congrammaticality, batteries of transformations and grammatical categories *in* "Structure of English and its Mathematical aspects." *Proc. 12th Symp. Appl. Math.* American Mathematical Society, Providence, R.I., 1961, pp. 43–50.
21. H. Hiż, Comments on Lambek's paper, *in* "Structure of Language and Its Mathematical Aspects." *Proc. 12th Symp. Appl. Math.* American Mathematical Society, Providence, R.I., 1961, pp. 264–265.
22. L. Hjelmslev, Essai d'une théorie des morphèmes. *Acte du IVe congrès international des linguistes, Copenhagen, 1938,* 140–151.
23. L. Ionescu, Asupra calculului tipurilor sintactice ale limbii române. *Studii Cercetări Lingvistice* **16** (3), 407–413 (1965).
24. R. Jakobson, Boas' view of grammatical meaning. *Am. Anthropologist* **61,** 139–145 (1959).
25. O. Jespersen, "The Philosophy of Grammar." New York, 1924.
26. J. Katz, Semi-sentences, *in* "Readings in Philosophy of Language" (J. Katz and J. Fodor, eds.). Prentice-Hall, Englewood Cliffs, N.J., 1963.
27. O. S. Kulagina, On one method of defining grammatical notions on the basis of set theory (in Russian). *Probl. Kibernetiki* **1,** 203–214 (1958).
28. J. Kurylowicz, J. "Esquisses Linguistiques." Wroclaw-Krakow, 1960, pp. 41–50.
29. J. Lambek, The mathematics of sentence structure. *Am. Math. Monthly* **65,** 154–170 (1958).
30. J. Lambek, Contributions to a mathematical analysis of the English verb phrase. *Can. Linguistic Assoc.* **5,** 83–89 (1959).
31. J. Lambek, On the calculus of syntactic types, *in* "Structure of Language and Its Mathematical Aspects." *Proc. 12th Symp. Appl. Math.,* American Mathematical Society, Providence, R.I., 1961, pp. 166–178.
32. S. Lesniewski, Grundzüge eines neuen Systems der Grundlagen der Mathematik. *Fund. Math.* **14,** 1–81 (1929).
33. S. Marcus, Asupra unui model logic al părţii de vorbire. *Studii Cercetări Matematice* **13** (1), 37–62 (1962).
34. S. Marcus, "Gramatici şi Automate Finite." Editura Academiei R. P. R., Bucureşti, 1964.
35. G. H. Matthews, Discontinuity and asymmetry in phrase structure grammars. *Inform. Control* **6,** 137–146 (1963).
36. G. H. Matthews, A note on asymmetry in phrase structure grammars. *Inform. Control* **7,** 360–365 (1964).
37. G. A. Miller, and N. Chomsky, Finitary models of languages users, *in* "Handbook of Mathematical Psychology," Vol. II (R. D. Luce, R. R. Bush, and E. Galanter, eds.). Wiley, New York, 1963, Chap. 13.
38. R. P. Mitchell, A note on categorial grammars, *Intern. Conf. Machine Translation*

Languages Appl. Language Analysis, **1961**.
39. H. Putnam, Some issues in the theory of grammar, *in* "Structure of Language and Its Mathematical Aspects. *Proc. 12th Symp. Appl. Math.,* American Mathematical Society, Providence, R.I., 1961, pp. 25–42.
40. I. I. Revzin, On some notions from the so-called set theoretic conception of language (in Russian). *Vopr. Jazykoznanija* **1960**, (6), 88–94.
41. I. I. Revzin, "Language Models" (in Russian). Izd. Akad. Nauk SSSR, Moscow, 1962.
42. I. I. Revzin, Some problems concerning the theory of language models (in Russian). *Naučhno. Tekhn. Inform.* **1964** (8), 42–46.
43. J. Ruvinskii, Consignes provisoires pour la mise en diagrammes des textes scientifiques. *Rapport GRISA* **5**, 1–27 (1960).
44. R. Suszko, Syntactic structure and semantical reference I. *Studia Logica* **8**, 213–244 (1958).
45. S. K. Šaumjan and P. A. Soboleva, "Applicational Generative Model and Transformational Calculus as Applied to the Russian Language. (in Russian)" Izd. Akad. Nauk SSSR, Moskow, 1963.
46. V. A. Uspenskii, On defining the part of speech in the set-theoretic system of the language (in Russian). *Byull. Obed. Probl. Mašinnogo Perevoda* **1957** (5), 22–26.
47. L. Wundheiler and A. Wundheiler, Some logical concepts for syntax. *in* "Machine Translation of Languages" (W. N. Locke and A. D. Booth, eds.). Wiley, New York, 1955, pp. 194–207.
48. B. Zelinka, Un langage adéquat non homogène, dont les classes sont disjointes deux à deux. *Rev. Roumaine Math. Pures Appl.* **10**, (8), 1249–1251 (1965).
49. P. Ziff, "Semantic Analysis." Cornell Univ. Press, Ithaca, N.Y., 1960.
50. P. Ziff, "About ungrammaticalness." Mimeographed, Univ. Pennsylvania, Philadelphia, 1961.

NOTE ADDED IN PROOF

The above model of parts of speech was used by T. Tobias (The parts of speech in Estonian language (in Russian), *Soobšč. Mašinnomu Perevodu* 1, 90–96 (1962)). An interesting discussion concerning parts of speech may be found in the books by A. Juilland and E. Chang-Rodriguez ("Frequency Dictionary of Spanish Words," Mouton, The Hague, 1964) and A. Juilland, P. M. H. Edwards and I. Juilland ("Frequency Dictionary of Rumanian Words," Mouton, The Hague, 1965). A presentation of syntactic calculus, with the aid of the Theory of Categories, is given by Ana Burghelea (Syntactic types and Theory of Categories, to appear in *Rev. Roumaine Math. Pures Appl.*). Concerning categorial grammars, see Martin Kay (A parsing program for categorial grammars, *Memorandum RM-4283-PR* Rand Corporation, 1964). New results concerning linguistic typology are obtained by B. Zelinka in several papers to appear in *Revue roumaine de math. pures et appl.* and *Bulletin math. de la Société de math. de la R. S. Roumanie.*

Chapter IV

Grammatical Gender

1. Introduction

Grammatical gender is one of the most interesting problems of the theory of grammar. It has been studied from several points of view, such as the relation between the gender of a noun and its semantic content (Lohmann [23]); the relation between the gender of a noun and its ending (Melčuk [30]); the gender, in the light of the correspondence between content and expression (Jakobson [17], Hjelmslev [14], Vasiliu [49]); the syntactic and contextual aspects of the grammatical gender (Diaconescu [6], Zaliznjak [50], Karpinskaja [20]); the study of the gender from the standpoint of its origin and evolution (that is, diachronic aspects; Graur [10, 11], Rosetti [42–44], Fodor [7]); synchronic aspects (Revzin [37–39]; Marcus [25, 27]).

Some of these points of view are, of course, closely connected; others, on the contrary, are very different. But almost all authors agree at present that the semantic criteria are not sufficient for understanding the complex nature of the grammatical gender. We must make use of all related facts concerning this category. In this respect, Hjelmslev writes [15]: On est souvent même amené à admettre la supériorité des définitions sémantiques ou par substance, qui prêtent souvent à l'équivoque et restent fuyantes et difficilement maniables. On ne saurait citer à cet égard un meilleur exemple que celui du genre grammatical: ici la définition sémantique paraît insuffisante ou même impossible, et ce n'est que la définition fonctionnelle, déterminant le genre comme un indice de concordance, qui fournit un point de vue solide et véridique.

Indeed, if we recognize that the grammatical gender is other than the natural one (that is, the sex), we must be consistent and recognize that the form and not the substance will be decisive in the problem we are considering.

We present in this chapter some mathematical models of grammatical gender. The mathematical starting points of these models are some notions and results investigated in the preceding chapters (especially the notions of mixed cells, chains—due to Revzin—and the corresponding results), whereas the linguistic one is the passing from the natural to the grammatical gender. As we shall see, all proposed models involve both morphologic and syntactic aspects, by means of the partitions P and S of the vocabulary Γ.

The analysis we develop has a purely synchronic character, but we hope that it may be useful for a better understanding and a more systematic presentation of the evolution of the structure of grammatical gender in any natural language. We intend also to discuss some very controversial problems such as the neuter gender, the ambiguous gender, the animate and the inanimate, personal genders, and others.

2. From the Natural to the Grammatical Gender

We begin by an attempt to explain, in an intuitive and practical fashion, the formal nature of the relation between natural and grammatical gender. This explanation will anticipate the mathematical models constructed in the next section.

Given a natural language, we shall take, as starting point, two nouns ξ and η representing the prototype of the natural gender (such as *man* and *woman* in English). In certain languages, even this operation, so simple at first sight, claims attention: In German, for instance, the noun *Weib* (woman) cannot be taken as the starting point in such a construction, since its grammatical gender is other than its natural one (the first is neuter, whereas the second is feminine). The problem we are concerned with is to characterize the masculine grammatical gender as well as the feminine so as to reveal clearly the mechanism, the operations by which these are obtained from the respective natural genders. It thus follows that every grammatically masculine noun should be in a formal well-determined relation with the noun ξ and that every grammatically feminine noun should be in a similar relation with the noun η. To obtain such a relation, we shall resort to a concept introduced by Revzin and studied in Section 10, Chapter I, namely, the concept of chain. Though it has already been defined, we shall explain it through some linguistic examples and recall some simple facts.

Each word is naturally associated with two sets of words: the set of its flectional forms and the set of the words occurring in the very same contexts with the given word. The first of these sets is the paradigm of the word, whereas the second is the class of distribution of the given word. For instance, the paradigm of the word *house* is {*house, houses*}, whereas the class of distribution is {*house, table, book,...*}. The flectional forms of each word are considered known and well-determined; therefore, the paradigms are also considered known. As far as the classes of distribution are concerned, they depend upon the set of sentences we have in view. It is desirable to consider, as a sentence, every grammatically well-constructed sequence of words. But this is a difficult task; *as long as no contrary statement is made, the set of sentences will consist, in all following examples, only of syntagms of the type noun + qualitative adjective in the positive degree or qualitative adjective in the positive degree + noun.*

Let us now consider the following four sequences of Latin words: (1) *dies, diem, rem*; (2) *lupi, lupus, urceolus, urceolorum, librorum, libros*; (3) *vir, viro, puero*; (4) *mulierem, aestatem, aestates, instructiones*. A common trait of all these sequences of words is the fact that, in each, two consecutive words are either in the same paradigm (that is, they are flectional forms of the same word) or in the same class of distribution (in other words, they appear in the same contexts). Thus, *lupi* and *lupus* are in the same paradigm, *urceolorum* and *librorum* are in the same class of distribution, etc. Such a sequence of words illustrates the notion of chain (Section 10, Chapter I) when P is the partition into paradigms, whereas S is the partition in families of the Latin vocabulary. We recall that the number of terms in a chain is called the length of the chain. Thus, chains (1) and (3) are of length equal to 3, chain (4) is of length 4, whereas chain (2) is of length 6. Chains (1), (2), (3), and (4) allow us to assert that the words *dies* and *rem* may be linked by a chain of length equal to 3; *lupi* and *libros* may be linked by a chain of length 6, etc.

The using of chains in defining the grammatical genders appears very natural, and indeed, the notion of chain is but a joining of the two fundamental grammatical aspects, the paradigmatic and the syntagmatic one. It is particularly such a joining that is needed in a theory of the gender, because (intuitively speaking) it does not necessarily follow from the fact that two nouns belong to the same gender, that they should belong to the same paradigm or to the same class of distribution. The interconnection alone of the paradigms with the distribution classes can be fruitful in such a problem. Otherwise, in some characterizations of the parts of speech we also use a special type of interconnection of the paradigms and distribution classes: the partition R'. We recall, in this respect, Theorem 4, Chapter II.

The notions of chain and chain length enable us to characterize the masculine and the feminine grammatical gender to be able to pass over from the natural to the grammatical gender. The rules we shall give are but a drawing out of the "formal carcass" of a great number of particular facts noticed in the English, French, Italian, Spanish, Rumanian, Russian, and German languages. All these facts will be explained as illustrations of the following rules.

A noun belongs to the masculine grammatical gender if any word of its paradigm may be joined to any word of the paradigm of ξ by a chain whose length is at most equal to 3. It follows immediately (as a tautological statement) that ξ is of the masculine grammatical gender.

A noun is of the feminine grammatical gender if any word of its paradigm may be joined with any form of η by a chain whose length is at most equal to 3. It follows immediately that η is of the feminine grammatical gender.

A noun is in the neuter if it is neither of the masculine nor of the feminine grammatical gender.

A noun is a double gender if it is both masculine and feminine.

By replacing, in the above rules, the nouns ξ and η by suitable corresponding nouns, we may apply these rules to characterize the grammatical genders of a great number of natural languages. The grammatical category of the gender of nouns is considered *not degenerate* in a language, if there is in that language at least one masculine noun which should not be feminine, and at least one feminine noun which should not be masculine.

3. Grammatical Genders in Natural Languages

Let us illustrate the above rules and procedures in several natural languages.

ENGLISH. The form of an English adjective changes only in function of its degree of comparison. It follows that, given two English nouns ξ' and x, there exists a chain of length not greater than 3, which joins ξ' and x. Indeed, the paradigm of x contains a word x' which is in the same distribution class as ξ', and we have the chain ξ', x', x. For instance, if $\xi' = book$ and $x = teachers$, then $x' = teacher$. If x belongs to the distributional class of ξ', we have the chain ξ', x; for instance, $\xi' = book$, $x = teacher$.

It follows that any English noun may be joined with *man* by a chain whose length is not greater than 3; the same is true if we replace *man* by *woman*. Therefore, any English noun is a double gender; *the grammatical gender of English nouns is degenerate.*

FRENCH. Let $\xi = homme$, $\eta = femme$. The nouns *colins, cahier, murs*, etc., are masculine, since we have the chains (a) *colins, colin, homme*, (b) *colins, hommes*, (c) *colin, homme, hommes*, (d) *cahier, homme*, (e) *cahiers, hommes, homme*, (f) *cahier, homme, hommes*, (g) *murs, mur, homme*, (h) *murs, hommes*, (i) *mur, homme, hommes*; the nouns *plumes, pluie, feuille*, etc., are feminine, since each form of their paradigms may be joined with any form of *femme* by a chain of a length not greater than 3; we have the chains *plumes, plume, femme*; *pluie, femme, femmes*; *feuille, femme*, etc. The nouns *cas, tas, tapis, nez, voix*, etc., whose singular form coincides with the plural, are neuter, since there exists no form of *homme* and no form of *femme* which belong to the distributional class of *cas* (we have *petit cas, petits cas*, but neither *petit hommes*, nor *petits homme*) and no form of *homme* and no form of *femme* which belongs to the distributional class of *voix* (we have *belle voix, belles voix*, but neither *belle femmes*, nor *belles femme*; we have *homme beau, hommes beaux*, but neither *voix beau* nor *voix beaux*). The nouns *camarade, élève, enfant*, etc, which may be preceded both by a masculine adjective and by a feminine adjective, are neuter since no form of *homme* and no form of *femme* belong to the distributional class of such a word. Indeed, we have *bon élève, bonne élève*, but neither *bon femme*, nor *bonne homme*; we have *bons élèves, bonnes élèves*, but neither *bons femmes*, nor *bonnes hommes*, etc.

Since there are French nouns which are masculine but not feminine (*cahier, mur, soleil*, etc. and those which are feminine but not masculine (*plume, pluie, feuille*, etc.), we deduce that *the grammatical gender of French nouns is not degenerate.*

ITALIAN. Let us consider as prototypes of the natural genders the noun *fratello* (masculine) and *donna* (feminine). The noun *frutto* is masculine since each of its forms may be joined to any one of the forms of *fratello* by a chain whose length is not greater than 3. For similar reasons, *castagno, bordone, giro,* etc., are masculine. The noun *boccola* is feminine, since each of its forms may be joined to any one of the forms of *donna* by a chain of length not greater than 3. For similar reasons, *confezione, maremma, roba,* etc., are feminine. Since *giro* is masculine without being feminine, whereas *roba* is feminine without being masculine, it follows that *the grammatical gender of Italian nouns is not degenerate.*

The nouns *nipote, consorte, cantante, giovane, paciente,* etc., which may be preceded both by a masculine and by a feminine adjective, are neuter since no form of *fratello* and no form of *donna* belong to the distributional class of such a word. Indeed, we have *buono giovane, buona giovane,* but neither *buono donna* nor *buona fratello,* etc.

SPANISH. Let us consider as prototypes of the natural genders the noun *padre* (masculine) and *madre* (feminine). The noun *libro* is masculine, since we have the chains *libro, padre; libro, padre, padres; libros, padres; libros, padres, padre.* The noun *casa* is feminine since we have the chains *casa, madre; casa, casas, madres; casas, madres, madre.* Since *libro* is masculine without being feminine, whereas *casa* is feminine without being masculine, it follows that *the grammatical gender of Spanish nouns is not degenerate.*

LATIN. Let $\xi = vir$, $\eta = mulier$. The noun *puer* is masculine, since each of its forms may be joined to each of the forms of *vir* by a chain whose length is not greater than 3. Since *vir* and *puer* each have seven distinct flectional forms, we obtain 49 chains (*puero, puer, vir; pueri, viri, virum; pueros, pueris, viris,* etc.).

The noun *aestas* is feminine, since each of its forms may be joined to each of the forms of *mulier* by a chain whose length is not greater than 3. Since each of the nouns *aestas* and *mulier* has eight distinct flectional forms, we obtain 64 chains (*aestas, mulier; aestatis, aestati, mulieri; aestate, muliere, mulieribus,* etc.).

The noun *tempus* is neither masculine nor feminine. Thus it is neuter.

It seems that our rules agree with the traditional genders of Latin nouns. But let us consider the noun *capra.* The shortest chain which joins the forms *caprae* and *mulieris* has length 4: *caprae, capra, mulier, mulieris.* Therefore, despite common intuition and traditional grammar, *capra* is not a feminine noun.

This example shows that the rules are not suitable for detecting the grammatical genders of Latin nouns in their customary form.

RUMANIAN. Let $\xi = b\breve{a}rbat$, $\eta = femeie$. To verify that *pom* is masculine, we must prove that any word of its paradigm may be joined to any word of the paradigm of *bărbat* by a chain having length less than or equal to 3. Since each paradigm has 7 words, the proof requires the building up of 49 chains. We note some of them, leaving the others to the reader: *pom, bărbat; pomi, bărbaţi, bărbatul; pomule, pomului, bărbatului*, etc. It follows that *pom* is of the masculine grammatical gender. In a similar way, we deduce that *par, copil, stîlp*, etc., are also masculine.

The noun *masă* is of the feminine grammatical gender, since each of its flectional forms belongs to the distributional class of some form of *femeie*. We have, for instance, the chains *masă, mesei, femeii; mesele, femeile, femeilor*, etc.

Pom and *femeie* cannot be joined by a chain whose length is less than 4, since no word of the paradigm of *pom* is in the same distribution class with *femeie* and no word of the paradigm of *femeie* enters the distribution class of *pom*. Therefore, *pom* is not feminine. It may be shown in a similar way that *masă* cannot be joined with *bărbat* through a chain whose length is less than 4. Hence *masă* is not masculine. Thus, we have proved that *in Rumanian the grammatical gender of nouns is not degenerate*.

We now remark that the above reasoning may be applied to any masculine and to any feminine noun; hence we deduce that *Rumanian has no double gender nouns*.

Let us consider the noun *scaun*. This is not a masculine noun, since *scaune* and *bărbaţi* can be joined only by a chain of length 4: *scaune, scaun, bărbat, bărbaţi*. On the other hand, *scaun* is not a feminine noun either, since *scaun* and *femeie* can be joined only by a chain having a length of 4: *scaun, scaune, femei, femeie*. It follows that *scaun* is a neuter noun.

RUSSIAN. Let $\xi = mu\check{z}\check{c}ina$ and $\eta = \check{z}en\check{s}\check{c}ina$. The noun *stol* has the masculine grammatical gender, since any form x' of *stol* belongs to the distribution class of some form of ξ. For instance, *stoly* belongs to the distribution class of *mužčiny*, etc. The noun *kniga* has the feminine grammatical gender, since each of its forms belongs to the distribution class of some form of η. There exist no Russian double-gender nouns, since the adjectives have, in the singular, different masculine and feminine forms, whereas there exist nouns (such as *stol*) which are masculine but not feminine and those (such as *kniga*) which are feminine but not masculine.

The noun *okno* is neither masculine nor feminine, since it belongs to no distribution class of form ξ or of form η. Therefore, *okno* is a neuter noun. The existence of neuter Russian nouns is because the adjectives that can be used with *okno* are not the same as the adjectives for ξ or η.

GERMAN. Let $\xi = Vater$ and $\eta = Mutter$. The noun *Titel* has the masculine gender, since we have the following chains: *Titel, Vater*; *Titel, Titels, Vaters*; *Titel, Titeln, Vätern*; *Titel, Vater, Väter*; *Titels, Vaters, Vater*; *Titels, Vaters, Väter*; *Titels, Vaters, Vätern*; *Titeln, Vätern, Vater*; *Titeln, Vätern, Väter*; *Titeln, Vätern, Vaters*. The noun *Gabel* has the feminine gender, since we have the chains *Gabel, Mutter*; *Gabel, Mutter, Muttern*; *Gabeln, Muttern*; *Gabeln, Muttern, Mutter*. The noun *Fenster* is neither masculine nor feminine; therefore there exist neuter German nouns. But let us consider the word *Knabe*. It is known as a masculine German noun. However, the shortest chain between *Knabe* and *Vater* has length 4. Indeed, *Knabe* and *Vater* do not belong to the same distribution class, since we may say *guten Vater* but not *guten Knabe*. Since *Knaben* and *Vätern* have the same distribution (*guten Knaben, guten Vätern*), we obtain the chain *Knabe, Knaben, Vätern, Vater*, the shortest chain between *Knabe* and *Vater*. It follows that our rules are inadequate for some German nouns.

In conclusion we make the following remarks:

(1) The rules considered permit us, in general, to detect the grammatical genders of English, French, Italian, Spanish, Rumanian, and Russian. Some minor discrepancies, such as the fact that in French the nouns *cas, tas, tapis,* etc., belong to the neuter gender, result from the level of grammaticality we have adopted (adjective + noun, noun + adjective). If we modify the set of marked strings correspondingly, such discrepancies disappear.

(2) The rules considered are not sufficiently adequate for Latin and German. One must seek other rules to detect in a better way the grammatical genders of these languages and, perhaps, of others.

(3) In view of the procedure adopted, a language cannot have more than four genders, whereas its fundamental genders are always the masculine and feminine. But there are situations which do not fall

into this scheme. A deeper analysis of a natural language may reveal the so-called personal genders, whereas in some languages (such as Swedish, where the fundamental genders are the *common* and the *neuter* gender) there is a fundamental distinction other than masculine-feminine.

(4) The grammatical genders have no absolute character. They are relative by a certain choice of the paradigms and sentences (marked strings). If we take, for instance, only isolated words in the function of the sentences, all the words will form but a single class of distribution so that, taking two words at random, we might join them by a chain of length equal to 2. In particular, all nouns will be both masculine and feminine, and therefore the grammatical gender will be degenerate. This remark reveals the essential contextual, syntagmatic character of grammatical gender.

Certain changes in the choice of the paradigms can also upset some of the conclusions obtained above. Thus, if by the paradigm of the Rumanian noun *scaun* we mean the totality of its flectional forms in the singular, and if by the paradigm of the noun *scaune* we understand all its flectional forms in the plural, then *scaun* is of the masculine gender, whereas *scaune* is feminine. Indeed, each of the words *scaun, scaunul, scaunului, scaunule* may be joined with any word of the paradigm of *bărbat* by a chain having at the most a length of 3. Each of the words *scaune, scaunelor, scaunele* may be joined with any word of the paradigm of *femeie* by a chain having, at most, a length equal to 3.

If we reorganize all the paradigms of the neuter Rumanian nouns as we have done above with the paradigm of *scaun*, and divide them into two paradigms, one singular and one plural, the neuter gender ceases to exist in Rumanian. Such a conclusion agrees with that of some others: Bujor[3], Gabinskiĭ[9], Hořejši[16].

Another reorganization of the paradigms which seems in a certain way natural, is the following: Let us put together the paradigms $P(x)$ and $P(y)$ of the nouns x and y obtained, one from another, by means of an inflection denoting the gender: in French $P(cousin)$ with $P(cousine)$, $P(époux)$ with $P(épouse)$, $P(loup)$ with $P(louve)$, etc.; in Italian, $P(eroe)$ with $P(eroina)$, $P(re)$ with $P(regina)$, $P(signore)$ with $P(signora)$, etc.; in Rumanian, $P(profesor)$ with $P(profesoară)$, $P(elev)$ with $P(elevă)$, etc. By such an operation, all the nouns mentioned become double-gender nouns. If we consider, for instance, the French noun *cousin*, we see that it is masculine, because any word from $P(homme)$ is in the same distribution class as a certain word from $P(cousin)$. It is also a feminine noun, because any flectional form of *femme* is in the same distribution class with a certain word from the former paradigm of *cousine, P(cousine)*, and thus from the present enlarged paradigm *P(cousin)* ∪ *P(cousine)*. Therefore, *cousin* has a double gender. In the same way one can show that *eroe, re,* and *signore* become double-gender nouns in Italian, whereas *profesor* and *elev* become double-gender nouns in Rumanian. This is the way the existence of the double-gender nouns is obtained, as well as that of the four distinct genders, for the nouns in Rumanian. A similar idea, but in a different way, has been expressed by Moisil[31]. For the double-gender nouns in Rumanian, see also Pătruţ [34]. The legitimacy of such operations of reorganizing the paradigms must be justified either by practical necessities, such as the making up of algorithms for translating from one language into another[31], or by a more lucid understanding of the logical structure of the paradigms. (A logical pattern of the notion of paradigm has been studied by Marcus[26].)

All the above facts require a general treatment, more formalized and more supple, for us to detect a greater part of the complexity of the grammatical gender. This task will be accomplished in the following sections.

4. Mathematical Models of Grammatical Gender

Let $\{\Gamma, P, \Phi\}$ be an arbitrary language. We shall say that two words $a \in \Gamma$ and $b \in \Gamma$ *belong to the same gender,* and we shall write $a\,\gamma\,b$ if, for any $a' \in P(a)$ and any $b' \in P(b)$, at least one of the following two conditions is fulfilled: $P(a) \cap S(b') \neq 0$; $P(b) \cap S(a') \neq 0$. We shall say that a and b *belong to the same restricted gender* and we shall write $a\,\rho\,b$ if, for any $a' \in P(a)$ and any $b' \in P(b)$, we have $P(a) \cap S(b') \neq 0 \neq P(b) \cap S(a')$.

Proposition 1. The relation γ is reflexive and symmetric, but not transitive in Γ.

PROOF. If $b = a$, we have, for $a' \in P(a)$, $a' \in P(b) \cap S(a')$. Hence, $P(b) \cap S(a') \neq 0$ and $a\,\gamma\,a$, that is, γ is reflexive.

Since the definition of γ is symmetric with respect to a and b, it follows that γ is symmetric: $a\,\gamma\,b \Rightarrow b\,\gamma\,a$.

To prove that γ is not transitive, let us consider the language used in the proof of Proposition 1, of Chapter II. We have $\Gamma = \{a, b, c, d\}$, $P(a) = \{a\}$, $P(b) = \{b\}$, $P(c) = \{c, d\}$, $\Phi = \{ab, cb, ad, cd\}$. Hence $S(a) = \{a, c\}$ and $S(b) = \{b, d\}$. We have $a \gamma c$; indeed, $P(a) \cap S(c) = \{a\} \cap \{a, c\} = \{a\} \neq 0$ and $P(c) \cap S(a) = \{c, d\} \cap \{a, c\} = \{c\} \neq 0$. We have $c \gamma b$; indeed, $P(c) \cap S(b) = \{c, d\} \cap \{b, d\} = \{d\} \neq 0$ and $P(b) \cap S(d) = \{b\} \cap \{b, d\} = \{b\} \neq 0$. On the other hand, we do not have $a \gamma b$, since $P(a) \cap S(b) = P(b) \cap S(a) = 0$.

REMARKS. Two words may belong to the same gender, although they do not belong to the same part of speech. Indeed, as was shown in the proof of the Proposition 1, Chapter II, we have in the above language $P = P'$. It follows that a and c do not belong to the same part of speech. But they belong to the same gender, as was shown in the proof of Proposition 1.

This fact introduces a discrepancy between the grammatical gender and its mathematical model, because the gender concerns a well-determined part of speech.* For instance, the grammatical gender of the adjective is quite different than the grammatical gender of nouns; our models concern only nouns, which is revealed by the next proposition.

Proposition 2. Given a language $\{\Gamma, P, \Phi\}$, if $b \in P(a)$, then $a \gamma b$.

PROOF. We have, for any $a' \in P(a)$ and for any $b' \in P(b)$, $b' \in P(a) \cap S(b')$ and $a' \in P(b) \cap S(a')$, since $P(a) = P(b)$. Therefore $P(a) \cap S(b') \neq 0 \neq P(b) \cap S(a')$.

REMARK. Since two different forms of an adjective may have different genders, it follows from Proposition 2 that the model considered does not concern adjectives.

Proposition 3. There exist a language $\{\Gamma, P, \Phi\}$ and two words $x \in \Gamma$, $y \in \Gamma$ such that $y \in S(x)$, but we do not have $x \gamma y$.

PROOF. Let us consider the following language. $\Gamma = \{a, b, c, d\}$, $P(a) = \{a, c\}$, $P(b) = \{b, d\}$, $\Phi = \{ac, bc, cd\}$. We have $S(a) = \{a, b\}$, $S(c) = \{c\}$, $S(d) = \{d\}$. But a and b do not belong to the same gender, since $d \in P(b)$, $c \in P(a)$, but $P(a) \cap S(d) = P(b) \cap S(c) = 0$.

REMARK. An illustration of Proposition 3 may be found in Rumanian. The nouns *scaun* and *pom* belong to the same class of distribution, although the first is a neuter noun, whereas the second is masculine. The nouns *caiete* and *scaune* belong to the same distribution class,

*This discrepancy will be removed by Proposition 8.

although the first is a feminine noun, whereas the second is neuter.

Proposition 4. Given a language $\{\Gamma, P, \Phi\}$, if $a\rho b$, then $a\gamma b$, but the converse is not true.

PROOF. The implication $a\rho b \Rightarrow a\gamma b$ follows from the definitions. On the other hand, in the language considered in the proof of Proposition 1 we have $a\gamma c$, but not $a\rho c$, since $d \in P(c)$ and $P(a) \cap S(d) = \{a\} \cap \{b, d\} = 0$.

Proposition 5. If $b \in P(a)$, then $a\rho b$.

PROOF. The proof follows immediately from the proof of Proposition 2.

Proposition 6. We have $a\gamma b$ if and only if, for any $a' \in P(a)$ and any $b' \in P(b)$, there exists a chain which joins a' and b' and whose length is not greater than 3.

PROOF. Let $a\gamma b$, $a' \in P(a)$, and $b' \in P(b)$. If $P(a) \cap S(b') \neq 0$, there exists a word $a_1 \in P(a) \cap S(b')$. Hence $a_1 \in P(a') \cap S(b')$, and we have the chain a', a_1, b'. If $P(b) \cap S(a') \neq 0$, there exists a word $b_1 \in P(b) \cap S(a')$. Hence $b_1 \in P(b') \cap S(a')$ and we have the chain a', b_1, b'.

Conversely, let us suppose that, for any $a' \in P(a)$ and any $b' \in P(b)$, there exists a chain which joins a' and b' and whose length is not greater than 3. If the length is equal to 1, we have $a' = b$. Hence $a = b$ and, in view of Proposition 1, it follows that $a\gamma b$. If the length is equal to 2, we have $b' \in P(a')$ or $b' \in S(a')$. If $b' \in P(a')$, then $b' \in P(a)$ — since $P(a') = P(a)$ — and it follows that $P(a) \cap S(b') \neq 0$. Hence $a\gamma b$. If $b' \in S(a')$, then $b' \in P(b) \cap S(a')$. Hence $P(b) \cap S(a') \neq 0$ and $a\gamma b$. If the length is 3, the chain has the form a', c, b', where $c \in P(a')$, $b' \in S(c)$, or $c \in S(a')$, $b' \in P(c)$. In the first case, we have $c \in P(a') \cap S(b') = P(a) \cap S(b') \neq 0$. Hence $a\gamma b$; in the second case we have $c \in P(b') \cap S(a') = P(b) \cap S(a') \neq 0$. Hence $a\gamma b$.

Let us denote by $G(a)$ the set of all words having the same gender as a. Let us recall that $R(a)$ denotes the set of all words which may be joined with a by a chain (see Section 10, Chapter I). We then have a further proposition.

Proposition 7. In any language $\{\Gamma, P, \Phi\}$ and for any $a \in \Gamma$ we have $G(a) \subseteq R(a)$.

PROOF. The Proposition follows immediately from Proposition 6. We remarked, after the proof of Proposition 1, that two words belonging to the same gender may belong, in our model, to different parts of speech. But, in view of Proposition 1, Chapter II, the language used in the proof of Proposition 1 is not adequate, whereas the natural languages are adequate. We may ask whether this situation is still possible in an adequate language. If the answer is negative, the discrepancy we mentioned after the proof of Proposition 1 is considerably diminished. This is precisely the case, since we have Proposition 8.

Proposition 8. In an adequate language, two words belonging to the same gender belong to the same part of speech.

PROOF. Let $\{\Gamma, P, \Phi\}$ be an adequate language and let $a \in \Gamma$. In view of Proposition 7, we have $G(a) \subseteq R(a)$. On the other hand, since the language is adequate, we may apply Theorem 2, Chapter II, and deduce that R is finer than P', that is, we have, for any $a \in \Gamma$, that $R(a) \subseteq P'(a)$. It follows that $G(a) \subseteq P'(a)$; but $P'(a)$ is precisely the part of speech of a. Thus Proposition 8 is proved.

We may ask whether the relation γ may still be nontransitive in an adequate language.

Proposition 9. There exists an adequate language $\{\Gamma, P, \Phi\}$ such that γ is not transitive in Γ.

PROOF. Let $\Gamma = \{a, b, c, d, e, f, g, i, k, l, m, n, p, r\}$, $P(a) = \{a, c, e, n\}$, $P(b) = \{b, d, f, k\}$ $P(g) = \{g, i\}$, $P(l) = \{l, m\}$, $P(p) = \{p, r\}$, $\Phi = \{ab, cd, ef, gb, rb, ik, ld, mk, nk, pf\}$. We have $S(a) = \{a, g, r\}$, $S(b) = \{b\}$, $S(c) = \{c, l\}$, $S(d) = \{d\}$, $S(e) = \{e, p\}$, $S(f) = \{f\}$, $S(i) = \{i, m, n\}$, $S(k) = \{k\}$. We have the following marked P-structures: $P(a)P(b)$, $P(g)P(b)$, $P(l)P(b)$, and $P(p)P(b)$. All other P-structures are unmarked. It follows immediately that $P'(a) = P(a) \cup P(g) \cup P(l) \cup P(p) = \{a, c, e, n, p, r, g, i, l, m\}$, $P'(b) = P(b) = \{b, d, f, k\}$, and $S(x) \subseteq P'(x)$ for every $x \in \Gamma$. Therefore, the language is adequate.

To show that γ is not transitive in Γ, we shall prove that $r \gamma a$ and $a \gamma l$, but we do not have $r \gamma l$. Let $r' \in P(r)$. If $r' = r$, then $P(a) \cap S(r') = P(a) \cap S(r) = \{a\} \neq 0$. If $r' = p$, then $P(a) \cap S(r') = P(a) \cap S(p) = \{a\} \neq 0$. It follows that $r \gamma a$. Let $l' \in P(l)$. If $l' = l$, then $P(a) \cap S(l') = P(a) \cap S(l) = \{c\} \neq 0$. If $l' = m$, then $P(a) \cap S(l') = P(a) \cap S(m) = \{n\} \neq 0$ and we have $a \gamma l$. But we do not have $r \gamma l$, since $P(r) \cap S(l) = P(r) \cap S(m) = P(l) \cap S(p) = P(l) \cap S(r) = 0$.

REMARK. To illustrate Proposition 9, we may consider the following fragment of Rumanian: $a = profesor$, $b = frumos$, $c = profesoară$, $d = frumoasă$, $e = profesori$, $f = frumoşi$, $g = scaun$, $i = scaune$, $k = frumoase$, $l = carte$, $m = cărţi$, $n = profesoare$; P and Φ are defined as in the proof of Proposition 9. Thus, we obtain all types of Rumanian noun syntagms having the noun first and the adjective second.

Proposition 9 shows the necessity of introducing a new notion, which generalizes that of double gender, considered in Sections 2 and 3. Given a subset A of Γ, we shall say that

$$\bigcap_{x \in A} G(x)$$

is the *archigender induced by* A. Every gender is an archigender, since we may take $A = \{x\}$. Thus, the double gender is the archigender induced by the set $A = \{a, b\}$, where a is a masculine noun, whereas b is feminine. The term archigender, used in a similar way by Diaconescu [6], follows from the well-known similar term *archiphonem*. See, for instance, Martinet [29].

Let us consider a set $A \subseteq \Gamma$ containing at least two words x and y for which $G(x) \neq G(y)$. If the archigender induced by A is nonvoid, it is called a *proper archigender*.

Given a word x, we shall define the *order of gender multiplicity of* x as the greatest number n such that there exist n words $a_1, a_2, \ldots, a_n$ for which the following two conditions are fulfilled:

(1) if $1 \leqslant i \leqslant n$, $1 \leqslant j \leqslant n$, and $i \neq j$, then a_i and a_j do not belong to the same gender;

(2) x belongs to every $G(a_i)$ ($1 \leqslant i \leqslant n$). If $n > 1$, we shall say that x has a multiple gender.

The structure of genders may be better understood with the aid of some topological notions.

Recall that a *topology* for a nonvoid set X is a class $\mathcal{T}$ of subsets of X such that: (1) 0 and X are members of $\mathcal{T}$, (2) the intersection of each finite subfamily of $\mathcal{T}$ is a member of $\mathcal{T}$ and (3) the union of each subfamily of $\mathcal{T}$ is a member of $\mathcal{T}$. The ordered pair $(X, \mathcal{T})$ is said to be a *topological space*.

We may define for the set Γ of words the following topology: A subset A of Γ belongs to $\mathcal{T}$ if for every $x \in A$ we have $G(x) \subseteq A$. It is easy to see that the conditions (1), (2), and (3) are fulfilled. But this topology has a property which is stronger than (2): The intersection of each subfamily of $\mathcal{T}$ is a member of $\mathcal{T}$. Hartnett called such a topology a *total topology*[13]. A topological space $(X, \mathcal{T})$ for which $\mathcal{T}$ is a total topology is said to be a *total space*.

The members of a topology are said to be *open sets*, whose complements are then *closed sets*. Therefore, a total topology has the property that the intersection of an arbitrary collection of open sets is an open set.

We say that a topological space $(X, \mathscr{T})$ has *the smallest open set property* if, for each $x \in X$, there exists a unique member $H(x)$ of $\mathscr{T}$ such that $x \in H(x)$ and $H(x) \subseteq H$ for each open set H such that $x \in H$. Hartnett has obtained the following result[13].

Proposition 10. Let $(X, \mathscr{T})$ be a topological space. Then $(X, \mathscr{T})$ is a total space if and only if $(X, \mathscr{T})$ has the smallest open set property.

PROOF. If $(X, \mathscr{T})$ is a total space and $x \in X$, let $H(x)$ be the intersection of all the open sets to which x belongs. Clearly, $H(x)$ satisfies the definition above, and so the space is total.

Conversely, suppose that $(X, \mathscr{T})$ has the smallest open set property. If $\{H_i; i \in I\}$ is a family of open sets indexed by I, $H = \bigcap \{H_i; i \in I\}$ and $x \in H$, then $x \in H_i$ for each i. But each H_i is an open set and so $\{x\} \subseteq H(x) \subseteq H_i$, where $H(x)$ is the smallest open set to which x belongs. Hence, $H(x) \subseteq \bigcap \{H_i; i \in I\}$ for each $x \in H$ and, therefore,

$$H = \bigcup \{\{x\}; x \in H\} \subseteq \bigcup \{H(x); x \in H\}$$
$$\subseteq \bigcap \{H_i; i \in I\} = H.$$

Hence H is an open set and $\mathscr{T}$ is a total topology.

It is interesting to establish the linguistic significance of the sets $H(x)$ in the total space $(\Gamma, \mathscr{T})$. In this aim, let us put $G_1(x) = \bigcup \{G(y); y \in G(x)\}$, $G_2(x) = \bigcup \{G(y); y \in G_1(x)\}, \ldots, G_n(x) = \bigcup \{G(y); y \in G_{n-1}(x)\}, \ldots, G_\infty(x) = \bigcup G_n(x)$. It is easy to see that $G_n(x) \subseteq G_{n+1}(x)$ for $n = 1, 2, \ldots$.

Proposition 11. In the total space $(\Gamma, \mathscr{T})$ we have $H(x) = G_\infty(x)$ for each $x \in \Gamma$.

PROOF. Let $y \in G_\infty(x)$. There exists an integer n such that $y \in G_n(x)$. Hence $G(y) \subseteq G_{n+1}(x) \subseteq G_\infty(x)$. Therefore $G_\infty(x)$ is an open set. Since $x \in G_\infty(x)$ and $H(x)$ is the intersection of all the open sets to which x belongs, it follows that $H(x) \subseteq G_\infty(x)$. On the other hand, there exists a finite sequence of words $x_1, x_2, \ldots, x_n$, such that $x_1 \in G(x)$, $x_2 \in G(x_1), \ldots, x_n \in G(x_{n-1})$ and $x_n = y$. Since $H(x)$ is open, we have $G(x_i) \subseteq H(x)$ for $1 \leqslant i \leqslant n$. Therefore $y \in H(x)$ and $G_\infty(x) \subseteq H(x)$.

Corollary 1. Given two words x and y, we have either $H(x) = H(y)$, or $H(x) \cap H(y) = 0$ [that is, the relation $b \in H(a)$ is an equivalence relation].

PROOF.   The proof follows immediately from Proposition 11.

Corollary 2.   A language possesses no proper archigender if and only if $G(x) = H(x)$ for each word x.

PROOF.   Let us suppose that no proper archigender exists. Given two words x and y such that $y \in G(x)$, we have $G(x) \cap G(y) \neq 0$ (in view of Proposition 1). Hence $G(y) = G(x)$. It follows that $G_1(x) = G(x)$. Therefore $G_n(x) = G(x)$ for $n = 1, 2, \ldots$ and, in view of Proposition 11, $H(x) = G(x)$.

Conversely, if $H(x) = G(x)$ for each $x \in \Gamma$, then, by Corollary 1, the relation γ is an equivalence relation in Γ. Hence $G(x) \cap G(y) \neq 0$ implies $G(x) = G(y)$ and no proper archigender exists.

Corollary 3.   We have $G(x) = H(x)$ for every $x \in \Gamma$ if and only if no word has a multiple gender.

PROOF.   It is enough to remark that a word has a multiple gender if and only if it belongs to a proper archigender and to take into account Corollary 2.

A *base* $\mathscr{B}$ for a topology for a set is a subfamily of the topology such that each open set is the union of members of $\mathscr{B}$. The family of all bases for a total space has the following property[13].

Proposition 12.   Let $(X, \mathscr{T})$ be a total space.   For each $x \in X$, let $H(x)$ be the smallest open set such that $x \in H(x)$ and let $\mathscr{B}_1 = \{H(x); x \in X\}$. Then for any base $\mathscr{B}$ of $\mathscr{T}$ we have $\mathscr{B}_1 \subseteq \mathscr{B}$ (that is, $\mathscr{B}_1$ is a minimal base for $\mathscr{T}$).

PROOF.   If H is an open set and $y \in H$, then $\{y\} \subseteq H(y) \subseteq H$ and so $H = \cup \{\{y\}; y \in H\} \subseteq \cup \{H(y); y \in H\} \subseteq H$. Therefore, $\mathscr{B}_1$ is a base. To show that $\mathscr{B}_1$ is a minimal base, let $\mathscr{B}$ be an arbitrary base for the total topology. For each $x \in X$, $H(x)$ is open, $H(x) = \cup \{B_i; B_i \in \mathscr{B}\}$, and so $x \in B_j \subseteq H(x)$ for some $B_j \in \mathscr{B}$. But then $B_j = H(x)$ because $H(x)$ is the smallest open set to which x belongs. Hence $H(x) \in \mathscr{B}$ for each $x \in X$ and $\mathscr{B}_1 \subseteq \mathscr{B}$.

We now may characterize some types of isomorphism concerning the structure of grammatical gender. We say that two languages $\{\Gamma_1, P_1, \Phi_1\}$ and $\{\Gamma_2, P_2, \Phi_2\}$ are *isomorphic with respect to the gender* if there exists a $1:1$ mapping f of Γ_1 onto Γ_2, such that for any $x \in \Gamma_1$, we have $f(G(x)) = G(f(x))$. We say that $\{\Gamma_1, P_1, \Phi_1\}$ and $\{\Gamma_2, P_2, \Phi_2\}$ are *isomorphic in the broad sense with respect to the gender*, if there exists a $1:1$ mapping g of Γ_1 onto Γ_2, such that, for any $x \in \Gamma_1$ we have $g(H(x)) = H(g(x))$.

Let us recall two well-known notions.

Given two topological spaces $(X, \mathscr{T})$ and $(Y, \mathscr{J})$, a mapping φ of X into Y is said to be *continuous* if for any open subset K of Y the set $\varphi^{-1}(K) = \{x; \varphi(x) \in K\}$ is open in $(X, \mathscr{T})$. Moreover, if φ is $1:1$ and onto and its inverse φ^{-1} is also continuous, then φ is said to be a *homeomorphism* between $(X, \mathscr{T})$ and $(Y, \mathscr{J})$. Two topological spaces are called *homeomorphic* if there is a homeomorphism between them.

Proposition 13. Let $(X, \mathscr{T})$ and $(Y, \mathscr{J})$ be total spaces, let $a \in X$, and let $\varphi : X \to Y$. φ is continuous if and only if $\varphi(H(a)) \subseteq H(\varphi(a))$ for each $a \in X$; φ is a homeomorphism if and only if φ is $1:1$, onto, and $\varphi(H(a)) = H(\varphi(a))$ for each $a \in X [13]$.

PROOF. The first assertion follows from the fact that continuity can be described in terms of the bases for the topologies and Proposition 10. Let us prove the second assertion. If φ is a homeomorphism, then φ and φ^{-1} are continuous and so, for each $a \in X$, $\varphi(H(a)) \subseteq H(\varphi(a))$ and $\varphi^{-1}(H(\varphi(a))) \subseteq H(\varphi^{-1}(\varphi(a))) = H(a)$. From the latter inclusion, we have $\varphi(\varphi^{-1}(H(\varphi(a)))) = H(\varphi(a)) \subseteq \varphi(H(a))$, and hence $\varphi(H(a)) = H(\varphi(a))$. On the other hand, if $\varphi(H(a)) = H(\varphi(a))$ for each $a \in X$, φ is $1:1$ and onto, then φ is continuous because $\varphi(H(a)) \subseteq H(\varphi(a))$. But φ^{-1} is continuous at each $b \in Y$ because $b = \varphi(a)$ for a unique $a \in X$, $\varphi^{-1}(H(b)) = \varphi^{-1}(H(\varphi(a))) = \varphi^{-1}(\varphi(H(a))) = H(a) = H(\varphi^{-1}(b))$, and therefore $\varphi^{-1}(H(b)) \subseteq H(\varphi^{-1}(b))$.

From Proposition 13 follows Proposition 14.

Proposition 14. Given two languages $L_1 = \{\Gamma_1, P_1, \Phi_1\}$ and $L_2 = \{\Gamma_2, P_2, \Phi_2\}$, the corresponding total spaces $(\Gamma_1, \mathscr{T}_1)$ and $(\Gamma_2, \mathscr{T}_2)$ are homeomorphic if and only if L_1 and L_2 are isomorphic in the wide sense with respect to the gender.

In Section 6, Chapter II, we defined the notion of *PS*-isomorphism. Since the genders of a language are completely determined by the partitions P and S, Proposition 15 follows.

Proposition 15. If two languages are PS-isomorphic, they are isomorphic with respect to the gender.

It would be interesting to establish whether the converse of Proposition 15 is also true.

Proposition 16. There exist two P-isomorphic and S-isomorphic languages, which are not isomorphic with respect to the gender.

PROOF. Let us consider the languages used in the proof of Proposition 43, Chapter II: $\Gamma_1 = \Gamma_2 = \{a, b, c, d\}$, $P_1(b) = \{b, c, d\} = P_2(b)$, $\Phi_1 = \{ab, ac, ad\}$, $\Phi_2 = \{ad, bd, cd\}$. It is easy to see that $S_1 = P_1$ and $S_2(a) = \{a, b, c\}$. Since $P_1(a) = S_1(a) = \{a\}$, it follows that $G_1(a) = \{a\}$. In view of Proposition 2, we have $\{b, c, d\} \subseteq G_1(b) \cap G_1(c) \cap G_1(d)$. Since $P_1(a) \cap S_1(b') = P_1(b) \cap S_1(a') = 0$ for any $b' \in P_1(b)$ and $a' \in P_1(a)$; $P_1(a) \cap S_1(c') = P_1(c) \cap S_1(a') = 0$ for any $c' \in P_1(c)$ and $a' \in P_1(a)$, and $P_1(a) \cap S_1(d') = P_1(d) \cap S_1(a') = 0$ for any $d' \in P_1(d)$ and $a' \in P_1(a)$, it follows that $G_1(b) = G_1(c) = G_1(d) = \{b, c, d\}$. On the other hand, we have $P_2(c) \cap S_2(a) = \{b, c\} \neq 0$ and $P_2(d) \cap S_2(a) = \{b, c\} \neq 0$, $P_2(a) \cap S_2(d) = P_2(b) \cap S_2(a) = 0$; in view of Proposition 2, it follows that $G_2(a) = \{a, c, d\}$, $G_2(b) = \{b, c, d\}$, $G_2(c) = \{a, b, c, d\}$, and $G_2(d) = \{a, b, c, d\}$. Since $G_1(x)$ contains at most three words for any $x \in \Gamma_1$, whereas $G_2(y)$ contains four words for some $y \in \Gamma_2$, it follows that the languages considered are not isomorphic with respect to the gender. On the other hand, in view of Proposition 43, Chapter II, these languages are both P- and S-isomorphic.

Proposition 17. If two languages are isomorphic with respect to the gender, they are isomorphic in the broad sense with respect to gender.

PROOF. Let us suppose that L_1 and L_2 are isomorphic with respect to the gender, that is, there exists a $1:1$ mapping f of Γ_1 onto Γ_2 such that $f(G(x)) = G(f(x))$. Let $y \in H(x)$. In view of Proposition 11, there exists a finite sequence $x_1, x_2, \ldots, x_i, \ldots, x_n$ such that $x_i \in G(x_{i-1})$ $(2 \leq i \leq n)$, $x_1 = x$ and $x_n = y$. Since $f(G(u)) = G(f(u))$ for any $u \in \Gamma_1$, it follows that $f(x_i) \in G(f(x_{i-1}))$ $(2 \leq i \leq n)$. Hence, using Proposition 11 again, we get $f(y) \in H(f(x))$ and $f(H(x)) \subseteq H(f(x))$. In a similar way one proves that $H(f(x)) \subseteq f(H(x))$.

Proposition 18. There exist two languages which are isomorphic in the broad sense with respect to the gender, but not isomorphic with respect to the gender.

PROOF. Let $\Gamma_1 = \{a, b, c, d, e, f, g, h, i, j\}$, $P_1(a) = \{a, b, c, d, e\}$, $P_1(f) = \{f\}$, $P_1(g) = \{g, h, i, j\}$, $\Phi_1 = \{ag, bg, ch, di, ej, fj\}$, $\Gamma_2 = \{a', b', c', d', e', f', g', h', i', j'\}$, $P_2(a') = \{a', c'\}$, $P_2(b') = \{b', d'\}$, $P_2(e') = \{e', f'\}$, $P_2(g') = \{g', h', i', j'\}$, $\Phi_2 = \{a'g', b'g', c'h', d'i', e'j', f'h'\}$. We have $S_1(a) = \{a, b\}$, $S_1(c) = \{c\}$, $S_1(e) = \{e, f\}$, $S_1(g) = \{g\}$, $S_1(h) = \{h\}$, $S_1(i) = \{i\}$, $S_1(j) = \{j\}$, $S_2(a') = \{a', b'\}$, $S_2(c') = \{c', f'\}$, $S_2(d') = \{d'\}$, $S_2(e') = \{e'\}$, $S_2(g') = \{g'\}$, $S_2(h') = \{h'\}$, $S_2(i') = \{i'\}$, $S_2(j') = \{j'\}$. It is easy to see that $G(a) = \{a, b, c, d, e, f\}$, $G(g) = \{g, h, i, j\}$ (we make use of Proposition 2), $G(a') = \{a', c'\}$, $G(b') = \{b', d'\}$, $G(e') = \{e', f'\}$, $G(g') = \{g', h', i', j'\}$, $H(a) = H(b) = H(c) = H(d) = H(e) = H(f) = \{a, b, c, d, e, f\}$, $H(g) = H(h) = H(i) = H(j) = \{g, h, i, j,\}$, $H(a') = H(b') = H(c') = H(d') = H(e') = H(f') = \{a', b', c', d', e', f'\}$, $H(g') = H(h') = H(i') = H(j') = \{g', h', i', j'\}$. Let us define φ as follows: $\varphi(x) = x'$, where $x = a, b, c, d, e, f, g, h, i, j$. We have $\varphi(H(x)) = H(\varphi(x))$ for every $x \in \Gamma_1$. Hence the languages considered are isomorphic in the broad sense with respect to the gender, since $G(a)$ contains six words, whereas $G(x')$ contains at most four words, for any $x' \in \Gamma_2$.

REMARK. The languages considered in the proof of Proposition 18 become fragments formed by nominal syntagms of Latin and Rumanian, respectively, if we take $a = vir$, $b = viri$, $c = viro$, $d = virum$, $e = viris$, $f = generis$, $g = fortis$, $h = forti$, $i = fortem$, $j = fortibus$, $a' = scaun$, $b' = pom$, $c' = scaune$, $d' = pomi$, $e' = carte$, $f' = cărți$, $g' = frumos$, $h' = frumoase$, $i' = frumosi$, $j' = frumoasă$.

5. Grammatical Genders in Homogeneous Languages

The grammatical genders of a homogeneous language present some important particulars.

Proposition 19. If $\{\Gamma, P, \Phi\}$ is a homogeneous language, then γ is transitive in Γ.

PROOF. Let $a \in \Gamma$, $b \in \Gamma$, and $c \in \Gamma$ such that $a \gamma b$ and $b \gamma c$. We shall show that $a \gamma c$. Let $a' \in P(a)$ and $c' \in P(c)$. Since $a \gamma b$, we have at least one of the relations (1) $P(a) \cap S(b) \neq 0$ or (2) $P(b) \cap S(a') \neq 0$.

Since $b \gamma c$, we have at least one of the relations (3) $P(c) \cap S(b) \neq 0$; (4) $P(b) \cap S(c') \neq 0$. If we have (1) and (3), then $b \in R(a)$ and $c \in R(b)$. Hence, because R is a partition of Γ, $c \in R(a)$. If we have (1) and (4), we deduce from (1) that $b \in R(a)$, whereas (4) implies, in view of the homogeneity, that $P(c') \cap S(b) \neq 0$. But $P(c') = P(c)$. Hence $P(c) \cap S(b) \neq 0$ and $c \in R(b)$; therefore, $c \in R(a)$. If we have (2) and (3), we deduce from (2), in view of the homogeneity, that $S(b) \cap P(a') \neq 0$; but $P(a') = P(a)$. Hence $P(a) \cap S(b) \neq 0$ and $b \in R(a)$. On the other hand, (3) implies $c \in R(b)$; therefore, $c \in R(a)$. If we have (2) and (4), we deduce, in view of the homogeneity, that $S(b) \cap P(a') \neq 0 \neq S(b) \cap P(c')$. Hence, since $P(a') = P(a)$ and $P(c') = P(c)$, $b \in R(a)$, $c \in R(b)$, and, therefore, $c \in R(a)$. We have thus proved that $a \gamma b$ and $b \gamma c$ imply $c \in R(a)$. But in view of Theorem 10, Chapter II, we have for each word x of a homogeneous language, $K(x) = R(x)$. Hence $c \in K(a)$. It follows that we have at least one of the relations $P(c) \cap S(a) \neq 0$, $P(a) \cap S(c) \neq 0$. But in each of these cases we have $c \in G(a)$. Hence $a \gamma c$.

Proposition 20. In any homogeneous language, γ is an equivalence relation in Γ.

PROOF. The proof follows from Propositions 1 and 19.

Proposition 21. In any homogeneous language we have $G(x) = H(x)$ for each word x.

PROOF. Let $x_1 \in G(x)$. In view of Proposition 20, we have $G(x_1) = G(x)$. Hence $G_1(x) = G(x)$. It follows, by induction, that $G_n(x) = G(x)$ for every word x and every positive integer n. Therefore $G_\infty(x) = G(x)$. By Proposition 11, we deduce $H(x) = G(x)$ for each word x.

Proposition 22. In a homogeneous language there exists no proper archigender.

PROOF. The proof follows from Proposition 21 and Corollary 2.

Proposition 23. In a homogeneous language no word has a multiple gender.

PROOF. This proof follows from Proposition 21 and Corollary 3.

Proposition 24. If two words in a homogeneous language have the same gender, they belong to the same part of speech.

PROOF. This follows from Theorem 8, Chapter II, and Proposition 8.

Proposition 25. If $\{\Gamma, P, \Phi\}$ is homogeneous, the associated total space $(\Gamma, \mathcal{T})$ has the following property: For each $x \in \Gamma$, $G(x)$ is the smallest open set to which x belongs.

PROOF. The proof follows from Propositions 10 and 21.

REMARKS. The total topology of a homogeneous language is the topology of an equivalence relation, in the sense that each open set is a union of γ-equivalence classes, that is, a union of genders. Conversely, every union of genders is an open set, in view of Proposition 25. Since the complement of a union of γ-equivalence classes is also a union of γ-equivalence classes, it follows that every closed set is open, and conversely. A systematic investigation of the topology induced by an equivalence relation has been made by Tondeur [48]. Some properties of total topologies have been given by Marcus [24] (see also the corrections indicated in [28]).

The results just obtained enable us to reconsider some facts concerning grammatical genders in natural languages. In Section 2 we found that every English noun has a double gender. But in fact no English noun has a multiple gender in the sense of our definition, because the masculine and feminine genders are not distinct in English. On the other hand, in Section 8, Chapter II, we established that all English nouns which are neither singularia tantum nor pluralia tantum are nonhomogeneous. This situation suggests that the converse of Proposition 23 is not true. In fact, all English nouns belong to the same grammatical gender.

We remarked in Section 2 that some choice of paradigms yields the existence of the nouns having double gender in French, Rumanian, and other languages. In the light of the last results, we may explain the reason for this situation.

Let us ignore the singularia tantum and the pluralia tantum. In this case, as we remarked in Section 8, Chapter II, the French nouns become homogeneous and, in view of Proposition 23, the existence of nouns having a multiple gender is not possible. However, let us consider, in contrast to the customary situation, that *bergère* is an inflected form of *berger*. Hence $P(berger) = \{berger, bergère, bergers, bergères\}$.

Berger and *maison* are of the same gender, since we have the chains *bergère, maison; bergères, maisons.* Hence *berger* and *bergers* may be joined with any form of *maison* by a chain of length not greater than 3. For similar reasons, we find that *berger* and *crayon* have the same gender. Since *maison* and *crayon* do not have the same gender (there exists no chain joining *crayon* and *maison*), it follows that *berger* has a multiple gender. But this situation—which seems to contradict Proposition 23—becomes possible because the reorganizing of some paradigms requires the sacrifice of the homogeneity, even in the absence of singularia tantum and pluralia tantum. Indeed, we shall show that, with the new paradigms, the fragment of French noun syntagms is not homogeneous. We have $P(berger) \cap S(feuille) = \{bergère\} \neq 0$, whereas $P(feuille) \cap S(berger) = 0$.

A similar situation occurs in Italian and in Spanish, but a quite different one occurs in Rumanian. As we established in Section 8, Chapter II, most Rumanian nouns are not homogeneous and, as is easy to see, the nonhomogeneity persists when we reorganize some paradigms following the above procedure.

Let us return to the results just proved. Propositions 19–23 show the simplicity of the structure of genders in homogeneous languages. It is known that the genders in Slavic languages have a more complex structure than in the Western romance languages. Propositions 22 and 23 enable us to understand the formal nature of this difference. Moreover, we may ask whether this simplicity is characteristic for homogeneous languages, for instance, if the converse of Proposition 20 is true. The answer is negative, as shown in the next proposition.

Proposition 26.   There exists an adequate nonhomogeneous language in which γ is an equivalence relation.

PROOF.   Let us consider the language used in the proof of Theorem 1, Chapter III: $\Gamma = \{a, b_1, b_2, c_1, c_2, d\}$, $P(a) = \{a, b_1, c_1\}$, $P(b_2) = \{b_2, c_2\}$, $P(d) = \{d\}$, $\Phi = \{aa, b_1c_1, b_1c_2, b_2c_1, b_2c_2, d\}$. As shown by Theorem 1, Chapter III, this language is adequate and nonhomogeneous. We have $S(a) = \{a\}$, $S(b_1) = \{b_1, b_2\}$, $S(c_1) = \{c_1, c_2\}$, $S(d) = \{d\}$. Since $P(a) \cap S(b_2) \neq 0 \neq P(a) \cap S(c_2)$, a and b_2 have the same gender; since $P(a) = P(b_1) = P(c_1)$, we have also $b_1 \gamma b_2$ and $c_1 \gamma b_2$. Since $P(a) \cap S(b_2) \neq 0 \neq P(a) \cap S(c_2)$, we have $a \gamma c_2$. In a similar way, we find that $b_1 \gamma c_2$ and $c_1 \gamma c_2$. Since $G(d) = \{d\}$ and in view of Proposition 2, we have $G(a) = G(b_1) = G(c_1) = G(b_2) = G(c_2) = \{a, b_1, c_1, b_2, c_2\}$ and γ is an equivalence relation in Γ.

REMARK. By comparing the proof of Theorem 1, Chapter III, with the proof of Proposition 26, we find that $K(x) = G(x)$ for each $x \in \Gamma$. It would be interesting to establish whether in each adequate language whose genders form a partition of Γ, the above equality holds. In any case we have a further proposition.

Proposition 27. If, in an adequate language, γ is an equivalence relation in Γ, the corresponding partition G of Γ fulfills the equalities $P' = G' = R'$.

PROOF. We have, in view of Propositions 2 and 7, $P(x) \subseteq G(x) \subseteq R(x)$ for each $x \in \Gamma$. On the other hand, since the language is adequate, we may apply Theorem 4, Chapter II and deduce that $P' = R'$. Then, by Lemma 1, Chapter II, $G' = P'$.

Proposition 28. If, in an adequate language, γ is an equivalence relation in Γ and the classes form a partition of Γ, then $G'(x) = K'(x)$ for every $x \in \Gamma$.

PROOF. We have, by Proposition 7, Chapter I, $P(x) \subseteq K(x) \subseteq R(x)$ for each $x \in \Gamma$. Since the language is adequate, we have, in view of Theorem 4, Chapter II, that $P' = R'$. Since the classes define a partition of Γ, we deduce from Lemma 1, Chapter II, that $P' = K' = R'$. In view of Proposition 27, we have $K' = G'$.

We shall now give a result which makes the structure of the grammatical genders in homogeneous languages quite precise.

Proposition 29. In a homogeneous language the genders coincide with the classes, that is, we have $G(x) = K(x)$ for each word x.

PROOF. In view of Proposition 7 we have $G(x) \subseteq R(x)$ for every word x. On the other hand, since the language is homogeneous, we have, by Theorem 10, Chapter II, that $K(x) = R(x)$ for any $x \in \Gamma$. Thus, Proposition 29 will be proved if we show that $K(x) \subseteq G(x)$ for each $x \in \Gamma$. Let $y \in K(x)$. We have at least one of the inequalities $P(x) \cap S(y) \neq 0$ or $P(y) \cap S(x) \neq 0$. Let $x' \in P(x)$ and $y' \in P(y)$. If $P(x) \cap S(y) \neq 0$, then, since $P(x) = P(x')$, $P(x') \cap S(y) \neq 0$ and, in view of the homogeneity, $P(y) \cap S(x') \neq 0$. If $P(y) \cap S(x) \neq 0$, since $P(y) = P(y')$, $P(y') \cap S(x) \neq 0$, and in view of the homogeneity, we have $P(x) \cap S(y') \neq 0$. Hence $y \in G(x)$ and Proposition 29 is proved.

REMARK.   Since, in view of Theorem 10, Chapter II, in any homogeneous language, the classes form a partition of Γ, it follows from Proposition 29 that *the genders of a homogeneous language form a partition of Γ.* Thus, Proposition 29 is an improvement of Proposition 20.

The converse of Proposition 29 is not true, as shown by the language used in the proof of Proposition 26. The same language shows the existence of a nonhomogeneous language in which $K(x) = G(x) = R(x)$ for any $x \in \Gamma$.

An illustration of Proposition 29 is given by French nouns, if we ignore the singularia and pluralia tantum. Thus we get a homogeneous language in which the nouns form two classes: one contains all masculine nouns, the other all feminine nouns.

Another peculiarity of homogeneous languages is given by Proposition 30.

Proposition 30.   In any homogeneous language we have $S(x) \subseteq G(x)$ for any $x \in \Gamma$.

PROOF.   In view of Proposition 7, Chapter I, we always have $S(x) \subseteq K(x)$ for any $x \in \Gamma$. Then, by Proposition 29 and since the language is homogeneous, $S(x) \subseteq G(x)$.

REMARK.   Proposition 30 shows an important difference between nonhomogeneous and homogeneous languages. Indeed, by Proposition 3, there exists a nonhomogeneous language in which two words belong to the same gender, although they are not in the same family.

Proposition 31.   There exist adequate nonhomogeneous languages, in which the coincidence between the genders and the classes is no longer valid.

PROOF.   Indeed, let us consider the language used in the proof of Theorem 9, Chapter II. We have $\Gamma = \{a, b, c, d\}$, $P(a) = \{a, b\}$, $P(c) = \{c, d\}$, $\Phi = \{ad, bb, ab, bc, bd, dc, db, dd\}$, $S(a) = \{a\}$, $S(b) = \{b, d\}$, $S(c) = \{c\}$. In view of Theorem 9, Chapter II, this language is adequate and nonhomogeneous. On the other hand, it is easy to see that $G(b) = \{a, b\}$, $K(b) = \{a, b, c, d\}$. Hence $G(b) \neq K(b)$.

Proposition 32.   In any homogeneous language, the restricted genders coincide with the genders; that is, we have $\gamma = \rho$.

PROOF.   Let $a \in \Gamma$, $b \in \Gamma$. Since $a \rho b$ implies $a \gamma b$, it remains to prove that the converse holds. But, in view of Proposition 29, $a \gamma b$ implies

$b \in K(a)$. Therefore we have at least one of the relations $P(a) \cap S(b) \neq 0$ or $P(b) \cap S(a) \neq 0$. But, by virtue of the homogeneity, both these relations are true. Hence, for any $a' \in P(a)$ and $b' \in P(b)$, we have $P(a) \cap S(b') \neq 0 \neq P(b) \cap S(a')$; therefore, $a \rho b$.

It would be interesting to find the particular characteristics of the genders in other types of languages studied in Chapter II.

6. Categories in the Sense of Revzin

As we remarked at the end of Section 2, Chapter I, Revzin has defined a language as a system $\{\Gamma, P, \Phi, \mathscr{V}, \varphi\}$, where Γ, P, and Φ maintain their customary acception, whereas $\mathscr{V}$ is a collection of subsets of Γ, called *categories*, and φ is a function which associates to each word x the intersection of all categories containing x; $\varphi(x)$ is called the *elementary category* of x ([38], p. 42–43). We may take $\mathscr{V}$ large enough to contain such important sets of words as the parts of speech and the grammatical genders of the considered language.

Following Revzin, a category $V \in \mathscr{V}$ is said to be *paradigmatic* if, for any $x \in V$, we have $P(x) \subseteq V$: the category V is said to be *syntagmatic* if for any $x \in V$ we have $S(x) \subseteq V$ ([38, 39]).

It is obvious that the parts of speech are paradigmatic categories. In order that every part of speech of a language L be a syntagmatic category, it is necessary and sufficient that L be adequate.

We recall that the word a *dominates* the word b if for any pair of strings x and y such that $xay \in \Phi$, we have $xby \in \Phi$. If any word of a set A dominates any word of a set B, we say that A *dominates* B and we write $A \rightarrow B$. If no word c exists such that $c \rightarrow A$, and $c \notin A$, we say that A is an *initial set*. Let us denote by A_1 the set of all words b such that $A \rightarrow b$. The set $\mathscr{G}(A) = A \cup A_1$ is called a *grammatical category*; it is the *grammatical category generated by* A. If A is a family, then $\mathscr{G}(A)$ is called an *elementary grammatical category*.

It is easy to see that, in general, a grammatical category is neither paradigmatic nor syntagmatic, whereas an elementary grammatical category is always syntagmatic. Since most grammatical categories which occur in linguistics are unions of elementary grammatical categories, it follows that most customary grammatical categories are syntagmatic.

As it was shown by Propositions 2 and 3, the grammatical genders are paradigmatic, but not always syntagmatic categories. Moreover, in view of Proposition 30, we deduce that the grammatical genders of any homogeneous language are both paradigmatic and syntagmatic.

Proposition 33. (Revzin [38] and [39], Theorem 3). If V is both paradigmatic and syntagmatic, for any word $x \in V$ we have $R(x) \subseteq V$.

PROOF. Let $x \in V$ and $y \in R(x)$. There exists a chain $x = x_1, x_2, \ldots, x_i, x_{i+1}, \ldots, x_n = y$, that is, $x_{i+1} \in P(x_i) \cup S(x_i)$ for $1 \leqslant i \leqslant n-1$. Since V is both paradigmatic and syntagmatic, and $x \in V$, it follows that $x_2 \in V$. Hence $P(x_2) \cup S(x_2) \subseteq V$. This implies $x_3 \in V$. Continuing in this way, we obtain $x_n \in V$, that is, $y \in V$.

REMARK. Since in any homogeneous language the grammatical genders are both paradigmatic and syntagmatic, it follows that in such a language we always have $R(x) \subseteq G(x)$ for any $x \in \Gamma$. Since $G(x) \subseteq R(x)$ in any case, we deduce that $G(x) = R(x)$ for each $x \in \Gamma$. In another way, this result was obtained in Proposition 29; indeed, in a homogeneous language we have $K(x) = R(x)$ for any $x \in \Gamma$ (Theorem 10, Chapter II).

Following Revzin, a category V is *P-uniformly distributed* if, for any pair of words x and y such that $y \in R(x)$ and $P(x) \cap V \neq 0$, we have $P(y) \cap V \neq 0$. V is *S-uniformly distributed* if from $y \in R(x)$ and $S(x) \cap V \neq 0$ it follows that $S(y) \cap V \neq 0$.

Proposition 34. If $\{\Gamma, P, \Phi\}$ is homogeneous, the grammatical genders are both P-uniformly and S-uniformly distributed.

PROOF. Let $y \in R(x)$ and $P(x) \cap G(u) \neq 0$. In view of the remark following Proposition 33, we have $R(x) = G(x)$. Hence, by Proposition 20, $G(y) = G(x)$. Since, by Proposition 2, $P(x) \subseteq G(x)$, it follows, in view of Proposition 20, that $G(u) = G(y)$; but $P(y) \subseteq G(y)$. Hence $P(y) \cap G(u) = P(y) \cap G(y) = P(y) \neq 0$. Therefore $G(u)$ is a paradigmatic category.

Suppose now that $y \in R(x)$ and $S(x) \cap G(u) \neq 0$. We have, by Proposition 30, $S(x) \subseteq G(x)$. Hence, by virtue of the homogeneity, $G(x) = G(y) = G(u)$ and $S(y) \cap G(u) = S(y) \cap G(y) = S(y) \neq 0$. Therefore $G(u)$ is a syntagmatic category.

Proposition 34 is a particular case of a more general result, due to Revzin ([38] and [39], Theorem 5).

Proposition 35. If $\{\Gamma, P, \Phi\}$ is homogeneous, every syntagmatic category is P-uniformly distributed, whereas every paradigmatic category is S-uniformly distributed.

PROOF. Let V be a syntagmatic category, that is, $x \in V$ implies $S(x) \subseteq V$. Let $y \in R(x)$ and $P(x) \cap V \neq 0$. Let $z \in P(x) \cap V$. Since $P(x) \subseteq K(x) = R(x)$ (Theorem 10, Chapter II), we have $z \in K(x)$ and $y \in K(x)$. Hence $z \in K(y)$. Therefore, in view of the homogeneity, $S(z) \cap P(y) \neq 0 \neq P(z) \cap S(y)$. Let $u \in S(z) \cap P(y)$. Since $z \in V$ and V is syntagmatic, we have $S(z) \subseteq V$. Hence $u \in V$. Therefore $u \in P(y) \cap V \neq 0$ and V is P-uniformly distributed.

To prove the second part of Proposition 35, we proceed in a similar fashion, replacing P by S and S by P.

The coincidence between genders and classes in homogeneous languages receives new support by virtue of Proposition 36.

Proposition 36 (Revzin [38] and [39], Theorem 4). Let V_1 and V_2 be two distinct categories contained in some R-cell $R(x)$, where $x \in \Gamma$ and $\{\Gamma, P, \Phi\}$ is an arbitrary language. If both V_1 and V_2 are paradigmatic, at least one is not P-uniformly distributed. If both V_1 and V_2 are syntagmatic, at least one is not S-uniformly distributed.

PROOF. Let us admit that both V_1 and V_2 are P-uniformly distributed. We shall show that $V_1 = V_2$.

Given $y \in V_2$, let x be such that $P(x) \cap V_1 \neq 0$. Since $V_2 \subseteq R(x)$, we have $y \in R(x)$ and, since V_1 is P-uniformly distributed, it follows that $P(y) \cap V_1 \neq 0$. But V_1 is paradigmatic. Therefore $P(y) \subseteq V_1$, and thus $y \in V_1$ and $V_2 \subseteq V_1$. In a similar way, but replacing V_1 by V_2 and V_2 by V_1, we obtain $V_1 \subseteq V_2$.

The second part of Proposition 36 may be obtained by replacing P by S in the proof above.

REMARK. If $\{\Gamma, P, \Phi\}$ is homogeneous, $x \in \Gamma$, and $G(u)$ and $G(v)$ are two genders such that $G(u) \cup G(v) \subseteq R(x)$. Then, in view of Proposition 36 and since $G(u)$ and $G(v)$ are both paradigmatic and syntagmatic, it follows that either $G(u) = G(v)$ or $G(u) \neq G(v)$ and neither $G(u)$ nor $G(v)$ are P-uniformly distributed and neither $G(u)$ nor $G(v)$ are S-uniformly distributed. The second possibility contradicts Proposition 34. Hence $G(u) = G(v) = R(x)$. This result agrees with Proposition 29, since $K(x) = R(x)$.

7. Subparadigms and Subfamilies

Given a language $\{\Gamma, P, \Phi\}$ and a word $x \in \Gamma$, we shall define the *subparadigm* $Ps(x)$ of x, as the set of words y which fulfill the following three conditions: (1) $y \in P(x)$; (2) if $x' \in S(x)$, then $P(x') \cap S(y) \neq 0$; (3) if $y' \in S(y)$, then $P(y') \cap S(x) \neq 0$. We shall also define the *subfamily* $Ss(x)$ of x as the set of words z which fulfill the following three conditions: (a) $y \in S(x)$; (b) if $x_1 \in P(x)$, then $S(x_1) \cap P(z) \neq 0$; (c) if $z_1 \in P(z)$, then $S(z_1) \cap P(x) \neq 0$. These notions were introduced by Revzin ([38], p. 45).

Proposition 37. The relations $y \in Ps(x)$ and $z \in Ss(x)$ are equivalence relations in Γ.

PROOF. We have $x \in P(x)$, $x' \in P(x') \cap S(x)$ for each $x' \in S(x)$, and $y' \in P(y') \cap S(x)$ for each $y' \in S(x)$. Hence $x \in Ps(x)$. The definition of $y \in Ps(x)$ is symmetric with respect to x and y. Hence $y \in Ps(x)$ implies $x \in Ps(y)$. To prove the transitivity, let $y \in Ps(x)$ and $z \in Ps(y)$. We have $y \in P(x)$ and $z \in P(y)$. Hence $z \in P(x)$. If $x' \in S(x)$, then $P(x') \cap S(y) \neq 0$. Let $u \in P(x') \cap S(y)$. Since $u \in S(y)$, we have $P(u) \cap S(z) \neq 0$. But $P(u) = P(x')$. Hence $P(x') \cap S(z) \neq 0$. If $z' \in S(z)$, then $P(z') \cap S(y) \neq 0$. Let $v \in P(z') \cap S(y)$. Since $v \in S(y)$, we have $P(v) \cap S(x) \neq 0$. But $P(v) = P(z')$. Therefore, $P(z') \cap S(x) \neq 0$ and the relation considered is transitive.

In a similar way (by replacing P by S and S by P) one can prove that $z \in Ss(x)$ is also an equivalence relation.

Proposition 38. There exist a nonadequate language $\{\Gamma, P, \Phi\}$ and a word $x \in \Gamma$ such that $P(x) \neq Ps(x) = Ss(x) \neq S(x)$.

PROOF. Let $\Gamma = \{a, b, c, d\}$, $P(a) = \{a\}$, $P(b) = \{b\}$, $P(c) = \{c, d\}$, $\Phi = \{ab, cb, ad, cd\}$. We have $S(a) = \{a, c\}$, $S(b) = \{b, d\}$. Since $c \in P(d)$, $a \in S(c)$, but $P(a) \cap S(d) = 0$, it follows that $Ps(c) = \{c\}$. Hence $Ps(c) \neq P(c)$. Since $c \in S(a)$, $d \in P(c)$, but $S(d) \cap P(a) = 0$, it follows that $Ss(c) = \{c\}$. Hence $Ss(c) \neq S(c)$. The word $x = c$ fulfills the required conditions. On the other hand, in view of the proof of Proposition 1, Chapter II, the language considered is not adequate.

Proposition 39. There exist an adequate language $\{\Gamma, P, \Phi\}$ and a word $x \in \Gamma$ such that $P(x) \neq Ps(x) = Ss(x) \neq S(x)$.

PROOF. Let $\Gamma = \{a, b, c, d\}$, $P(a) = \{a, b\}$, $P(c) = \{c, d\}$, $\Phi = \{ad,$ $bb, ab, bc, bd, dc, db, dd\}$. We have $S(a) = \{a\}$, $S(b) = \{b, d\}$, $S(c) =$ $\{c\}$. Since $b \in P(a)$, $d \in S(b)$ and $P(d) \cap S(a) = 0$, we have $Ps(b) =$ $\{b\}$. Hence $Ps(b) \neq P(b)$. Since $b \in S(d)$, $a \in P(b)$, and $S(a) \cap P(d) = 0$, we have $Ss(b) = \{b\}$. Hence $Ss(b) \neq S(b)$. The word $x = a$ fulfills the required conditions. On the other hand, in view of the proof of Theorem 9, Chapter II, the language considered is adequate.

The linguistic significance of the subparadigms may be illustrated by the following example. Consider the Rumanian neuter nouns, such as *scaun*. The paradigms of these nouns have the specific property that each inflected form of the singular belongs to the family of some masculine noun, whereas each inflected form of the plural belongs to the family of some feminine noun. For instance, we have $P(scaun) =$ $P_1(scaun) \cup P_2(scaun)$, where $P_1(scaun) = \{scaun, scaunului, scaunule,$ *scaunul*}, $P_2(scaun) = \{scaune, scaunele, scaunelor\}$. Each element of $P_1(scaun)$ belongs to the singular, whereas each element of $P_2(scaun)$ belongs to the plural. We have *scaun* $\in S(pom)$, *scaunului* $\in S(pomului)$, *scaunule* $\in S(pomule)$, *scaunul* $\in S(pomul)$, whereas *pom*, *pomului*, *pomule*, and *pomul* belong to the masculine grammatical gender and belong to the same gender in the sense of the definition given in Section 4. We have also *scaune* $\in S(cărți)$, *scaunele* $\in S(cărțile)$, *scaunelor* $\in$ $S(cărților)$, whereas *cărți*, *cărțile*, and *cărților* belong to the feminine grammatical gender and belong to the same gender in the sense of the definition given in Section 4. On the other hand, *scaun* and *pom* do not belong to the same gender, and the same is true for *scaune* and *cărți*. However, if we consider $P_1(scaun)$ and $P_2(scaun)$ as two distinct paradigms and we adopt this convention for all neuter Rumanian nouns, *scaun* is the same gender as *pom*, whereas *scaune* is the same gender as *cărți*; the Rumanian neuter no longer exists.

The differences between $P_1(scaun)$ and $P_2(scaun)$ may be detected with the aid of subparadigms. Indeed, it is easy to see that $Ps(scaun) =$ $P_1(scaun)$, whereas $Ps(scaune) = P_2(scaun)$. That *scaune* does not belong to $Ps(scaun)$ results from the relations *scaune* $\in P(scaun)$, *cărți* $\in S(scaune)$, $P(cărți) \cap S(scaun) = 0$.

There are Rumanian nouns which belong to the same family, although they do not have the same gender. For instance, *scaun* $\in S(pom)$, *scaune* $\in S(cărți)$ but *scaun* and *pom*, *scaune* and *cărți* do not have the same gender. We may detect this peculiarity with the aid of the subfamilies. Indeed, two Rumanian nouns which belong to the same family have the same gender if and only if they belong to the same subfamily. For the sake of illustration, let us prove that *scaun* does not belong to $Ss(pom)$. We have $pomi \in P(pom)$, but $S(pomi) \cap P(scaun) = 0$.

The linguistic significance of subparadigms and subfamilies, particularly concerning Slavic languages, are discussed by Revzin [38, 39].

It is not accidental that all linguistic illustrations of subparadigms and subfamilies are taken from languages such as Rumanian and Russian, in which, as we have already proved, most nouns are not homogeneous words (see, for instance, Section 8, Chapter II). Indeed, we have Proposition 40.

Proposition 40. If the language $\{\Gamma, P, \Phi\}$ is homogeneous, the subparadigms coincide with the paradigms, whereas the subfamilies coincide with the families.

PROOF. Since in any case $Ps(x) \subseteq P(x)$ for each $x \in \Gamma$, let us prove that $P(x) \subseteq Ps(x)$. Let $y \in P(x)$ and $y' \in S(y)$. We have $y \in P(x) \cap S(y) = P(x) \cap S(y') \neq 0$. Hence, in view of the homogeneity, $P(y') \cap S(x) \neq 0$. Now let $x' \in S(x)$. We have $x \in P(y) \cap S(x) = P(y) \cap S(x') \neq 0$. Thus, in view of the homogeneity, $P(x') \cap S(y) \neq 0$; therefore, $y \in Ps(x)$.

In the same way, but replacing P by S and S by P, we prove that $Ss(x) = S(x)$.

Given two words x and y such that $y \in S(x)$, we cannot deduce that x and y belong to the same categories. In a nonadequate language, x and y may belong to different parts of speech, whereas in a nonhomogeneous language x and y may have different genders. It is interesting to decompose $S(x)$ into subsets $S_1, S_2, \ldots, S_n$ such that, for $y \in S_i$, $z \in S_i$ ($1 \le i \le n$), y and z belong to the same categories. If, for each word x, the subfamilies of $S(x)$ yield such a decomposition, we shall say that the language considered is *S-regular* (Revzin [38], p. 45). The *S*-regularity and the homogeneity are very close properties. Indeed, if we consider as categories only the grammatical categories (in the sense defined in the first part of this section), the parts of speech and the genders, then, in view of Theorem 10, Chapter II, and of Propositions 2 and 40, this Chapter, any homogeneous language is *S*-regular. As a matter of fact, it would be interesting to see whether there exists a part of speech or a gender in a homogeneous language, which is not a grammatical category.

Another interesting problem is to investigate the notions introduced in Chapter II, when $S(x)$ is replaced by $Ss(x)$, whereas $P(x)$ is replaced by $Ps(x)$.

8. A Measure of the Difference between Genders

We shall now study the problem of finding a measure of the difference between two given genders. To this aim, we shall introduce the notion of *distance between two genders G(x) and G(y)*, defined as the smallest number *n* having the property that any word of *G(x)* may be joined with any word of *G(y)* by a chain of a length smaller than, or equal to *n* + 1. In case there is no natural number having this property, we shall say that *the distance between G(u) and G(y) is infinite*.

Let us denote by $\delta(x, y)$ the distance between *G(x)* and *G(y)*. It is easy to see that $\delta(x, y) \geq 0$; $\delta(x, y) = \delta(y, x)$; $\delta(x, y) \leq \delta(x, z) + \delta(z, y)$ for any word *z*. Thus, $\delta(x, y)$ fulfills almost all the properties of a distance. It is useful especially whenever the genders are pairwise disjoint (as in most of the following examples).

To establish the distances between genders in various natural languages, we shall reconsider the results of Section 3 in the light of the definitions given in Section 4. We do not claim completeness; we intend only to illustrate the notion of distance and its linguistic significance.

ENGLISH.   We have, for two arbitrary nouns *x* and *y*, $G(x) = G(y)$ and $\delta(x, y) = 2$.

FRENCH.   Let us consider the following six genders: *G(crayon)* (first masculine), *G(arbre)* (second masculine), *G(maison)*, (feminine), *G(cas)* (first neuter), *G(voix)* (second neuter), *G(enfant)* (third neuter), and *G(camarade)* (fourth neuter). Since the strings *bel arbre* and *bels arbres* are correct, whereas the strings *bel crayon, bels crayons* are not, we have $\delta(crayon, arbre) = \infty$. Since the strings *beau crayon* and *beaux crayons* are correct, whereas *beau maison* and *beaux maisons* are not, it follows that $\delta(crayon, maison) = \infty$. Since the strings *nouveau cas* and *nouveaux cas* are correct, whereas the strings *nouveaux crayon* and *nouveau crayons* are not, we have $\delta(crayon, cas) = \infty$. Since *beau voix* and *beaux voix* are not correct strings, it follows that $\delta(crayon, voix) = \infty$. Since the correct strings *belle enfant* and *belles enfants* are no longer correct when we replace *enfant* by *crayon* and *enfants* by *crayons*, we have $\delta(crayon, enfant) = \infty$. Since the correct strings *belle maison* and *belles maisons* become incorrect when we replace *maison* by *arbre* and *maisons* by *arbres*, it follows that $\delta(arbre, maison) = \infty$. Since the strings *bel arbre, bels arbres* are correct, whereas *bel cas* and *bels cas* are not, we have $\delta(arbre, cas) = \infty$. Since *bel voix, bels voix* are not correct, it follows $\delta(arbre, voix) = \infty$. Since the strings *belle enfant* and *belles enfants* are correct, whereas *belle arbre, belles arbres* are not, we have $\delta(arbre, enfant) = \infty$. Since *grande voix* and *grandes voix* are correct strings, whereas *grande maisons* and *grandes maison* are not, it follows that $\delta(maison, voix) = \infty$. Since the strings *bel enfant* and *bels enfants* are correct, whereas *bel maison* and *bels maisons* are not, we have $\delta(maison, enfant) = \infty$. In the same way we find $\delta(maison, cas) = \infty$, $\delta(cas, voix) = \infty$ and $\delta(voix, enfant) = \infty$. Since the strings *beau camarade, beaux camarades, belle camarade*, and *belles camarades* are all correct, whereas *beaux camarade, beau camarades, belles camarade, belle camarades, bel camarade*, and *bels camarades* are not, it follows that $\delta(crayon, camarade) = \delta(arbre, camarade) = \delta(maison, camarade) = \delta(cas, camarade) = \delta(voix, camarade) = \delta(enfant, camarade) = \infty$.

It is easy to see that two different genders are always disjoint.

ITALIAN. Let us consider the following three genders: $G(fratello)$ (masculine), $G(bocolla)$ (feminine), $G(giovane)$ (neuter). Since the strings *buono fratello* and *buoni fratelli* are correct, whereas the strings *buono bocolla* and *buoni bocolle* are not, we have $\delta(fratello, bocolla) = \infty$. Since *buona giovane* and *buone giovani* are correct strings, whereas *buona fratello* and *buone fratelli* are not, we have $\delta(fratello, giovane) = \infty$. Since *buono giovane* and *buoni giovani* are correct strings, whereas *buono bocolla* and *buoni bocolle* are not, it follows that $\delta(bocolla, giovane) = \infty$. It is easy to see that two distinct genders are always disjoint.

SPANISH. Let us consider the genders $G(padre)$ and $G(madre)$. For similar reasons we find $\delta(padre, madre) = \infty$.

RUMANIAN. Let us consider the following six genders: $G(pom)$ (masculine), $G(carte)$ (feminine), $G(scaun)$ (first neuter), $G(ochi)$ (second neuter), $G(\hat{i}nv\breve{a}\underline{t}\breve{a}toare)$ (third neuter), and $G(nume)$ (fourth neuter).

The shortest chain between *pomi* and *carte* is of a length equal to 6: *pomi–pom–scaun–scaune–cărţi–carte*. Since any word of $P(pom)$ may be joined with any word of $P(carte)$ by a chain of length not greater than 6, it follows that $\delta(pom, carte) = 5$. The shortest chain between *pomi* and *scaune* is equal to 4: *pomi–pom–scaun–scaune*. Since any word of $P(pom)$ may be joined with any word of $P(scaun)$ by a chain of length not greater than 4, we have $\delta(pom, scaun) = 3$.

The shortest chain between *pom* and *ochi* is of length 4: *pom–pomului–ochiului–ochi*. Since any word of $P(pom)$ may be joined with any word of $P(ochi)$ by a chain of length not greater than 4, we have $\delta(pom, ochi) =$ 3. The shortest chain between *pomi* and *învățătoare* is of length 6: *pomi–pom–scaun–scaunelor–învățătoarelor–învățătoare*. Since any word of $P(pom)$ may be joined with any word of $P(\hat{i}nv\u{a}\u{t}\u{a}toare)$ by a chain no longer than 6, it follows that $\delta(pom, \hat{i}nv\u{a}\u{t}\u{a}toare) = 5$. Since for any $x \in P(pom)$ and any $y \in P(nume)$ we have the chain $x–pomului–numelui–y$, it follows that $\delta(pom, nume) = 3$.

For each $x \in P(carte)$ and each $y \in P(scaun)$ we have the chain $x–c\u{a}r\u{t}i–scaune–y$. Hence $\delta(carte, scaun) = 3$. For each $x \in P(carte)$ and $y \in P(ochi)$ we have the chain $x–c\u{a}r\u{t}i–scaune–scaunului–ochiului–y$; hence $\delta(carte, ochi) = 5$. For each $x \in P(carte)$ and $y \in P(\hat{i}nv\u{a}\u{t}\u{a}toare)$ we have the chain $x–c\u{a}r\u{t}ii–\hat{i}nv\u{a}\u{t}\u{a}toarei–y$. Hence $\delta(carte, \hat{i}nv\u{a}\u{t}\u{a}toare) = 3$. For each $x \in P(carte)$ and $y \in P(nume)$ we have the chain $x–c\u{a}r\u{t}ilor–numelor–y$. Hence $\delta(carte, nume) = 3$.

In the same way we find that $\delta(scaun, ochi) = 3$, $\delta(scaun, \hat{i}nv\u{a}\u{t}\u{a}toare) = 3$, $\delta(scaun, nume) = 3$, $\delta(ochi, \hat{i}nv\u{a}\u{t}\u{a}toare) = 5$, $\delta(ochi, nume) = 3$, $\delta(\hat{i}nv\u{a}\u{t}\u{a}toare, nume) = 3$. Moreover, it is easy to see that two distinct genders are always disjoint.

RUSSIAN. Let us consider the genders $G(stol)$ (masculine), $G(kniga)$ (feminine), and $G(okno)$ (neuter). We use the following remark: A plural form of a Russian adjective is the same for all genders. It follows that two plural noun forms having the same case are in the same family. If $x \in G(stol)$, $y \in G(kniga)$, and $z \in G(okno)$ and x', y', z' are the corresponding forms of nominative plural, we have the chains $x–x'–y'–y$; $x–x'–z'–z$; $y–y'–z'–z$. Hence $\delta(stol, kniga) = \delta(stol, okno) = \delta(kniga, okno) = 3$.

GERMAN. Let us consider the genders $G(Titel)$ (masculine), $G(Gabel)$ (feminine), $G(Fenster)$ (neuter). For reasons similar to those concerning Russian we find $\delta(Titel, Gabel) = \delta(Titel, Fenster) = \delta(Gabel, Fenster) = 3$.

LATIN. Let us consider the genders $G(puer)$ (masculine), $G(aestas)$ (feminine) and $G(tempus)$ (neuter). We use the following remark: A dative plural form of a Latin adjective is the same for all genders. It follows that two dative plural noun forms belong to the same family. If $x \in G(puer)$, $y \in G(aestas)$, and $z \in G(tempus)$, we have the chains $x–pueris–aestatibus–y$; $x–pueris–temporibus–z$; $y–aestatibus–temporibus–z$. It follows that $\delta(puer, aestas) = \delta(aestas, tempus) = \delta(puer, tempus) = 3$.

We notice that the distance between masculine and feminine is maximum in French, Italian, and Spanish (being equal to ∞) and minimum in Russian, German, and Latin (where it is equal to 3). Rumanian is, in this respect, intermediate. Unlike Russian, German, and Latin (where the three genders exhibit, in their reciprocal relations, identically strong oppositions — based on the constant value of all the distances), in Rumanian some of the neuter genders are obviously inferior compared to the masculine and the feminine. For instance, the distance between masculine and feminine is equal to 5, whereas that between masculine and first neuter is equal to 3.

The conditions under which we have settled the existence of the neuter in Rumanian and the conditions under which we have settled its disappearance (see Sections 3 and 7) define a specific position in this much argued problem of the neuter [1–5, 10, 11, 17, 18, 35, 37, 41–44, 47, 49]. In any event the neuter, under the condition that it exists in Rumanian, is fundamentally different from both the Latin and the Russian neuter, through its relatively weaker opposition in relation to the masculine and the feminine. It is of interest that the diachronic analysis of Rumanian neuter leads to the conclusion that it continues neither the Latin neuter nor the Slavic one (see in this respect the paper of Rosetti [43]). The Rumanian neuter corresponds to neither the Slavic nor the Latin neuter, neither in form nor in semantic content. In sum and substance, as Rosetti [43] and Jakobson [18] have already mentioned, the first Rumanian neuter is an appanage of the inanimate alone, which does not exclude, of course, the existence of some masculine or feminine inanimate.

As far as French neuter is concerned, as well the second, the third and fourth Rumanian neuter, they are exclusively a result of some phenomena of morphologic homonymy. Hence they are, in some sense, secondary genders.

9. Personal Genders in Rumanian

Until now we have adopted as marked (correct) strings only those of the form *noun + qualifying adjective in the positive degree* or *qualifying adjective in the positive degree + noun*. But as soon as we take other sentences into consideration, we feel the need of detecting more shades of difference in grammatical genders.

Let us consider the Rumanian language. To understand in a better fashion the discussion we made, we shall also give here the English translation of all Rumanian strings we use.

If we enlarge sufficiently the set of sentences (marked strings) so that they also contain sentences of the type *cheamă pe băiat* (call the boy) or *dau lui Ion o carte* (I give John a book), we observe, in relation to the above definition, that each of the words *pom* (tree), *băiat* (boy), and *Ion* (John) has its own characteristic gender. Indeed, if we admit the sentence *cheamă pe băiat* (call the boy), we can never accept the sentence *cheamă pe pom* (call the tree); it follows that *băiat* (boy) and *pom* (tree) are not in the same distribution class as they were when we considered a more restricted set of sentences. Hence it still follows that *băiat* (boy) and *pom* (tree) can no longer be joined by anything except a chain having a length of 4: *băiat* (boy), *băiatului* (of (to) the boy), *pomului* (of (to) the tree), *pom* (tree); therefore, *băiat* (boy) and *pom* (tree) are not of the same gender.

If we admit the sentence *dau lui Ion o carte* (I give John a book), but do not agree to sentences such as *dau lui pom o carte*, (*pom* = tree) or *dau lui băiat o carte** (*băiat* = boy), it follows that *Ion* is neither in the same distribution class with *pom* nor with *băiat*. Since the paradigm of *Ion* is cut down to this single word [we are leaving aside the form *Ioane* (John) in the vocative], it follows that there is no chain, however long, that could join *Ion* to *băiat* or *Ion* to *pom*. Thus, the grammatical gender of *Ion* differs both from the grammatical gender of *băiat* and from that of *pom*. This conclusion is still valid even if we take into consideration the form *Ioane* (John, in the vocative). The only new factor in such a case is the possibility of joining *Ion* with *băiat* and with *pom* by a chain having a length equal to 4.

The grammatical gender of *pom* (tree) will be called *nonpersonal masculine gender*. The grammatical gender of *Ion* will be named *personal masculine gender of proper nouns*, whereas the grammatical gender of *băiat* (boy) will be called *abstract personal masculine gender*.

A similar analysis may be carried out for words such as *masă* (table), *Maria* and *fată* (girl). The outcome is that *fată* and *masă* are not in the same distribution class, because we do admit the sentence *cheamă pe fată* (call the girl) and reject the sentence *cheamă pe masă* (call the table). *Fată* and *masă* may be joined only by a chain of a length equal to 4: *fată*, *fetei* [of (to) the girl], *mesei* [of (to) the table], *masă*. Therefore *fată* and *masă* are not of the same gender. In a similar manner

*Nothing in English corresponds to the incorrectness of the two sentences.

it may be proved that *Maria* and *masă* are not of the same gender either; they may be joined only by a chain of a length equal to 4: *Maria, Mariei* (Mary's or to Mary), *mesei* [of (to) the table], *masă*. We notice here a difference from the situation of the masculine nouns. If *Ion* and *pom* cannot be joined by any chain, *Maria* and *masă* can be joined by a chain.

The question of whether *Maria* and *fată* are of the same gender must now be settled. The answer to this question is different from the one given to the analogous situation for the masculine, because, if we do admit the sentence *dau lui Ion o carte* (I give John a book), we reject the sentence *dau lui Maria o carte* (Mary is a feminine proper name).

But if we take into consideration sentences of the type *Maria cea silitoare* (Mary the diligent) we notice that *Maria* does not belong to the same class of distribution with *fată* because the sentence *fată cea silitoare* (girl the diligent) is not admitted. The smallest chain uniting *Maria* with *fată* is, in this case, a chain of a length equal to 4: *Maria, Mariei* (Mary's or to Mary), *fetei* (the girl's or to the girl), *fată* (girl); therefore *Maria* and *fată* are not of the same gender.

Let us consider now a feminine proper noun to which the article *lui* may be added, for instance, *Mimi*. For such a word, we apply the same reasoning as for the word *Ion*. The result is that *Mimi* belongs to a different gender from that of *fată* (girl) as well as from that of *casă* (house). At the same time, we notice that there is no chain to join *Mimi* with *Maria*, which means that these two nouns also have different genders.

As far as the neuter genders are concerned, it is not difficult to see that their existence has not been affected by the fact that the set of sentences has been enriched.

In conclusion, we have obtained the following grammatical genders of Rumanian nouns, with respect to the set of enriched sentences as shown above:

(1) *the nonpersonal masculine gender* [*pom* (tree), *stîlp* (pillar), etc.];

(2) *the first personal masculine gender* or *the abstract personal masculine gender* [*băiat* (boy), *copil* (child), etc.];

(3) *the second personal masculine gender* or *the personal masculine gender of proper nouns* (*Ion, Gheorghe, Vasile*, etc.);

(4) *the nonpersonal feminine gender* [*casă* (house), *carte* (book), *ploaie* (rain), etc.];

(5) *the first nonpersonal feminine gender* or *the abstract personal feminine gender* [*fată* (girl), *copilă* (little girl), *femeie* (woman), etc.];
(6) *the second personal feminine gender* or *the personal feminine gender of proper nouns* (*Maria*, *Sanda*, etc.);
(7) *the third personal feminine gender* or *the personal semifeminine gender of proper nouns* (*Mimi*, *Jeni*, etc.);
(8) *the neuter genders* [*scaun* (chair), *caiet* (exercise book), etc.].
We are not yet sure that we have thus exhausted the Rumanian genders. The analysis of names of towns, of countries, of generic names of animals, and of other categories of words, as well as the enriching of the set of sentences, might reveal new grammatical genders. However, we shall not investigate this problem now.

The problem of determining the reciprocal distance between the above genders of the Rumanian language seems quite natural. We shall record here some of these distances; using the code MN = nonpersonal masculine, $I\,MP$ = first person masculine, $II\,MP$ = second person masculine, FN = nonpersonal feminine, $I\,FP$ = first person feminine, $II\,FP$ = second person feminine, $III\,FP$ = third person feminine, N = first neuter. We obtain the results contained in Table 4 (filling in the empty spaces may form the object of another investigation).

TABLE 4

	MN	$I\,MP$	$II\,MP$	FN	$I\,FP$	$II\,FP$	$III\,FP$
MN	2	3	∞	5			
$I\,MP$	3	2	∞				
$II\,MP$	∞	∞	2				
FN	5			2	3	3	∞
$I\,FP$				4	2		∞
$II\,FP$				4		2	∞
$III\,FP$				∞	∞	∞	2

It is worthwhile to observe that the opposition between the nonpersonal masculine and the first person masculine is weaker than the opposition between the first person masculine and the second person masculine. The first person masculine is nearer to the nonpersonal masculine than to the second person masculine. Likewise, the opposition between the third person feminine and any other feminine gender is stronger than the opposition between the nonpersonal feminine and any of the two first person feminine genders.

As shown above, the widely accepted current thesis, according to which Rumanian has only one masculine and one feminine gender, corresponds in fact to a relatively low level of grammaticalness, namely, to the one supplied by the syntagms consisting of a noun and an adjective in the positive degree. As soon as we move to a higher level of grammaticalness in the Rumanian language the number of masculine and feminine genders increases considerably.

We might raise the problem of the necessity of passing at first through lower levels of grammaticalness; might it not be possible to consider the entire grammaticalness at once? The answer is negative. In truth, the actual idea of such a consideration is an illusion. We can keep in mind a higher grammaticalness compared to a preceding stage of the investigation, but something will always escape our endeavor, because grammaticalness is inexhaustible. Besides (and, perhaps, this is the most important fact) this gradual passing from one level of grammaticalness to another superior one, enables us to identify certain simple, but essential, connections which could not be detected otherwise. Thus, at the level of the syntagms *noun + adjective* we could detect the mechanism of the passing from the natural gender to the grammatical one, a mechanism which no longer appears at superior levels of grammaticalness, because, for example, *bărbat* (man) and *pom* (tree) cease, under such conditions, to be of the same gender.

As we have seen above, the personal genders occur, in Rumanian, at a superior level of grammaticalness. These genders arise within the genders already detected at an inferior level of grammaticalness; two personal genders arise within the masculine and another three genders within the feminine. This situation tallies roughly with the results of the diachronic analysis [43]; yet, some details differ. We do observe, at the same time, that the passing on to a superior level of grammaticalness does not cancel the results of the analysis done at an inferior level, but enlarges them, also adding a more subtle description.

Concerning personal genders in Rumanian, see also Chiţimia [4], Graur [10, 11], Hjelmslev [14], Nandriş [32], Niculescu [33], Racoviţă [36], Rosetti [42], Seidel [46]. Concerning genders in Slavic languages see also [8], [12], [19], [21], [22], and [45]. Concerning genders in Italian see [40].

REFERENCES

1. C. Bazell, Has Rumanian a third gender? *Cashiers Sextil Puşcariu* **1**, 77–85 (1952).
2. G. Bonfante, Esiste il neutro in italiano? *Quaderni dell'Istituto di glottologia, Bologna* **6**, 103–109 (1961–1962).
3. I. I. Bujor, Genul substantivelor în limba română. *Limba Română* **4**, 51–64 (1955).
4. I. C. Chiţimia, Genul personal în limbile polonă şi română, *Romanoslavica* **3**, 31–41 (1958).
5. I. Coteanu, Despre pluralul substantivelor neutre în româneşte. *Limbă şi Literatură* **1**, 103–117 (1955).
6. P. Diaconescu, Le nombre et le genre du substantif roumain. (Analyse contextuelle). *Rev. Roumaine Linguistique* **9**, (2) 171–193 (1964).
7. I. Fodor, The origin of grammatical gender. *Lingua* **8** (1–2) (1959).
8. I. Fodor, La typologie des langues slaves et le genre grammatical, *in* "Slavjanska Filologija". Vol. 3, Sofia, 1963.
9. M. A. Gabinskii, Autochtonous elements in Moldavian (in Russian). *Vopr. Jazykoznanija* **1956**, 85–93.
10. A. Graur, Contributions à l'étude du genre personnel en roumain. *Bull. Linguistique* **13**, 97–105 (1945).
11. A. Graur, "Studii de lingvistică generală." Editura Academiei R.P.R., Bucureşti, 1960.
12. G. L. Hall and I. S. Clair-Sobell, Animate gender in Slavonic and Romance languages. *Lingua* **4**, 194–201 (1954).
13. W. E. Hartnett, Total topological spaces (in press).
14. L. Hjelmslev, Animé et inanimé, personnel et non-personnel. *Trav. Inst. Linguistique Paris* **1**, 155–199 (1956).
15. L. Hjelmslev, Essais linguistiques. *Trav. Cercle linguistique Copenhague* **12**, 142–143 (1959).
16. V. Hořejši, Problema substantivelor aşa zise "neutre" în limba română, în lumina legăturilor cu alte limbi. *Studii Cercetări Lingvistice* **8** (4), 415–429 (1957).
17. R. Jakobson, Zur Struktur des russischen Verbums, *in* "Charisteria G. Mathesio... oblata." Prague, 1932, pp. 74–79.
18. R. Jakobson, On the Rumanian neuter. *Cercetări Lingvistice.* **3**, 237–238 (1958).
19. R. Jakobson, The gender pattern of Russian, "Omagiu lui Al. Graur cu prilejul împlinirii a 60 de ani." *Studii Cercetări Lingvistice* **11** (3), 541–543 (1960).
20. O. G. Karpinskaja, Typology of genders in Slavonic languages (in Russian). *Vopr. Jazykoznanija* **13** (6), 61–76 (1964).
21. J. Kurylowicz, "Esquisses Linguistiques." Wroclaw-Krakow, 1960, pp. 160–163.
22. J. Kurylowicz, Personal and animate genders in Slavic. *Lingua* **11**, 249–255 (1962).
23. J. Lohmann, "Genus und Sexus." Göttingen, 1930.
24. S. Marcus, Structures linguistiques et structures topologiques. *Rev. Math. Pures Appl.* **6** (3), 501–506 (1961).
25. S. Marcus, Le genre grammatical et son modèle logique. *Cahiers Linguistique Théor. Appl.* **1**, 103–122 (1962).

154   IV. Grammatical Gender

26. S. Marcus, Aspectul logic al opoziţiilor lingvistice, II. Opoziţii ordonate, paradigme, morfeme şi quasi-morfeme. *Studii Cercetări Matematice* **13** (4), 539–551 (1962).

27. S. Marcus, A synchronic analysis of the grammatical gender. *Rev. Linguistique* **8**, (1), 99–111 (1963).

28. S. Marcus, Modèles mathématiques pour la catégorie grammaticale du cas. *Rev. Math. Pures Appl.* **8** (4), 585–610 (1963).

29. A. Martinet, Neutralisation et archiphonème. *Trav. Cercle Linguistique Prague* **6,** (1936).

30. I. A. Melčuk, Statistics and dependence of French nouns gender on its ending (in Russian). *Vopr. Statistiki Reč* 1958, 112–130.

31. Gr. C. Moisil, Problèmes posés par la traduction automatique. La déclinaison en roumain écrit. *Cahiers Linguistique Théor. Appl.* **1,** 123–134 (1962).

32. O. Nandriş, Le genre, ses réalisations et le genre personnel en roumain. *Rev. Linguistique Romane* **25,** 47–74 (1961).

33. A. Niculescu, "Sur l'objet direct prépositionnel dans les langues romanes." Recueil Lisbonne, Editura Academiei R.P.R., Bucureşti, 1959, pp. 167–185.

34. I. Pătruţ, "Sur le genre 'neutre' en roumain." Mélanges Oslo, Editura Academiei R.P.R., Bucureşti, 1957, pp. 291–301.

35. S. Puşcariu, "Limba Romînă," Vol. 1. Bucureşti, 1940, pp. 135–136.

36. C. Racoviţă, Sur le genre personnel en roumain. *Bull. Linguistique* **8** (1), 154–158 (1940).

37. I. I. Revzin, "Language Models" (in Russian). Izd. Akad. Nauk SSSR, Moskow, 1962.

38. I. I. Revzin, Some problems concerning the theory of language models (in Russian). *Naučn. Tekhn. Inform.* **1964** (8), 42–46.

39. I. I. Revzin, Marked strings, algebra of fragments, categories (in Russian). (In press).

40. G. Rohlfs, "Historische Grammatik der italienischen Sprache." Berna, 1949.

41. A. Rosetti, Neutrul în română. *Studii Cercetări Lingvistice* **1,** 233–234 (1950).

42. A. Rosetti, Despre genul neutru şi genul personal în limba română. *Studii Cercetări Lingvistice* **8,** 407–413 (1957).

43. A. Rosetti, Remarques sur la catégorie du genre en roumain. *Studia Linguistica* **13,** 133–136 (1959).

44. A. Rosetti, Contribuţii la studiul neutrului în limba română. *Studii Cercetări Lingvistice* **14** (4), 433–438 (1963).

45. A. M. Schenker, Gender categories in Polish. *Language* **31** (3), (1955).

46. E. Seidel, Gibt es ein Genus personale? *Bull. Linguistique* **16,** 5–93 (1948).

47. K. Togeby, Le neutre en roumain et en albanais. *Cahiers Sextil Puşcariu* **2** (2), 121–131 (1953).

48. P. Tondeur, Ein Beispiel zur allgemeinen Topologie: die Topologie einer Äquivalenzrelation. *Ann. Acad. Sci. Fennicae, Ser. A, I. Math.* **344,** 1–7 (1964).

49. E. Vasiliu, Observaţii asupra categoriei genului în limba română. *Studii Cercetări Lingvistice* **11** (3), 463–464 (1960).

50. A. A. Zaliznjak, On the grammatical categories of gender and animateneѕs in modern Russian (in Russian). *Vopr. Jazykoznanija* **13** (4), 25–40 (1964).

NOTE ADDED IN PROOF

A new mathematical model of grammatical genders is studied by I. I. Revzin (Applying a set-theoretical model to a language with grammatical homonymity (in Russian), *Naučn. Tekhn. Inform.* **1965** (3), 34–38). In this model, two distinct genders are always disjoint. For some homogeneous languages, Revzin's model coincides with the above one. An application of the model studied in Chapter IV to genders in Western Slavic languages is made by J. Horecký (Model gramatického rodu v západoslovanských jazykoch, *Jazykovedný Časopis* **17** (1), 3–12 (1966). Concerning genders in Rumanian see also V. Horejsí (A propos des noms ambigènes (neutres) roumains, *Philologica Pragensia*, **7** (4), 401–407 (1964)). Some concepts and theorems discussed in Chapters I–IV can be included in a general algebraic theory of so-called R-systems (M. Novotný, On some algebraic concepts of Mathematical Linguistics, *Prague Studies in Mathematical Linguistics* **1**, 125–140 (1966)).

Chapter V

Configurations

1. Introduction

In this chapter we intend to make a systematic investigation of one of the basic notions of any syntactic description — the notion of syntactic dependence. To this aim, we concentrate on the theory of syntactic configurations, initiated by Ljapunov and Kulagina [26]. There are many notions in literature which express the fact that some groups of words (or morphemes) may behave, in some contexts, as a single word. Thus, we recall the notions of *syntagm* (see, for instance, Mikuš [29]), *constituent* (Bloomfield [4, 5], Pike [37], Wells [45]), *construction* (Gleason [17]). A configuration is none of these, but it has something in common with each of them. It permits us to detect, by a recursive procedure, various degrees of syntactic dependence. (For the signification of recursive definitions in empirical sciences see Bar-Hillel [1].) Consider, for instance, the well-formed German string *ein sehr alter Mann*. The dependence of *sehr* upon *alter* may be recognized from the possibility of removing the word *sehr* and the impossibility of removing the word *alter*, without affecting the correctness of the sentence. (The string *ein alter Mann* is correct, whereas the string *ein sehr Mann* is not.) The group of words *sehr alter* behaves as the single word *alter*, that is, *sehr alter* and *alter* have (approximatively) the same distribution. But we intuitively agree that we also have another dependence: *alter* depends upon *Mann*. Nevertheless, this dependence may not be detected in the same way, since neither *alter* nor *Mann* may be removed without affecting the correctness of the sentence. But as soon as we replace the group *sehr alter* by the "resultant" of this group, *alter*, we obtain a sentence where the dependence of *alter* upon *Mann* may be detected as the dependence of *sehr* upon *alter* in the first sentence. Indeed, in the well-formed string *ein alter Mann* the group *alter Mann* behaves as the single word

Mann. It follows that the dependence of *alter* upon *Mann* is of another degree than the dependence of *sehr* upon *alter*. Precisely such distinctions will be the object of our study in this chapter. We shall define syntactic configurations of various orders, and we shall then apply them in the classification of dependence relations.

2. *P*-Configurations and *P*-Structures of Order *n*

Let us consider a language $\{\Gamma, P, \Phi\}$. We recall that a *P*-structure is a finite sequence $P_1, P_2, \ldots, P_n$ of *P*-cells; *n* is the *length of the P-structure*. The *P*-structure is marked if there exists a marked string $a_1 a_2 \ldots a_n$ over Γ such that $P(a_i) = P_i (1 \le i \le n)$.

Every *P*-structure will be considered in the present chapter as a *P-structure of rank zero*. The set of all *P*-structures will be denoted by $\mathscr{S}_0$. We consider also the *empty P-structure*, whose length is equal to 0.

Let us consider a *P*-structure $\mathscr{P}$ which fulfills the two conditions (1) the length of $\mathscr{P}$ is not less than 2 and (2) there exists a word $a \in \Gamma$ such that $\mathscr{P}$ and $P(a)$ are *P*-equivalent, that is, given two *P*-structures $\mathscr{P}_1$ and $\mathscr{P}_2$, the *P*-structures $\mathscr{P}_1 \mathscr{P} \mathscr{P}_2$ and $\mathscr{P}_1 P(a) \mathscr{P}_2$ are either both marked or both unmarked. Then we shall say that $\mathscr{P}$ is a *P-configuration of the first rank*. The *P*-cell $P(a)$ will be called a *resultant of* $\mathscr{P}$.

Let $\mathscr{P}$ be a *P*-structure such that no *P*-structures $\mathscr{P}_1$ and $\mathscr{P}_2$ exist for which $\mathscr{P}_1 \mathscr{P} \mathscr{P}_2$ is a marked *P*-structure. We shall say that $\mathscr{P}$ is a *parasitic P-structure*. Moreover, $\mathscr{P}$ may be both a parasitic *P*-structure and a *P*-configuration of the first rank. In such a situation, we shall say that $\mathscr{P}$ is a *parasitic P-configuration of the first rank*.

Let $\mathscr{S}$ be a subset of $\mathscr{S}_0$. We shall say that two *P*-structures $\mathscr{P}_1$ and $\mathscr{P}_2$ are *P-equivalent with respect to* $\mathscr{S}$ if for any pair of *P*-structures $\mathscr{P}_3$ and $\mathscr{P}_4$, such that $\mathscr{P}_3 \mathscr{P}_1 \mathscr{P}_4$ and $\mathscr{P}_3 \mathscr{P}_2 \mathscr{P}_4$ belong to $\mathscr{S}$, the *P*-structures $\mathscr{P}_3 \mathscr{P}_1 \mathscr{P}_4$ and $\mathscr{P}_3 \mathscr{P}_2 \mathscr{P}_4$ are either both marked or both unmarked.

Let $\mathscr{P}$ be a *P*-structure which fulfills the following condition. If $\mathscr{P}_1$ and $\mathscr{P}_2$ are *P*-structures for which $\mathscr{P}_1 \mathscr{P} \mathscr{P}_2 \in \mathscr{S}$, then $\mathscr{P}_1 \mathscr{P} \mathscr{P}_2$ is an unmarked *P*-structure. In this case, we shall say that the *P*-structure $\mathscr{P}$ is *parasitic with respect to* $\mathscr{S}$.

The following proposition is obvious.

Proposition 1. If $\mathscr{S}'$ and $\mathscr{S}''$ are two subsets of $\mathscr{S}_0$ such that $\mathscr{S}'' \subseteq \mathscr{S}'$ and if the *P*-structures $\mathscr{P}_1$ and $\mathscr{P}_2$ are *P*-equivalent with respect to $\mathscr{S}'$, then $\mathscr{P}_1$ and $\mathscr{P}_2$ are also *P*-equivalent with respect to $\mathscr{S}''$

Given two P-structures $\mathcal{P}$ and $\mathcal{P}_1$, we shall say that $\mathcal{P}$ *contains* $\mathcal{P}_1$ if there exist two P-structures $\mathcal{P}_2$ and $\mathcal{P}_3$ such that $\mathcal{P} = \mathcal{P}_2 \mathcal{P}_1 \mathcal{P}_3$. ($\mathcal{P}_2$ or $\mathcal{P}_3$ may be the empty P-structure).

We shall say that a P-structure $\mathcal{P}$ is a *P-structure of the first rank* if $\mathcal{P}$ contains no P-configuration of the first rank. The set of all P-structures of the first rank will be denoted by $\mathcal{S}_1$.

Let us consider a P-structure $\mathcal{P}$ which fulfills the following two conditions: (1) the length of $\mathcal{P}$ is not less than 2; (2) there exists a word $a \in \Gamma$ such that $\mathcal{P}$ and $P(a)$ are P-equivalent with respect to $\mathcal{S}_1$. Then we shall say that $\mathcal{P}$ is a *P-configuration of the second rank*. The P-cell $P(a)$ will be called a *resultant of* $\mathcal{P}$.

If $\mathcal{P}$ is both a P-configuration of the second rank and a parasitic P-structure with respect to $\mathcal{S}_1$, we shall say that $\mathcal{P}$ is a *parasitic P-configuration of the second rank*.

We shall say that a P-structure $\mathcal{P}$ is a *P-structure of the second rank* if $\mathcal{P}$ contains no P-configuration of the second rank. The set of all P-structures of the second rank will be denoted by $\mathcal{S}_2$.

Let us admit that we have defined, for every positive integer $p < n$, the P-configurations and the P-structures of rank p; let us denote by $\mathcal{S}_p$ the set of all P-structures of rank p. We shall say that the P-structure $\mathcal{P}$ is a *P-configuration of rank n* if the following two conditions are fulfilled: (1) the length of $\mathcal{P}$ is not less than 2; (2) there exists a word $a \in \Gamma$ such that $\mathcal{P}$ and $P(a)$ are P-equivalent with respect to $\mathcal{S}_{n-1}$. The P-cell $P(a)$ will be called a *resultant of* $\mathcal{P}$.

If $\mathcal{P}$ is both a P-configuration of rank n and a parasitic P-structure with respect to $\mathcal{S}_{n-1}$, we shall say that $\mathcal{P}$ is a *parasitic P-configuration of rank n*.

We shall say that a P-structure $\mathcal{P}$ is a *P-structure of rank n* if $\mathcal{P}$ contains no P-configuration of rank n. The set of all P-structures of rank n will be denoted by $\mathcal{S}_n$.

Let us denote by $\mathcal{C}_n$ the set of all P-configurations of rank n.

Theorem 1. We have $\mathcal{S}_0 \supseteq \mathcal{S}_1 \supseteq \cdots \supseteq \mathcal{S}_n \supseteq \mathcal{S}_{n+1} \supseteq \cdots$ and $\mathcal{C}_1 \subseteq \mathcal{C}_2 \subseteq \cdots \subseteq \mathcal{C}_n \subseteq \mathcal{C}_{n+1} \subseteq \cdots$. Moreover, if $\mathcal{P} \in \mathcal{C}_n$ and $\mathcal{P}$ admits the resultant $P(a)$, then $P(a)$ is also a resultant of $\mathcal{P}$ conceived as an element of $\mathcal{C}_{n+1}$.

PROOF. Since $\mathcal{S}_0$ is the set of all P-structures, the inclusion $\mathcal{S}_0 \supseteq \mathcal{S}_1$ is obvious. Then, in view of Proposition 1, we have $\mathcal{C}_1 \subseteq \mathcal{C}_2$, and any resultant of $\mathscr{P} \in \mathscr{C}_1$ is also a resultant of $\mathscr{P}$ conceived as an element of $\mathscr{C}_2$.

Let us admit that $\mathscr{S}_{p-1} \supseteq \mathscr{S}_p$ and $\mathscr{C}_p \subseteq \mathscr{C}_{p+1}$ for every positive integer $p < n$. Let $\mathscr{P}$ be a *P*-structure of rank n. $\mathscr{P}$ contains no *P*-configuration of rank n and, since $\mathscr{C}_{n-1} \subseteq \mathscr{C}_n$, $\mathscr{P}$ contains no *P*-configuration of rank $n-1$. It follows that $\mathscr{S}_n \subseteq \mathscr{S}_{n-1}$. Then, in view of Proposition 1, we have $\mathscr{C}_n \subseteq \mathscr{C}_{n+1}$ and any resultant of $\mathscr{P} \in \mathscr{C}_n$ is also a resultant of $\mathscr{P}$ conceived as an element of $\mathscr{C}_{n+1}$. Theorem 1 is proved.

Theorem 1 makes the following definitions natural.

A *P*-structure $\mathscr{P}$ is said to be *of finite order* if there exists an integer n (obviously unique) such that $\mathscr{P} \in \mathscr{S}_n - \mathscr{S}_{n+1}$. The number n is the *order of* $\mathscr{P}$. If no such n exists, then $\mathscr{P}$ is said to be *of infinite order*. Let us denote by $\mathscr{S}_\infty$ the set of all *P*-structures of infinite order.

A *P*-structure $\mathscr{P}$ is said to be a *P-configuration of order n* if we have $\mathscr{P} \in \mathscr{C}_n - \mathscr{C}_{n-1}$. (We put $\mathscr{C}_0 = 0$.) It is easy to see that the rank of a *P*-structure $\mathscr{P}$ is less than or equal to the order of $\mathscr{P}$, whereas the rank of a *P*-configuration $\mathscr{P}$ is greater than or equal to the order of $\mathscr{P}$. Moreover, if $\mathscr{P}$ is a *P*-structure of order n, then $\mathscr{P}$ is a *P*-structure of rank k for every $k \leq n$; if $\mathscr{P}$ is a *P*-configuration of order n, then $\mathscr{P}$ is a *P*-configuration of rank i for every $i \geq n$. Therefore, the order of a *P*-structure is its maximum rank, whereas the order of a *P*-configuration is its minimum rank.

A *P*-structure $\mathscr{P}$ is said to be a *P-configuration of infinite order* if the two conditions are fulfilled (1) the length of $\mathscr{P}$ is not less than 2 and (2) there exists a word $a \in \Gamma$ such that $\mathscr{P}$ and $P(a)$ are *P*-equivalent with respect to $\mathscr{S}_\infty$. The *P*-cell $P(a)$ is a *resultant of* $\mathscr{P}$. We shall denote by $\mathscr{C}_\infty$ the set of all *P*-configurations of infinite order. We may now develop a transfinite classification of the *P*-structures and *P*-configurations of a given language, but we do not insist on this idea.

Proposition 2. We have $\mathscr{S}_\infty \subseteq \mathscr{S}_n$ for every integer $n \geq 0$ and $\mathscr{C}_n \subseteq \mathscr{C}_\infty$ for every positive integer n.

PROOF. If $\mathscr{P} \in \mathscr{S}_\infty$, then $\mathscr{P} \in \mathscr{S}_n - \mathscr{S}_{n+1}$ holds for no integer $n \geq 0$. Since, in any case, $\mathscr{P} \in \mathscr{S}_0$, it follows, in view of Theorem 1, that

$$\mathscr{P} \in \bigcap_{n=1}^{\infty} \mathscr{S}_n,$$

and the first inclusion is proved. From $\mathscr{S}_\infty \subseteq \mathscr{S}_n$ $(n \geq 0)$ and in view of Proposition 1, the second inclusion immediately follows.

3. The *P*-Configuration and the *P*-Structure Types of Language

Theorem 2.   For every positive integer n, the equality $\mathscr{C}_n = \mathscr{C}_{n+1}$ implies $\mathscr{S}_n = \mathscr{S}_{n+1}$, whereas the equality $\mathscr{S}_{n-1} = \mathscr{S}_n$ implies $\mathscr{C}_n = \mathscr{C}_{n+1}$.

PROOF.   Let $\mathscr{C}_n = \mathscr{C}_{n+1}$. In view of Theorem 1 we have, in any case, $\mathscr{S}_{n+1} \subseteq \mathscr{S}_n$. It remains to prove the other inclusion. Let $\mathscr{P} \in \mathscr{S}_n$; $\mathscr{P}$ contains no *P*-configuration of rank n. Hence, since $\mathscr{C}_n = \mathscr{C}_{n+1}$, $\mathscr{P}$ contains no *P*-configuration of rank $n+1$. Therefore $\mathscr{P} \in \mathscr{S}_{n+1}$ and $\mathscr{S}_n \subseteq \mathscr{S}_{n+1}$.

Now let $\mathscr{S}_{n-1} = \mathscr{S}_n$. In view of Theorem 1 we have, in any case, $\mathscr{C}_n \subseteq \mathscr{C}_{n+1}$. It remains to prove the other inclusion. Let $\mathscr{P} \in \mathscr{C}_{n+1}$. There exists a word $a \in \Gamma$ such that $\mathscr{P}$ and $P(a)$ are *P*-equivalent with respect to $\mathscr{S}_n$. Since $\mathscr{S}_n = \mathscr{S}_{n-1}$, it follows that $\mathscr{P}$ and $P(a)$ are *P*-equivalent with respect to $\mathscr{S}_{n-1}$; on the other hand, the length of $\mathscr{P}$ is not less than 2, because $\mathscr{P} \in \mathscr{C}_{n+1}$. It follows that $\mathscr{P} \in \mathscr{C}_n$ and $\mathscr{C}_{n+1} \subseteq \mathscr{C}_n$. Theorem 2 is so proved.

Corollary 1.   If there exists an integer n such that $\mathscr{C}_n = \mathscr{C}_{n+1}$, then $\mathscr{C}_n = \mathscr{C}_m$ for any $m > n$. If there exists an integer n such that $\mathscr{S}_n = \mathscr{S}_{n+1}$, then $\mathscr{S}_n = \mathscr{S}_m$ for any $m > n$.

PROOF.   In view of Theorem 2, $\mathscr{C}_n = \mathscr{C}_{n+1}$ implies $\mathscr{S}_n = \mathscr{S}_{n+1}$, which implies $\mathscr{C}_{n+1} = \mathscr{C}_{n+2}$, which implies $\mathscr{S}_{n+1} = \mathscr{S}_{n+2}$, which implies $\mathscr{C}_{n+2} = \mathscr{C}_{n+3}$ etc.

Corollary 2.   If the language $\{\Gamma, P, \Phi\}$ has no *P*-configuration of order n, it has no *P*-configuration of order $m > n$. The same is true for the *P*-structures.

PROOF.   If no *P*-configuration of order n exists, then $\mathscr{C}_n - \mathscr{C}_{n-1} = 0$. Hence, in view of Theorem 1, $\mathscr{C}_{n-1} = \mathscr{C}_n$ and, by Corollary 1, $\mathscr{C}_m = \mathscr{C}_{m-1}$ for every integer $m \geqslant n$. Therefore, $\mathscr{C}_m - \mathscr{C}_{m-1} = 0$ for $m \geqslant n$ and no *P*-configuration of order m exists. A similar proof holds for the *P*-structures.

Corollary 2 makes the following definitions natural.

Let us suppose the existence of an integer N which fulfills the following conditions: (1) there exists a *P*-configuration of order N; (2) there exists no *P*-configuration of order $N+1$. In this case, we shall say that *the considered language has a finite, positive P-configuration*. By definition, *the P-configuration is equal to N*. If $\mathscr{C}_1 = 0$, we shall say that *the P-configuration is equal to* 0. If no such integer N exists, and if $\mathscr{C}_1 \neq 0$, we shall say that *the P-configuration is infinite.*

The *P*-configuration of a language L is a measure of the complexity of the dependence relations which exist in L. Unfortunately, we know nothing about the *P*-configuration of the natural languages. This seems to be a difficult problem.

Let us suppose the existence of an integer M which fulfills the following conditions: (1) there exists a *P*-structure of order M; (2) there exists no *P*-structure of order $M + 1$. In this case, we shall say that *the considered language has a finite nonnegative P-structure type.* By definition, *the P-structure type is equal to* M. If $\mathscr{S}_0 = \mathscr{S}_1$, we shall say that *the P-structure type is equal to* -1. If no such integer M exists and if $\mathscr{S}_0 \neq \mathscr{S}_1$, we shall say that *the P-structure type is infinite.*

In the general case, denote by M the *P*-structure of a language L and by N its *P*-configuration. We always have $-1 \leqslant M \leqslant \infty$, $0 \leqslant N \leqslant \infty$.

Proposition 3. If $\mathscr{C}_1 = 0$, then $\mathscr{C}_n = 0$ and $\mathscr{S}_n = \mathscr{S}_0$ for every positive integer n.

PROOF. If $\mathscr{C}_1 = 0$ and $\mathscr{P} \in \mathscr{S}_0$, then $\mathscr{P}$ contains no *P*-configuration of the first rank. Hence $\mathscr{P} \in \mathscr{S}_1$ and $\mathscr{S}_0 \subseteq \mathscr{S}_1$. Since, in view of Theorem 1, we have in any case $\mathscr{S}_1 \subseteq \mathscr{S}_0$, it follows that $\mathscr{S}_1 = \mathscr{S}_0$. Now, by Corollary 1, $\mathscr{S}_n = \mathscr{S}_0$ for every n. In view of Theorem 2, the last equality implies that $\mathscr{C}_n = \mathscr{C}_1$ for every n and, since $\mathscr{C}_1 = 0$, $\mathscr{C}_n = 0$ for every n.

Proposition 4. If $\mathscr{S}_1 = \mathscr{S}_0$, then $\mathscr{C}_n = 0$ for every positive integer n.

PROOF. In view of Proposition 3, it is enough to show that $\mathscr{C}_1 = 0$. Let us admit that $\mathscr{C}_1 \neq 0$ and let $\mathscr{P} \in \mathscr{C}_1$. There exist in any case some *P*-structures which do not contain $\mathscr{P}$ (for instance, every *P*-structure whose length is equal to 1), therefore $\mathscr{S}_0 - \mathscr{S}_1 \neq 0$. But this fact contradicts the assumption that $\mathscr{S}_1 = \mathscr{S}_0$. It follows that $\mathscr{C}_1 = 0$ and Proposition 4 is proved.

Propositions 3 and 4 yield Proposition 5.

Proposition 5. The *P*-configuration of a language L is equal to zero if and only if the *P*-structure type of L is equal to -1.

We shall say that L is *of finite P-structure type* if $M < \infty$; L is *of finite P-configuration* if $N < \infty$.

In the general case, the *P*-configurational type and the *P*-structure type are related by Theorem 3.

Theorem 3. Let M be the P-structure type of a language L and let N be its P-configurational type. M and N are either both finite or both infinite. If M and N are finite, then $N = M + 1$.

PROOF. Theorem 3 will be deduced from the following two propositions: (1) If N is finite, then $N = M + 1$; (2) if M is finite, then N is finite.

Let us prove (1). If $N = 0$, in view of Proposition 5, $M = -1$. Hence $N = M + 1$. If $N = 1$, we have $\mathscr{C}_1 \neq 0$ and $\mathscr{C}_2 - \mathscr{C}_1 = 0$. The first relation implies $\mathscr{S}_0 - \mathscr{S}_1 \neq 0$ and $M \geq 0$. In view of Theorem 1, the second relation implies $\mathscr{C}_1 = \mathscr{C}_2$ and, by Theorem 2, we obtain $\mathscr{S}_1 = \mathscr{S}_2$ and $\mathscr{S}_1 - \mathscr{S}_2 = 0$. Therefore $M < 1$. Thus, $M = 0$ and $N = M + 1$. If $N > 1$, we have $\mathscr{C}_N - \mathscr{C}_{N-1} \neq 0$ and $\mathscr{C}_{N+1} - \mathscr{C}_N = 0$. In view of Theorem 2, the first relation implies $\mathscr{S}_{N-1} \neq \mathscr{S}_{N-2}$. Hence $\mathscr{S}_{N-1} - \mathscr{S}_{N-2} \neq 0$ and $M \geq N - 1$. In view of Theorem 1, the second relation is equivalent to $\mathscr{C}_N = \mathscr{C}_{N+1}$. By Theorem 2, we obtain $\mathscr{S}_N = \mathscr{S}_{N+1}$. Therefore $\mathscr{S}_N - \mathscr{S}_{N+1} = 0$ and, in view of Corollary 2, $M < N$. It follows that $N = M + 1$ and (1) is proved.

Let us prove (2). If $M = -1$, in view of Proposition 5, $N = 0$. Hence $N = M + 1$. If M is finite and nonnegative, we have $\mathscr{S}_M - \mathscr{S}_{M+1} \neq 0$ and $\mathscr{S}_{M+1} - \mathscr{S}_{M+2} = 0$. In view of Theorem 1, the second relation is equivalent to $\mathscr{S}_{M+1} = \mathscr{S}_{M+2}$. By Theorem 2, we obtain $\mathscr{C}_{M+2} = \mathscr{C}_{M+3}$. Therefore $\mathscr{C}_{M+3} - \mathscr{C}_{M+2} = 0$ and, in view of Corollary 2, $N \leq M + 2$. Since M is finite, it follows that N is finite. Theorem 3 is proved.

Let us denote by $\mathscr{S}_n^*$ the set of all P-structures of order n and by $\mathscr{C}_n^*$ the set of all P-configurations of order n. We always have $\mathscr{S}_n^* \cap \mathscr{S}_m^* = \mathscr{C}_n^* \cap \mathscr{C}_m^* = 0$ for $m \neq n$. If $\mathscr{S}_\infty = 0$, then $\mathscr{S}_n = \mathscr{S}_n^* \cup \mathscr{S}_{n+1}^* \cup \cdots$ for each integer $n \geq 0$ and $\mathscr{C}_n = \mathscr{C}_1^* \cup \mathscr{C}_2^* \cup \cdots \cup \mathscr{C}_n^*$ for each positive integer n. Hence $\mathscr{C}_n = \mathscr{C}_{n-1} \cup \mathscr{C}_n^*$. On the other hand, let us denote by $\mathscr{S}_\infty$ the set of P-structures of infinite order and by $\mathscr{C}_\infty$ the set of P-configurations of infinite order. It is easy to see that $\mathscr{S}_\infty = 0$ implies $\mathscr{C}_\infty = 0$.

4. Examples of E-Configurations

To illustrate these notions and facts, we present several examples.

EXAMPLE 1. Let us consider the following language. $\Gamma = \{a, b\}$, $P = E$ (the unit partition), $\Phi = \{a^3, \ldots, a^{2n+1}, \ldots, b^2, b^4, \ldots, b^{2n}, \ldots\}$. For every integer $n > 1$, the string b^{2n-1} is an E-configuration of the first rank, having as resultant the word b. Indeed, if x and y are two strings over Γ, we have $xb^{2n-1}y \in \Phi$ if and only $x = b^m$, $y = b^p$, and $m + p$ is an odd positive integer. Under the same conditions we have $xby \in \Phi$. Hence b^{2n-1} and b are E-equivalent with respect to $\mathscr{S}_0$.

The strings of the form a^n are not E-configurations of the first rank. Indeed, if n is odd, neither a nor b may be resultants of a^n, since a and b do not belong to Φ; if n is even, neither a nor b may be resultants of a^n, since a^2 and ab do not belong to Φ. No string of the form b^{2n} may be an E-configuration of the first rank, since a and b do not belong to Φ. No string containing both a and b may be an E-configuration of the first rank, since there exist (infinitely many) marked strings containing a and (infinitely many) marked strings containing b, whereas no marked string exists containing both a and b. Thus, there exists no parasitic E-configuration of the first rank and we have $\mathscr{C}_1 = \{b^3, b^5, \ldots, b^{2n+1}, \ldots\}$. The set $\mathscr{S}_1$ may be obtained by replacing in all strings every E-configuration of the first rank by its resultant.

It follows that $\mathscr{S}_1$ is formed by the strings over Γ that do not contain a substring of the form $b^n (n > 2)$.

Since there exists no pair of strings u and v, such that $ub^n v \in \mathscr{S}_1$ $(n > 2)$, it follows that b^n is a parasitic E-configuration of the second rank, having resultants a and b, for any $n > 2$. We have no other E-configuration of the second rank. It follows that $\mathscr{C}_1 \subset \mathscr{C}_2$, but every E-configuration of the second rank is parasitic.

This example shows that the same P-structure may be a nonparasitic P-configuration of the first rank, but a parasitic P-configuration of the second rank.

It is easy to see that $\mathscr{S}_2 = \mathscr{S}_1$. In view of Theorems 1 and 2, we have $\mathscr{C}_2 = \mathscr{C}_n$ for $n \geq 2$ and $\mathscr{S}_n = \mathscr{S}_1$ for every positive integer n. Thus, all the E-configurations of the form b^{2n+1} $(n \geq 1)$ are of the first order, whereas those of the form $b^{2n} (n > 1)$ are second order. The E-configuration of the considered language is equal to 2. In view of Theorem 3, the E-structure type is 1.

EXAMPLE 2. Let us consider the language $\{\Gamma, P, \Phi\}$, where $\Gamma = \{a\}$, $P = E$, and $\Phi = \{a^{q_1}, \ldots, a^{q_n}, \ldots\}$, where $1 = q_1, q_2, \ldots, q_n, \ldots$ is the sequence of prime numbers. We shall show that this language has no E-configuration of the first rank. (Thus in view of Proposition 3, it has no E-configuration of rank n, for any positive integer n.) Let us admit the existence of an E-configuration of the first rank; it necessarily has the form a^p and its resultant is a.

Let q be a prime number. Since a^p has the resultant a, it follows that

$$a^q, a^{q+(p-1)}, a^{q+2(p-1)}, \ldots, a^{q+n(p-1)}, \ldots$$

are marked strings. Hence the numbers q, $q+(p-1)$, $q+2(p-1), \ldots$, $q+n(p-1), \ldots$ are prime. But these numbers form an infinite arithmetic progression. A theorem of Erdös asserts that, for each positive integer n, there exist two consecutive prime numbers whose difference is greater than n[12]. This theorem makes the existence of the above infinite sequence of prime numbers as an arithmetic progression impossible. Thus, the language considered has no E-configuration. The E-configuration is equal to zero, whereas the E-structure type is -1.

It is shown [27] that the language considered is not a finite-state language.

EXAMPLE 3. Let us consider the language of Kleene ([25], p. 40): $\Gamma = \{a\}$, $P = E$, $\Phi = \{a^{n^2}\}(1 \leqslant n < \infty)$. Let us admit that a^p is an E-configuration of the first rank. Since the resultant may not be other than a, it follows that

$$a, a^{1+(p-1)}, a^{1+2(p-1)}, \ldots, a^{1+n(p-1)}, \ldots$$

are marked strings. Hence the numbers 1, $1+(p-1)$, $1+2(p-1), \ldots$, $1+n(p-1), \ldots$ are perfect squares. But these numbers form an infinite arithmetic progression, and no infinite arithmetic progression exists whose terms are perfect squares. Indeed, the difference of two consecutive perfect squares is $n^2 - (n-1)^2 = 2n - 1$. Hence it tends to ∞ when $n \to \infty$. It follows that the language of Kleene has no E-configuration.

Kleene has shown that this language is not a finite-state language [25]. Gladkii has proved (unpublished paper) that the language of Kleene may be generated by a context-sensitive grammar in the sense of Chomsky [9], but not by a context-free grammar (see also Bar-Hillel *et al.* [2]). As Gladkii has shown, all these conclusions hold for the language discussed in Example 2.

EXAMPLE 4. Let us consider the following language of Curry ([11], p. 57): $\Gamma = \{a, b\}$, $P = E$, $\Phi = \{ab^n\}$, where $0 \leqslant n < \infty$ (b^0 is the empty string). There exists no parasitic E-configuration of order 1. Every string of the form b^n, where $n \geqslant 2$, is an E-configuration of the first rank, whose resultant is b. Every string of the form ab^n ($0 \leqslant n < \infty$), that is, every marked string is an E-configuration of first order, whose resultant is a. All the E-configurations of the first rank are parasitic E-configurations of the second rank. Every nonempty string over Γ, other than a and b that contains no string of the form b^n ($n \geqslant 2$) and no string of the form ab^n ($n \geqslant 1$) is a parasitic E-configuration of order 2, with resultant b. It follows that $\mathscr{S}_2 = \mathscr{S}_1$. In view of Theorems 1 and 2, we have $\mathscr{S}_n = \mathscr{S}_1$ for $n \geqslant 1$ and $\mathscr{C}_n = \mathscr{C}_2$ for $n \geqslant 2$. Every E-configuration of the first rank is of order 1. The E-configuration is equal to 2, whereas the E-structure is 1 (see Theorem 3).

The language considered, which will be designed by L_1, is the first step of a model concerning the mathematical language ([11]; see also Section 7, Chapter II). The second step is given by the language L_2: $\Gamma = \{a, b, c\}$, $P = E$, $\Phi = \{ab^n cab^m\}$, where m and n are arbitrary nonnegative integers, b^0 being the empty string. It is easy to see that L_2 has the same E-configurations as L_1. As shown in [11], L_2 is a model of the set of mathematical (true or not) propositions. L_2 is a finite-state language [28]. The third step is given by the language L_3: $\Gamma = \{a, b, c\}$, $P = E$, $\Phi = \{ab^n cab^n\}$, where n takes the values of all nonnegative integers. In contrast to L_1 and L_2, L_3 has no E-configuration of the first rank. Hence, in view of Proposition 3, L_3 has no E-configuration of rank $n \geqslant 1$. L_3 may be considered a model of the set of theorems [11]. As was shown in Section 7, Chapter II, L_3 is not a finite-state language; but it is a context-free language [28] (for the notion of a context-free language see also Section 10, Chapter III).

EXAMPLE 5. Let $\Gamma = \{a,b,c\}$, $P = E$, $\Phi = \{ab,c\}$. The unique E-configuration of the first rank is ab, and its resultant is c. This example shows that a P-configuration does not always contain its resultant.

EXAMPLE 6. Let $\Gamma = \{a,b,c,d\}$, $P = E$, $\Phi = \{ab,c,d\}$. The unique E-configuration of the first rank is ab and it admits two resultants c and d.

Examples 5 and 6 describe a fragment of English. Thus, we may put $a = very$, $b = large$, $c = great$, $d = short$. It follows that a syntagm of the form $adverb + adjective$ may have as resultant an adjective other than that contained in the syntagm.

EXAMPLE 7. Let $\Gamma = \{a, b, c\}$, $P = E$, $\Phi = \{c, cb, cab, ca^2b, \ldots, ca^nb, \ldots\}$. For every $n \geqslant 2$, a^n is an E-configuration of order 1, with resultant a. For every positive integer n, the strings a^nb and ca^n are E-configurations of the first order having the resultants b and c, respectively. We obtain $\mathscr{S}_2 = \mathscr{S}_1$, and every E-configuration of order 2 is parasitic.

In view of Theorems 1 and 2, we have $\mathscr{C}_n = \mathscr{C}_2$ for $n \geqslant 2$ and $\mathscr{S}_n = \mathscr{S}_1$

for every $n \geq 1$. The E-configuration is equal to 2, whereas the E-structure type is 1.

Example 7 describes a short fragment of French syntax, namely, that concerning the strings of the forms noun, noun + adjective, noun + adverbs + adjective (such as *homme, homme grand, homme très grand, homme très très grand,..., homme (très)^n grand,...*). The strings of the form $(adverb)^n + adjective$ are E-configurations of the first order, having the adjective as resultant.

Example 7 also describes a similar fragment of the Rumanian syntax (*om, om mare, om foarte mare,..., om (foarte)^n mare,...*). Thus, there is an isomorphism between French and Rumanian, concerning the dependence structure of noun phrases.

EXAMPLE 8. Let $\Gamma = \{a, b, c, d, e, f\}$, $P = E$, $\Phi = \{cd, cdf, cde^m f, a^n bcd, a^n bcde^m f\}$, where $0 \leq m < \infty$ and $0 \leq n < \infty$. We have the following E-configurations of the first order: a^n with resultant a for every $n \geq 2$; e^m with the resultant e for every $m \geq 2$; $a^n b$ with the resultant b for every $n \geq 1$; $e^m f$ with the resultant f for every $m \geq 1$. We obtain $\Phi \cap \mathscr{S}_1 = \{cd, cdf, bcd, bcdf\}$. We have no nonparasitic E-configuration of the second order.

The above example becomes a fragment of English if we take $a = very$, $b = little$, $c = boys$, $d = look$, $e = many$, $f = pictures$.

EXAMPLE 9. Let $\Gamma = \{a, b, c, d, e, f\}$, $P = E$ and $\Phi = \{ab^n c^m de^p f^q\}$, where m, n, p, and q are integers such that $m \geq 0$, $n \geq 0$, $p \geq 0$, $q \geq 0$, and the implications $n > 0 \Rightarrow m > 0$ and $p > 0 \Rightarrow q > 0$ are valid. We have the following E-configurations of the first order: $b^n (n \geq 2)$ with the resultant b; $c^m (m \geq 2)$ with the resultant c; $e^p (p \geq 2)$ with the resultant e; $f^q (q \geq 2)$ with the resultant f; $b^n c^m (n \geq 1, m \geq 1)$ with the resultant c; $e^p f^q (p \geq 1, q \geq 1)$ with the resultant f. We have $\Phi \cap \mathscr{S}_1 = \{ad, acdf, adf, acd\}$, and no nonparasitic E-configuration of order 2 exists.

The above example becomes a fragment of Rumanian syntax if we take $a = elevul$, $b = foarte$, $c = silitor$, $d = studiază$, $e = multe$, $f = cărti$.

Examples 7 and 8 show the possibility that an E-configuration of the first order contains another first-order E-configuration. In Example 7, a^n is contained in ca^n and in $a^n b$. In Example 8, a^n is contained in $a^n b$, whereas e^m is contained in $e^m f$.

EXAMPLE 10 (Kulagina [26], p. 211). Let $\Gamma = \{a, b, c, d\}$, $P = E$, $\Phi = \{ab^n cd, dd, bc^m\}$, where $m \geq 0$ and $n \geq 0$. For every $n \geq 1$, ab^n is an E-configuration of the first order, with resultant a. We have $\mathscr{C}_1 = \{ab, ab^2, \ldots, ab^n, \ldots\}$ and $\Phi \cap \mathscr{S}_1 = \{acd, dd, bc^m\}$ $(m \geqslant 0)$. For every $m \geqslant 1$, bc^m is an E-configuration of order 2, with resultant b, and we have $\Phi \cap \mathscr{S}_2 = \{acd, dd, b\}$. We have two E-configurations of order 3 (with resultant b): acd and dd.

EXAMPLE 11. Let $\Gamma = \{a, b, c, d, e\}$, $P = E$, $\Phi = \{ab^mcde, bc^nde, cd^pe, de^r\}$, where $m \geqslant 0$, $n \geqslant 0$, $p \geqslant 0$, and $r \geqslant 0$. For every $m \geqslant 1$, ab^m is an E-configuration of order 1, with resultant a, and no other E-configuration of order 1 exists. We have $\Phi \cap \mathscr{S}_1 = \{acde, bc^nde, cd^pe, de^r\}$, where $n \geqslant 0, p \geqslant 0, r \geqslant 0$. For every $n \geqslant 1$, bc^n is an E-configuration of order 2, with resultant b and no other E-configuration of order 2 exists. Further, we find that cd^p is an E-configuration of order 3, with resultant c, for any $p \geqslant 1$ and de^r is an E-configuration of order 4, with resultant d, for any $r \geqslant 1$. Since $\Phi \cap \mathscr{S}_4 = \{acde, bde, ce, d\}$, we have three E-configurations of order 5 (with resultant d): $acde$, bde, and ce.

Example 11 shows how we can obtain, for every positive integer n, a language which admits nonparasitic E-configurations of order n.

It is not difficult to explain the significance of Examples 9 and 10 from the standpoint of dependence structure. For instance, in Example 10, b is dependent on a, c on b, d on c, and e on d. But these four dependencies are of different degrees, which implies the different orders of the corresponding E-configurations.

EXAMPLE 12 (Revzin [40], pp. 124–125). This example concerns the Russian language. Every marked S-structure of the form $S(a)S(b)$, where a is an adverb and b is an adjective (for instance, $a = vesma$, $b = malenkaja$) is an S-configuration of the first order with resultant $S(b)$, if we neglect Russian strings, such as *vesma i vesma* or *vesma vesma i vesma*. A marked S-structure of the form $S(b)S(c)$, where b is an adjective and c is a noun, is an S-configuration of the second rank, with resultant $S(c)$; but $S(b)S(c)$ may not be replaced by $S(c)$ in such marked S-structures as $S(a)S(b)S(c)$ (for instance $a = vesma$, $b = malenkaja$, $c = devočka$). It is easy to see that no word x exists such that $S(b)S(c)$ and $S(x)$ are S-equivalent with respect to $\mathscr{S}_0$. It follows that $S(b)S(c)$ is not an S-configuration of the first rank. Hence it is of order 2. There also exist S-configurations of the second order, formed by verbs, such as $S(dolgo)S(laskala)$, whose resultant is $S(laskala)$. If d is a transitive verb and e is its direct complement (for instance, $d = laskala$, $e = košku$), and f is an intransitive verb (for instance, $f = stojala$), then $S(laskala)$

$S(ko\check{s}ku)$, and $S(stojala)$ are S-equivalent with respect to $\mathscr{S}_2$. Hence $S(laskala)\ S(ko\check{s}ku)$ is an S-configuration of the third rank, with resultant $S(stojala)$; it is easy to see that this S-configuration is third order.

5. Removal of Parasitic Elements

Now let us remark on the above examples. Examples 1 and 4 show that the parasitic P-configurations may cause an increase in the P-configuration of a language. In both these examples, the E-configuration type is equal to 2, but all E-configurations of order 2 are parasitic. It is natural then to introduce the following definitions.

A language L *has a finite effective P-configurational type* if there exists an integer N_1 which fulfills the following conditions: (1) there exists a nonparasitic P-configuration of order N_1; (2) every P-configuration of order $N_1 + 1$ is parasitic. N_1 is *the effective P-configuration* of L (if every P-configuration of order 1 is parasitic, then, by definition, we put $N_1 = 0$). If no such integer exists, we say that L *has an infinite effective P-configuration* and we put $N_1 = \infty$. Thus, in Examples 1 and 4 we have $N_1 = 1$, whereas $N = 2$. In Examples 2 and 3 we have $N_1 = N = 0$. In Examples 5 and 6, $N_1 = N = 1$. In Example 7, $N_1 = 1$ *and* $N = 2$. In Examples 8 and 9, $N_1 = 1$ and in Example 10, $N_1 = 3$. In Example 11, $N_1 = 5$.

Consider a language $\{\Gamma, P, \Phi\}$ and a word $a \in \Gamma$. The word a is said to be *parasitic*, if a is contained in no marked string (that is, if $x = uav$, then x does not belong to Φ).

Proposition 6. We always have $N_1 \leqslant N$. If no parasitic word exists and if $N_1 = 0$, then $N = 0$.

PROOF. Since the inequality is obvious, let us prove the second assertion. Suppose $N_1 = 0$ and let $\mathscr{P}$ be a P-configuration of order 1 and $P(a)$ a resultant of $\mathscr{P}$. Thus, $\mathscr{P}$ and $P(a)$ are P-equivalent. Since a is not parasitic, there exists a marked string containing a: $a_1 a_2 \cdots a_{p-1} a a_{p+1} \cdots a_n$. Hence the P-structure $P(a_1) \cdots P(a_{p-1}) P(a) P(a_{p+1}) \cdots P(a_n)$ is marked. Since $\mathscr{P}$ and $P(a)$ are P-equivalent, the P-structure $P(a_1) \cdots P(a_{p-1}) \mathscr{P} P(a_{p+1}) \cdots P(a_n)$ is also marked. Hence $\mathscr{P}$ is not parasitic. But this fact contradicts the assumption that $N_1 = 0$. Therefore no *P*-configuration (parasitic or not) of order 1 exists and $N = 0$.

It is to be expected that the difference $N - N_1$ may not exceed any integer. In this respect, it would be interesting to find the smallest integer n (if it exists) such that $N - N_1 \leq n$ in every language.

In an obvious manner, we may define *the effective P-structure type* M_1 of a language. We always have $M_1 \leq M$. It is interesting to establish whether Theorem 3 remains true if M and N are replaced by M_1 and N_1, respectively.

6. Semiregular *P*-Configurations

The examples considered show that the most interesting *P*-configurations $\mathcal{P}$ are those which fulfill the following two conditions: (1) the length of $\mathcal{P}$ is exactly 2; (2) there exists a resultant of $\mathcal{P}$ which is contained in $\mathcal{P}$. If $\mathcal{P}$ fulfills condition (1), it is called *a minimal P-configuration*. If $\mathcal{P}$ fulfills condition (2), it is *a semiregular P-configuration*.

Among the languages considered in the above examples, only those of Examples 5 and 6 are finite languages. On the other hand, only in Examples 5 and 6 is there no semiregular *E*-configuration of the first order. These facts are explained by Theorem 4.

Theorem 4. Let L be a language containing no parasitic word. If L admits at least one semiregular *P*-configuration of order 1, then L is infinite.

PROOF. Let $\mathcal{P}$ be a semiregular *P*-configuration and let $a_i \in \Gamma$ such that $P(a_i)$ is a resultant of $\mathcal{P}$ contained in $\mathcal{P}$. Thus, there exist two *P*-structures $\mathcal{P}_1$ and $\mathcal{P}_2$ such that $\mathcal{P} = \mathcal{P}_1 P(a_i) \mathcal{P}_2$. Since a_i is not parasitic, there exist two *P*-structures $\mathcal{P}_3$ and $\mathcal{P}_4$, such that $\mathcal{P}_3 P(a_i) \mathcal{P}_4$ is a marked *P*-structure. But $\mathcal{P}$ and $P(a_i)$ are *P*-equivalent. Therefore the *P*-structure $\mathcal{P}_3 \mathcal{P} \mathcal{P}_4 = \mathcal{P}_3 \mathcal{P}_1 P(a_i) \mathcal{P}_2 \mathcal{P}_4$ is also marked. Further, again using the *P*-equivalence of $\mathcal{P}$ and $P(a_i)$, we deduce that the *P*-structure $\mathcal{P}_n = \mathcal{P}_3 (\mathcal{P}_1)^n P(a_i) (\mathcal{P}_2)^n \mathcal{P}_4$ is marked for every positive integer n. If we denote by p_1, p_2, p_3, p_4, and p_n the lengths of the *P*-structures $\mathcal{P}_1, \mathcal{P}_2, \mathcal{P}_3, \mathcal{P}_4$, and $\mathcal{P}_n$, respectively, we have $p_n = n(p_1 + p_2) + p_3 + p_4 + 1$. Since the length of $\mathscr{P}$ may not be less than 2, it follows that $p_1 + p_2 \geq 1$. Hence

$$\lim_{n \to \infty} p_n = \infty.$$

Since every $\mathscr{P}_n$ is a marked P-structure, there exists, for any positive integer n, a marked string of length p_n. Hence L is infinite.

Proposition 7. If the language L contains no parasitic word, then L admits no parasitic P-configuration of order 1.

PROOF. Let $\mathscr{P}$ be a P-configuration of order 1 and let $P(a)$ be a resultant of $\mathscr{P}$. Since a is not parasitic, the existence of two P-structures $\mathscr{P}_1$ and $\mathscr{P}_2$ such that $\mathscr{P}_1 P(a) \mathscr{P}_2$ is a marked P-structure follows. In view of the P-equivalence of $\mathscr{P}$ and $P(a)$, the P-structure $\mathscr{P}_1 \mathscr{P} \mathscr{P}_2$ is marked. Hence $\mathscr{P}$ is not parasitic.

REMARKS. Proposition 7 shows that all P-configurations occurring in Theorem 4 are nonparasitic. Moreover, Theorem 4 is a new confirmation of a general hypothesis adopted in algebraic linguistics. Every natural language is an infinite language. Indeed, the assumptions of Theorem 4 are fulfilled by every natural language; for every word a of a natural language L, there exists a sentence of L containing a, and every natural language admits semiregular configurations of order 1. For instance, in English an E-configuration of the form secondary adverb + adverb (such as *very clearly*) is of order 1 and semiregular, since it admits the resultant *adverb*.

Theorem 4 does not remain true if we remove the assumption that L contains no parasitic word. Indeed, we have another proposition.

Proposition 8. There exists a finite language which admits a semi-regular E-configuration of order 1.

PROOF. Let $\Gamma = \{a, b\}$ and $\Phi = \{aa\}$. The string ab is an E-configuration of order 1, with resultant b. Hence it is semiregular.

We also have Proposition 9.

Proposition 9. In a finite language, every semiregular P-configuration of order 1 is parasitic.

PROOF. Let $\mathscr{P}$ be a semiregular P-configuration of order 1 and let

$P(a)$ be a resultant of $\mathscr{P}$ contained in $\mathscr{P}$. Thus, there exist two P-structures $\mathscr{P}_1$ and $\mathscr{P}_2$ such that $\mathscr{P} = \mathscr{P}_1 P(a) \mathscr{P}_2$. If $\mathscr{P}$ is nonparasitic, we may find two P-structures $\mathscr{P}_3$ and $\mathscr{P}_4$ such that $\mathscr{P}_3 \mathscr{P}_1 P(a) \mathscr{P}_2 \mathscr{P}_4$ is a marked P-structure. We may replace successively $P(a)$ by $\mathscr{P}_1 P(a) \mathscr{P}_2$ and obtain infinitely many marked P-structures containing $P(a)$: $\mathscr{P}_3 (\mathscr{P}_1)^n P(a)(\mathscr{P}_2)^n \mathscr{P}_4$ ($1 \leqslant n < \infty$). As in the proof of Theorem 4, we deduce the existence of infinitely many marked strings containing the word a. This fact contradicts the assumption that the language is finite. Hence, $\mathscr{P}$ is parasitic.

The above examples suggest that, in any language without parasitic words, the existence of semiregular P-configurations of order n implies the existence of semiregular P-configurations of order p, for every positive integer $p < n$. But the validity of this conjecture requires an ulterior investigation.

To obtain a better approximation of the situations occurring in natural languages, we shall consider a particular case of semiregular configurations.

A P-configuration $\mathscr{P}$ of rank k is said to be *finally regular* if the following conditions are fulfilled: (1) the last term of $\mathscr{P}$ is a resultant of $\mathscr{P}$; (2) no other term of $\mathscr{P}$ is a resultant of $\mathscr{P}$. More precisely, if $\mathscr{P} = P(a_1)$ $P(a_2) \ldots P(a_n)$, then $\mathscr{P}$ and $P(a_n)$ are P-equivalent with respect to $\mathscr{S}_{k-1}$, but $\mathscr{P}$ and $P(a_i)$ ($1 \leqslant i < n$) are not P-equivalent with respect to $\mathscr{S}_{k-1}$. $\mathscr{P}$ is said to be *initially regular* if the first term of $\mathscr{P}$ is a resultant of $\mathscr{P}$, but no other term of $\mathscr{P}$ is a resultant of $\mathscr{P}$. It is obvious that, if $\mathscr{P}$ is finally (initially) regular of rank k, then $\mathscr{P}$ is not initially (finally) regular of rank k. $\mathscr{P}$ is said to be a *regular P-configuration of rank k* if it is either initially or finally regular of rank k.

It is obvious that any regular P-configuration of rank k is also a semiregular P-configuration of rank k; but the converse is not true, as is shown by the next proposition.

Proposition 10. There exist a language L and a semiregular E-configuration $\mathscr{P}$ of rank 1 in L, which is not regular in L.

PROOF. Let $\Gamma = \{a, b, c\}$, $\Phi = \{ab^n c, b\}$, where $n \geqslant 1$. It is obvious that $ab^n c$ is an E-configuration of rank 1, with resultant b. Hence it is semiregular, but not regular, since neither a nor c are resultants of $ab^n c$. Proposition 10 is proved.

7. Normal P-Configurations, Dependencies, and Constituents

A *P*-configuration $\mathscr{P}$ is said to be *initially normal* if it is minimal and initially regular. $\mathscr{P}$ is said to be *finally normal* if it is minimal and finally regular. $\mathscr{P}$ is said to be *normal* if it is minimal and regular. The most frequent configurations encountered in natural languages are normal. The establishment of the order of a configuration in a natural language is a difficult task, because it involves a large quantity of strings and requires many explanations concerning the marked strings. We shall enumerate some normal configurations in various natural languages, without specifying their order. Afterwards, for the sake of illustration and without claim of completeness and exactness, we shall indicate the (plausible) relative order of some normal *E*-configurations in natural languages.

Initially normal *E*-configurations: *cartea elevului* (*noun in nominative + noun in genitive*), *om mare* (*noun + qualitative adjective*), *citesc cărţi* (*transitive verb + direct object*) in Rumanian; *enfant obéissant* (*noun + qualitative adjective*), *écrire lentement* (*verb + adverb*) in French; *civis carus* (*noun + qualitative adjective*), *pater noster* (*noun + pronominal adjective*), *liber civium* (*nominative noun + genitive noun*), *gloria horum* (*noun + possessive adjective*), *imitatur patrem* (*transitive verb + direct object*) in Latin; *palabras nuevas* (*noun + qualitative adjective*), *expresado anteriormente* (*verb in participle + adverb*), *dices nada* (*transitive verb + direct object*) in Spanish; *rechnest gut* (*verb + adverb*) in German; *fetch me* (*verb + indirect object*), *go today* (*verb + adverb*) in English; *čitaet knigu* (*transitive verb + direct object*) in Russian.

Finally normal *E*-configurations: *foarte frumos* (*adverb + qualitative adjective*), *frumoasă carte* (*qualitative adjective + noun*), *trei pomi* (*cardinal numeral + noun*) in Rumanian; *très joli* (*adverb + qualitative adjective*), *merveilleux destin* (*qualitative adjective + noun*), *mon livre* (*possessive adjective + noun*), *ces fruits* (*demonstrative adjective + noun*) in French; *vestra domus* (*possessive adjective + noun*), *hoc praemium* (*demonstrative adjective + noun*), *tres partes* (*cardinal numeral + noun*) in Latin; *algunas horas* (*numeral + noun*), *nuevas ramas* (*qualitative adjective + noun*) in Spanish; *sehr gut* (*adverb + qualitative adjective*), *unsere Wohnung* (*possessive adjective + noun*), *schönes Gärtchen* (*qualitative adjective + noun*), *viele Blumen* (*indefinite adjective + noun*) in German; *my friend* (*possessive adjective + noun*), *very large* (*adverb + qualitative adjective*), *great house* (*qualitative adjective + noun*), *many boys* (*indefinite adjective + noun*), *almost surrounded* (*adverb + passive participle*) in English; *očen bolšoi* (*adverb + qualitative adjective*), *bolšoi dom* (*qualitative adjective + noun*) in Russian.

First let us remark that in every language the order of a normal E-configuration of the form *adverb + qualitative adjective* is less than the order of a normal E-configuration of the form *qualitative adjective + noun*. Indeed, the last configuration may be replaced by its resultant *noun* only after replacing the former with its resultant *qualitative adjective*. In the same way we find that the order of a normal E-configuration of the form *secondary adverb + adverb* is less than the order of a normal E-configuration of the form *adverb + qualitative adjective*, whereas the order of a normal E-configuration of the form *noun + qualitative adjective* is less than the order of a normal E-configuration of the form *transitive verb + direct object*. For instance, in the Rumanian string *mult prea frumoasă* (*secondary adverb + adverb + adjective*) we first replace the normal E-configuration *mult prea* by its resultant *prea*, and only after this we may replace the normal E-configuration *prea frumoasă* by its resultant *frumoasă*. In the Rumanian string *citesc cărți frumoase* (*transitive verb + noun + qualitative adjective*) we must first replace the normal E-configuration *cărți frumoase* by *cărți*, and only after this we may replace *citesc cărți* by *citesc*. So we have at least four different orders of E-configurations in most languages: *secondary adverb + adverb*, *adverb + qualitative adjective*, *qualitative adjective + noun* or *noun + qualitative adjective*, and *transitive verb + direct object*. This situation suggests that the effective E-configuration of a natural language is in any case greater than 4.

Normal E-configurations enable us to define a hierarchy of syntactic dependences, as follows. If *ab* is an initially (finally) normal E-configuration of order n, we shall say that *b depends upon a from the right* (*from the left*), and the order of this dependence is equal to n. In the first case, *a* is said to be the *nucleus* and *b* is said to be the *satellite* of *a*, whereas in the second case these functions are inverted. This terminology is very close to that of Pike [37] and of Pittman [38]. We may also say that *a* is the *center* of the initially normal E-configuration *ab*, whereas *b* is its *adjunct*. Thus, in a normal E-configuration of order n we have a nucleus or a center of order n and a satellite or an adjunct of order n. For other aspects concerning these notions see Revzin [39–41].

In descriptive linguistics, two notions play an important part in every syntactic description: the notions of constituent and immediate constituent. These notions are very closely related to E-configurations of different orders. An attempt to formalize the classical analysis in immediate constituents was given by Revzin [41, 42].

Let $x = a_1 a_2 \ldots a_n$ be a string over Γ and let us consider a language $\{\Gamma, \Phi\}$. We define the *constituents of x* as follows: (1) a_i is a constituent of x for every positive integer $i \le n$; (2) if there exists a constituent z of x such that the strings y and z are E-equivalent (that is, for every pair of strings u and v the strings uyv and uzv are either both in Φ or both in the complement of Φ), then y is a constituent of x. By rule (1) we always obtain finitely many constituents (n constituents), whereas rule (2) may introduce infinitely many constituents.

Let us consider the Rumanian string *Elevul silitor învaţă foarte bine.* By (1) we obtain the constituents *elevul, silitor, învaţă, foarte,* and *bine.* By (2) we obtain a very large number of constituents but we shall specify only the constituents contained in the given string. Thus we find the constituents *foarte bine* (E-equivalent to *bine*), *elevul silitor* (E-equivalent to *elevul*), and *învaţă foarte bine* (E-equivalent to *învaţă*). In the Russian string *bolšaja vorona vzletela na vysokiĭ kust*, Revzin finds the following constituents of length not less than 2 and contained in the given string [41]: *bolšaja vorona* (E-equivalent to *vorona*), *vysokiĭ kust* (E-equivalent to *kust*), and *vzletela na vysokiĭ kust* (E-equivalent to *vzletela*).

It is easy to see that a constituent of length ≥ 2 of the string $x = a_1 a_2 \ldots a_n$ is nothing but an E-configuration of rank 1, which admits at least one of the words a_i ($1 \le i \le n$) as resultant.

The above examples show the necessity of making a distinction between constituents of x contained in x (these constituents are said to be *proper*) and constituents of x not contained in x (said to be *improper*). In the above examples, all the specified constituents are proper, but *copilul* is an improper constituent of the Rumanian string considered, because *copilul* $\in S(elevul)$. It is immediately seen that every string admits only finitely many proper constituents.

The notion of proper constituent enables us to define another important notion of descriptive linguistics, that of an immediate constituent.

A constituent y of the string x is said to be an *immediate constituent of x* if it is a proper constituent of x and if y is contained in no proper constituent of x other than y. In other words, an immediate constituent has a maximal character. Thus, the above Rumanian string admits two immediate constituents: $y = elevul$ $silitor$ and $z = \hat{i}nva\c{t}\u{a}$ $foarte$ $bine$; y admits two immediate constituents: $elevul$ and $silitor$, whereas z admits the immediate constituents $\hat{i}nva\c{t}\u{a}$ and $u = foarte$ $bine$; u admits two immediate constituents $foarte$ and $bine$. The above Russian string admits two immediate constituents, $v = bol\check{s}aja$ $vorona$ and $w = vzletela$ na $vysokii$ $kust$; v is obviously formed by two immediate constituents, whereas w contains two immediate constituents $vzletela$ and $\lambda = na$ $vysokii$ $kust$; λ has two immediate constituents na and $vysokii$ $kust$.

Other aspects of the analysis of immediate constituents and some details concerning immediate constituents in finite-state languages have been investigated by Marcus ([27], pp. 215–219).

Let us remark that the notion of immediate constituent was tacitly considered in Sections 6–9, Chapter III. The theory of configurations of various orders is a considerable improvement of the above description of constituents.

8. *P*-Configurations, *P*-Structures, and Regularly Finer Partitions

In a customary syntactic analysis we often deal with sequences of words or morphemes, although our interest and the conclusions we derive concern sequences of some classes of words or morphemes (such as distributional classes or parts of speech). In this respect, Example 12 of Section 4 and the various examples of normal *E*-configurations given in Section 7 are very significant. The analysis carried out in Example 12 concerns the Russian string *malenkaja devočka dolgo laskala košku*. But we have tacitly transferred the result of our analysis to the *S*-structure of this string, that is, to the sequence of distribution classes to which *malenkaja, devočka, dolgo, laskala*, and *košku* belong. A similar tacit and unexplained transfer was made in Section 7. Thus, we state that *enfant obéissant, om mare, civis carus, palabras nuevas* are initially nomal *E*-configurations in French, Rumanian, Latin, and Spanish, respectively, but we show in parentheses that the associated parts of speech (*noun* and *qualitative adjective*) form a sequence with a similar property, that is, the *P'*-structures *P'* (*enfant*) *P'* (*obéissant*), *P'* (*om*) *P'* (*mare*), *P'* (*civis*) *P'* (*carus*), *P'* (*palabras*) *P'* (*nuevas*) are initially normal P'-configurations. Similarly the initially normal E-configurations *foarte frumos, très joli, sehr gut, very large, očen bolšoi* yield (in Rumanian, French, German, English, and Russian, respectively) the initially normal P'-configuration *adverb + qualitative adjective.*

It is the purpose in this section to investigate the legitimacy and the limits of the above procedure. We shall show that the dependence structure of a string $a_1 a_2 \ldots a_i \ldots a_n$ is isomorphic to the dependence structure of $S(a_1)S(a_2) \ldots S(a_i) \ldots S(a_n)$, whereas the dependence structure of $P(a_1)P(a_2) \ldots P(a_i) \ldots P(a_n)$ is isomorphic to the dependence structure of $P'(a_1)P'(a_2) \ldots P'(a_i) \ldots P'(a_n)$. The exact meaning of these assertions will be explained later.

In the following we shall frequently use the notion of regularly finer partition, introduced in Section 5, Chapter I. To avoid overloading notation, we shall denote by $P(x)$ and $Q(x)$ the P-structure and the Q-structure of x, where x is an arbitrary string over Γ.

Let us consider a language $\{\Gamma, \Phi\}$ and two partitions P and Q of Γ. We then have Proposition 11.

Proposition 11. If P is regularly finer than Q and if x and y are two strings for which $Q(x) = Q(y)$, then $P(x)$ and $P(y)$ are P-equivalent.

PROOF. Let $x = a_1 a_2 \ldots a_n$ and $y = b_1 b_2 \ldots b_m$. Since $Q(x) = Q(y)$, we have $n = m$ and $Q(a_i) = Q(b_i)$ for $1 \leq i \leq n$. Since P is finer than Q, it follows that $P(a_i) \subseteq Q(a_i)$ and $P(b_i) \subseteq Q(b_i)$. Hence $P(a_i) \subseteq Q(a_i) \supseteq P(b_i)$ for $1 \leq i \leq n$. Since P is regularly finer than Q, we deduce that $P(a_i)$ and $P(b_i)$ are P-equivalent for $1 \leq i \leq n$. Hence $P(x)$ and $P(y)$ are P-equivalent.

Proposition 12. If P is regularly finer than Q and if x is a string for which $P(x)$ is an unmarked P-structure, then $Q(x)$ is an unmarked Q-structure.

PROOF. Let us admit the existence of a marked string y such that $Q(y) = Q(x)$. In view of Proposition 11, it follows that $P(x)$ and $P(y)$ are P-equivalent. Since $P(x)$ is unmarked, $P(y)$ is also unmarked. On the other hand, since y is marked, $P(y)$ is marked. This contradiction proves that $Q(x)$ is an unmarked Q-structure.

Theorem 5 (Kulagina [26]). If P is regularly finer than Q and if x is a string over Γ, such that $P(x)$ is a P-configuration of rank 1, with resultant $P(a)$, then $Q(x)$ is a Q-configuration of rank 1 with resultant $Q(a)$.

PROOF. Since the length of $P(x)$ is not less than 2 and $Q(x)$ has the same length as $P(x)$, it follows that the length of $Q(x)$ is not less than 2. It remains to prove that $Q(x)$ and $Q(a)$ are Q-equivalent. Let x_1 and x_2 be two strings such that $Q(x_1)Q(x)Q(x_2)$ is a marked Q-structure. In view of Proposition 12, it follows that $P(x_1)P(x)P(x_2)$ is a marked P-structure. Since $P(x)$ is a P-configuration of rank 1, with resultant $P(a)$, it follows that $P(x_1)P(a)P(x_2)$ is a marked P-structure. Since P is finer than Q, it follows by Lemma 1, Chapter I, Section 6, that $Q(x_1)Q(a)Q(x_2)$ is a marked Q-structure. We have thus proved that $Q(x)$ Q-dominates $Q(a)$.

Conversely, if $Q(x_1)Q(a)Q(x_2)$ is a marked Q-structure, there exists a marked string y such that $Q(y) = Q(x_i)Q(a)Q(x_2)$. Hence, in view of Proposition 11 and since P is regularly finer than Q, $P(y)$ and $P(x_1)P(a)P(x_2)$ are P-equivalent. Since y is marked, it follows that $P(x_1)P(a)P(x_2)$ is a marked P-structure; but $P(a)$ and $P(x)$ are P-equivalent. Therefore $P(x_1)P(x)P(x_2)$ is a marked P-structure. Hence, by Lemma 1, Chapter 1, Section 6, $Q(x_1)Q(x)Q(x_2)$ is a marked Q-structure. We have therefore proved that $Q(a)$ Q-dominates $Q(x)$; thus $Q(x)$ and $Q(a)$ are Q-equivalent and Theorem 5 is proved.

Theorem 6 (Kulagina [26]). If P is regularly finer than Q and if x is a string over Γ such that $Q(x)$ is a Q-configuration of rank 1, with resultant $Q(a)$, then $P(x)$ is a P-configuration of rank 1, with resultant $P(a)$.

PROOF. Obviously, the length of $P(x)$ is equal to the length of $Q(x)$. Hence it is not less than 2.

Let x_1 and x_2 be two strings for which $P(x_1)P(x)P(x_2)$ is a marked P-structure. In view of Lemma 1, Chapter I, $Q(x_1)Q(x)Q(x_2)$ is a marked Q-structure. But $Q(x)$ and $Q(a)$ are Q-equivalent. Hence $Q(x_1)Q(a)Q(x_2)$ is a marked Q-structure. Now we may apply Proposition 12, Chapter V, and deduce that $P(x_1)P(a)P(x_2)$ is a marked P-structure. Hence $P(x)$ P-dominates $P(a)$.

Let x_1 and x_2 be two strings for which the P-structure $P(x_1)P(a)P(x_2)$ is marked. In view of Lemma 1, Chapter I, $Q(x_1)Q(a)Q(x_2)$ is a marked Q-structure. Since $Q(a)$ and $Q(x)$ are Q-equivalent, it follows that $Q(x_1)Q(x)Q(x_2)$ is marked; there exists a marked string y such that $Q(x_1)Q(x)Q(x_2) = Q(y)$. Hence, in view of Proposition 11, $P(y)$ and $P(x_1)P(x)P(x_2)$ are P-equivalent. But $P(y)$ is a marked P-structure. Therefore $P(x_1)P(x)P(x_2)$ is also marked and $P(a)$ P-dominates $P(x)$.

Proposition 13. Let P be regularly finer than Q and let x be any string over Γ. $P(x)$ is a P-structure of rank 1 if and only if $Q(x)$ is a Q-structure of rank 1.

PROOF. Let $P(x)$ be a P-structure of rank 1 and let us admit that $Q(x)$ contains a Q-configuration $Q(x_1)$ of rank 1. Hence there exist two strings x_2 and x_3 such that $Q(x)=Q(x_2)Q(x_1)Q(x_3)$. This implies $P(x)=P(x_2)P(x_1)P(x_3)$ and, by Theorem 6, $P(x_1)$ is a P-configuration of rank 1; thus, we obtain the absurd conclusion that $P(x)$ is not a P-structure of rank 1. It follows that $Q(x)$ contains no Q-configuration of rank 1. Hence it is a Q-structure of rank 1.

Conversely, let $Q(x)$ be a Q-structure of rank 1 and let us admit that $P(x)$ contains a P-configuration $P(x_1)$ of rank 1. We have, for some strings x_2 and x_3, $P(x)=P(x_2)P(x_1)P(x_3)$. Hence $Q(x)=Q(x_2)Q(x_1)Q(x_3)$. By Theorem 5, $Q(x_1)$ is a Q-configuration of rank 1 contained in $Q(x)$; but this fact contradicts the assumption that $Q(x)$ is a Q-structure of rank 1. Therefore, $P(x)$ is a P-structure of rank 1.

Theorem 7 (Kulagina [26]). Let P be regularly finer than Q and let x be a string over Γ. Then $P(x)$ is a P-configuration of rank n ($n \geqslant 1$) with resultant $P(a)$ if and only if $Q(x)$ is a Q-configuration of rank n, with resultant $Q(a)$. Moreover, if y is a string over Γ, then $P(y)$ is a P-structure of rank n if and only if $Q(y)$ is a Q-structure of rank n ($n \geqslant 1$).

PROOF. We proceed by induction. For $n=1$, Theorem 7 follows from Theorems 5 and 6 and Proposition 13. Let us admit that Theorem 7 is true for any positive integer $p < n$ and let us prove Theorem 7 for $p=n$. Let $P(x)$ be a P-configuration of rank n with resultant $P(a)$. We shall show that $Q(x)$ is a Q-configuration of rank n with resultant $Q(a)$. Since the length λ of $Q(x)$ is equal to the length of $P(x)$, which is not less than 2, it follows that $\lambda \geqslant 2$. It remains to prove that $Q(x)$ and $Q(a)$ are Q-equivalent with respect to $\mathscr{S}_{n-1}(Q)$ (equal the set of Q-structures of rank $n-1$). Consider two strings x_1 and x_2 such that the Q-structures

$$Q(x_1)Q(x)Q(x_2) \tag{1}$$

$$Q(x_1)Q(a)Q(x_2) \tag{2}$$

are of rank $n-1$. Since the theorem is supposed true for $p < n$, it follows that the P-structures

$$P(x_1)P(x)P(x_2) \tag{3}$$

$$P(x_1)P(a)P(x_2) \tag{4}$$

are of rank $n-1$; moreover, if (1) is marked, then, by Proposition 12, (3) is also marked and, since $P(x)$ and $P(a)$ are P-equivalent with respect to $\mathscr{S}_{n-1}(P)$ (equal the set of P-structures of rank $n-1$), (4) is marked. This implies, by Lemma 1, Chapter I, that (2) is marked. Conversely, if (2) is marked, then, by Proposition 12, (4) is also marked and, since $P(x)$ and $P(a)$ are P-equivalent with respect to $\mathscr{S}_{n-1}(P)$, (3) is marked. This implies, by Lemma 1, Chapter I, that (1) is marked. Hence $Q(x)$ is a Q-configuration of rank n, with resultant $Q(a)$.

Let us now suppose that $Q(x)$ is a Q-configuration of rank n, with resultant $Q(a)$. If (3) is marked, then in view of Lemma 1, Chapter I, (1) is marked and (2) is also marked, because $Q(x)$ and $Q(a)$ are Q-equivalent with respect to $\mathscr{S}_{n-1}(Q)$. By Proposition 12, it follows that (4) is marked. Conversely, if (4) is marked, then, by Lemma 1, Chapter I, (2) is marked, and (1) is also marked, because $Q(x)$ and $Q(a)$ are Q-equivalent with respect to $\mathscr{S}_{n-1}(Q)$. In view of Proposition 12, it follows that (3) is marked. Hence $P(x)$ is a P-configuration of rank n, with resultant $P(a)$.

We shall now prove the last part of Theorem 7. Let y be a string over Γ and suppose that $P(y)$ is a P-structure of rank n. If $Q(y)$ contains a Q-structure $Q(y_1)$ of rank n, we find two strings y_2 and y_3 such that $Q(y) = Q(y_2)Q(y_1)Q(y_3)$. Hence $P(y) = P(y_2)P(y_1)P(y_3)$. Since $Q(y_1)$ is a Q-configuration of rank n, $P(y_1)$ is a P-configuration of rank n (as we have just proved), in contradiction to the assumption that $P(y)$ contains no P-configuration of rank n. It follows that $Q(y)$ contains no Q-configuration of rank n. Hence it is a Q-structure of rank n. In the same way one proves that $P(y)$ is a P-structure of rank n if $Q(y)$ is a Q-structure of rank n. Theorem 7 is proved.

It is natural to ask whether Theorem 7 remains true if we replace the rank by the order. The answer is affirmative, as follows.

Corollary 3. Let P be regularly finer than Q and let x and y be two strings over Γ. Then $P(x)$ is a P-configuration of order n with resultant $P(a)$ if and only if $Q(x)$ is a Q-configuration of order n, with resultant $Q(a)$. $P(y)$ is a P-structure of order n if and only if $Q(y)$ is a Q-structure of order n.

PROOF. Let $P(x)$ be a P-configuration of order n with resultant $P(a)$. On one hand, $P(x)$ is of rank n. Hence, in view of Theorem 7, $Q(x)$ is a Q-configuration of rank n, with resultant $Q(a)$. On the other hand, $P(x)$ is of no rank less than n; using Theorem 7 again, it follows that $Q(x)$ is of no rank less than n. Hence it is a Q-configuration of order n with resultant $Q(a)$. Conversely, if $Q(x)$ is of order n, with resultant $Q(a)$, $P(x)$ is of order n, with resultant $P(a)$.

Consider now a P-structure $P(y)$ of order n. On one hand, $P(y)$ is of rank n. Thus, in view of Theorem 7, $Q(y)$ is also of rank n. On the other hand, $P(y)$ has no rank greater than n; again using Theorem 7, it follows that $Q(y)$ has no rank greater than n. Hence it is a Q-structure of order n. In the same way one can prove that, if $Q(y)$ is of order n, then $P(y)$ is also of order n.

Corollary 4. Let P be regularly finer than Q. Then the P-configurational type $N(P)$ of $L_1 = \{\Gamma, P, \Phi\}$ is equal to the Q-configurational type $N(Q)$ of $L_2 = \{\Gamma, Q, \Phi\}$, whereas the P-structure type $M(P)$ of L_1 is equal to the Q-structure type $M(Q)$ of L_2.

PROOF.   The proof follows immediately from Corollary 3.

Proposition 14. Let P be regularly finer than Q and let x be a string over Γ. Then, $P(x)$ is a parasitic P-configuration of rank n if and only if $Q(x)$ is a parasitic Q-configuration of rank n.

PROOF.   Let y and z be two strings over Γ. In view of Theorem 7, we have $P(yxz) \in \mathscr{S}_{n-1}(P)$ if and only if $Q(yxz) \in \mathscr{S}_{n-1}(Q)$ and $P(x) \in \mathscr{C}_{n-1}(P)$ if and only if $Q(x) \in \mathscr{C}_{n-1}(Q)$. Moreover, from Lemma 1, Chapter I, and Proposition 12, we deduce that $P(yxz)$ is a marked P-structure if and only if $Q(yxz)$ is a marked Q-structure. Proposition 14 follows immediately.

PROOF.   The proof follows immediately from Corollary 4 and Proposition 14.

Proposition 15. Let P be regularly finer than Q and let us adopt the notation of Corollary 4 Then, the effective P-configuration $N_1(P)$ of L_1 is equal to the effective Q-configuration $N_1(Q)$ of L_2, whereas the effective P-structure $M_1(P)$ of L_1 is equal to the effective Q-structure $M_1(Q)$ of L_2.

Proposition 16. Let P be regularly finer than Q and let x be a string over Γ. Then, $P(x)$ is a semiregular (initially regular, finally regular, minimal, initially normal, finally normal) P-configuration of order n if and only if $Q(x)$ is a semiregular (initially regular, finally regular, minimal, initially normal, finally normal, respectively) Q-configuration of order n.

PROOF.   Let $x = a_1 a_2 \ldots a_m$. $P(x)$, as P-configuration of rank n, admits the resultant $P(a_i)$ ($1 \le i \le m$) if and only if $Q(x)$, as Q-configuration of rank n, admits the resultant $Q(a_i)$ (see Theorem 7). Therefore, $P(x)$ is semiregular (initially regular, finally regular) if and only if $Q(x)$ is semiregular (initially regular, finally regular, respectively). The other assertions of Proposition 16 follow immediately from the fact that $P(x)$ and $Q(x)$ have the same length (equal to m) and by taking Corollary 3 into account.

Theorem 7, Corollaries 3 and 4, and Propositions 14–16 show that the most important properties concerning configurations and structures are invariant with respect to partitions one of which is regularly finer than others. This fact is very important from both a theoretical and practical point of view. Indeed, we know that every partition P is regularly finer than its derivative partition P' and we always have $E' = S$ (Section 5, Chapter I). We also have $R' = P'$ in every adequate language (Theorem 4, Chapter II) and $R' = K' = M' = N' = G' = P'$ in every homogeneous language (see Theorem 10, Corollaries 3 and 4, Chapter II, and Proposition 29, Chapter IV). Thus, the dependence structure of a customary string $a_1 a_2 \ldots a_n$ over Γ is the same as the dependence structure of the corresponding sequence of distributional classes $S(a_1) S(a_2) \ldots S(a_n)$, whereas the dependence structure of the sequence of paradigms $P(a_1) P(a_2) \ldots P(a_n)$ is the same as the dependence structure of the corresponding sequence of parts of speech $P'(a_1) P'(a_2) \ldots P'(a_n)$. It follows that Examples 1–11 investigated in Section 4 and concerning E-configurations and E-structures, are also valid with respect to the corresponding S-configurations and S-structures. The examples of normal E-configurations ab given in Section 7 remain valid if the word a is replaced by a word $a' \in P(a)$, whereas b is replaced by a suitable word $b' \in P(b)$. (For instance, in French, if $a = mon$, $b = livre$, and $a' = mes$, then $b' = livres$.) Thus Proposition 16 enables us to transfer the corresponding examples and results to P'-configurations and so we obtain normal configurations whose terms are parts of speech.

We may ask whether Theorem 7, Corollaries 3 and 4, and Propositions 13–16 remain true when P is merely finer (but not regularly finer) than Q. In this respect, we shall consider several examples due to Kulagina ([26], pp. 211–222).

Proposition 17. There exist a language $L = \{\Gamma, \Phi\}$, two partitions P and Q of Γ, P finer than Q, and two words a and b such that $P(a) P(b)$ is a P-configuration of rank 1 in L, whereas $Q(a) Q(b)$ is not a Q-configuration of rank 1 in L.

PROOF.   Let $\Gamma = \{a, b, c, d\}$ and $\Phi = \{dbcc, ab^n cd\}$ ($n \geqslant 0$). As before, b^0 means the zero string. Let $P = E$ and $Q(a) = \{a, d\}$, $Q(b) = \{b\}$, $Q(c) = \{c\}$. Obviously, E (the unit partition) is finer than Q. As before we shall denote by x both the element x and the E-cell of x. The E-structure ab is an E-configuration of rank 1 with resultant a. Indeed, by replacing ab by a in $ab^n cd$ ($n > 0$), we also get a marked E-structure; the same is true when we replace a by ab. On the other hand, $Q(a)Q(b)$ is not a Q-configuration of rank 1. Indeed, $Q(a)Q(b)$ is contained in the marked Q-structure $Q(a)Q(b)Q(c)Q(c)$ (this is the Q-structure of the marked string $dbcc$), whereas none of the Q-structures $Q(a)Q(c)Q(c)$, $Q(b)Q(c)Q(c)$, and $Q(c)Q(c)Q(c)$ is marked. Hence none of the Q-cells $Q(a)$, $Q(b)$, and $Q(c)$ may be a resultant of $Q(a)Q(b)$. It follows that $Q(a)Q(b)$ is not a Q-configuration of rank 1.

Proposition 18.   There exist a language $L = \{\Gamma, \Phi\}$, two partitions P and Q of Γ, P finer than Q, and two words a and b such that $Q(a)Q(b)$ is a Q-configuration of rank 1 in L, but $P(a)P(b)$ is not a P-configuration of rank 1 in L.

PROOF.   Let Γ, P, and Q be defined as in the proof of Proposition 17 and let $\Phi = \{dc, ab^n c\}$ ($n \geqslant 1$). Since each Q-structure of the form $(Q(a)Q(b))^n Q(c)$ ($n \geqslant 0$) is marked, it follows that $Q(a)Q(b)$ is a Q-configuration of rank 1, with resultant $Q(a)$. [$(Q(b))^0$ means the zero Q-structure.] On the other hand, we shall show that $P(a)P(b)$ is not a P-configuration of rank 1. Indeed, if we replace $P(a)P(b)$ by $P(a)$, $P(b)$, or $P(c)$ in the marked P-structure $P(a)P(b)P(c)$, we get the unmarked P-structure $P(a)P(c)$, $P(b)P(c)$, or $P(c)P(c)$, respectively; if we replace $P(a)P(b)$ by $P(d)$ in the marked P-structure $P(a)P(b)P(b)P(c)$, we get the unmarked P-structure $P(d)P(b)P(c)$. Hence, none of the P-cells $P(a)$, $P(b)$, $P(c)$, and $P(d)$ may be a resultant of $\mathscr{P} = P(a)P(b)$. Therefore $\mathscr{P}$ is not a P-configuration of rank 1 in L.

Proposition 19.   There exist a language $L = \{\Gamma, \Phi\}$, two partitions P and Q of Γ, P finer than Q, and two words b and c such that $P(b)P(c)$ is a P-configuration of order 2, with resultant $P(b)$, whereas $Q(b)Q(c)$ is a Q-configuration of order 1, with resultant $Q(b)$ in L.

PROOF.   Let $\Gamma = \{a, b, c, d\}$, $P = E$, $Q(a) = \{a, d\}$, $Q(b) = \{b, c\}$ and $\Phi = \{ab^n cd, dd, bc^m\}$ ($m \geqslant 0$, $n \geqslant 0$). Since the strings $ab^n cd$ and $ab^{n-1} cd$ are both marked for $n > 0$, it follows that ab is a P-structure of rank 1, with resultant a. The marked P-structures of rank 1 are acd, dd, and bc^m

($m \geq 0$). It is easily seen that bc is a P-configuration of order 2, with resultant b; indeed, the P-structures of rank 1 bc^m and bc^{m-1} are both marked for $m > 0$, and so bc is a P-configuration of rank 2, with resultant b, whereas the replacement of bc by b in the marked P-structure ab^ncd yields the unmarked P-structure ab^nd. Hence bc is not a P-configuration of rank 1, with resultant b. However, $Q(b)Q(c)$ is a Q-configuration of order 1, with resultant $Q(b)$, since we have the marked Q-structures $Q(a)(Q(b))^nQ(a)$ and $(Q(b))^n$ ($n \geq 0$) and the replacement of $Q(b)Q(c)$ [$= Q(b)Q(b)$] by $Q(b)$ or of $Q(b)$ by $Q(b)Q(c)$ transforms a marked Q-structure into a marked one and an unmarked Q-structure into an unmarked one.

Proposition 20. There exist a language $L = \{\Gamma, \Phi\}$, two partitions P and Q of Γ, P finer than Q, and two words c and d such that $P(d)P(c)$ is a P-configuration of order 1, with resultant $P(d)$, whereas $Q(d)Q(c)$ is a Q-configuration of order 2, with resultant $Q(d)$ in L.

PROOF. Let $\Gamma = \{a, b, c, d\}$, $P = E$, $Q(a) = Q(d) = \{a, d\}$, $Q(b) = \{b\}$, $Q(c) = \{c\}$, $\Phi = \{ba^nc, dc^m\}$ ($m \geq 0, n \geq 0$). The P-structure dc is a P-configuration of order 1, with resultant d, because the P-structures dc^m and dc^{m-1} are both marked for $m > 0$. However, the Q-structure $Q(d)Q(c)$ is not a Q-configuration of rank 1, with resultant $Q(d)$, because the replacement of $Q(d)Q(c)$ by $Q(d)$ in the marked Q-structure $Q(b)(Q(d))^nQ(c)$ ($n > 0$) yields the unmarked Q-structure $Q(b)(Q(d))^n$. But $Q(d)Q(c)$ is a Q-configuration of rank 2, with resultant $Q(d)$. Indeed, $Q(b)Q(a)$ is a Q-configuration of rank 1, with resultant $Q(b)$, and we obtain the following Q-structures of rank 1: $Q(b)Q(c)$ and $Q(d)(Q(c))^m$ ($m \geq 0$). It remains to remark that the replacement of $Q(d)Q(c)$ by $Q(d)$ or of $Q(d)$ by $Q(d)Q(c)$ in the marked Q-structure $Q(d)(Q(c))^m$ also yields a marked Q-structure.

Propositions 17–20 show that Theorem 7, Corollaries 3 and 4, and Proposition 13 do not remain true when P is finer, but not regularly finer, than Q.

9. Configurations in the Sense of Gladkiï

Gladkiï has introduced an important restriction in the definition of configurations of order higher than 1 [13]. We shall deal with E-configurations only; thus, we may adopt a simpler terminology and say configuration instead of E-configuration.

A string x over Γ is a *Gladkiĭ configuration of rank 1, with resultant $a \in \Gamma$, in the language* $L = \{\Gamma, \Phi\}$, if and only if x is a customary configuration (that is, in the sense of Section 2) of rank 1, with resultant a in L.

We recall that a string u is said to be contained in the string v if there exist two strings s and t such that $v = sut$. Given two strings x and y, we shall say that y *meets* x (or that x *meets* y) if there exists a nonvoid string z which is contained both in x and in y.

Let n be a positive integer greater than 1, and suppose we have defined, for every $i < n$ ($i \geq 1$), the Gladkiĭ configurations of rank i. A string x over Γ is a *Gladkiĭ configuration of rank n in L* if the following two conditions are fulfilled: (1) the length of x is not less than 2; (2) there exists a word a (called a *resultant of x*) such that, for every pair of strings y and z, we have: (a) if $yaz \in \Phi$, then $yxz \in \Phi$; (b) if yxz belongs to Φ and contains no Gladkiĭ configuration of rank less than n, which meets x but is not contained in x, then $yaz \in \Phi$.

Proposition 21 follows immediately.

Proposition 21.   Every Gladkiĭ configuration of rank n is of any rank greater than n.

The relation between the Gladkiĭ configurations and the customary ones is given by Theorem 8.

Theorem 8.   Every Gladkiĭ configuration of rank n, with resultant a, is a configuration of rank n, with resultant a, but the converse is not true. There exist a language $L = \{\Gamma, \Phi\}$ and a configuration of rank 2 in L which is not a Gladkiĭ configuration in L.

PROOF.   The first part of Theorem 8 follows from the remark: The definition of configurations of rank n may be obtained from the definition of Gladkiĭ configurations of rank n by replacing condition (2) by the next condition: (3) there exists a word $a \in \Gamma$ (called a resultant of x) such that for every pair of strings y and z, for which yxz and yaz contain no configuration of rank less than n, the strings yxz and yaz are either both marked or both unmarked. Indeed, it is easily seen that (2) implies (3).

To prove the second part of Theorem 8, let us consider the language L defined as follows. $\Gamma = \{a, b, c, d, e, f, g\}$, $\Phi = \{aec, gc, aef, gf, ec,$

bdc, ab, db}. The unique configuration of rank 1 is *ae*, with resultant *g*. The marked strings which do not contain *ae* are *gc*, *gf*, *ec*, *bdc*, *ab*, *db*. It follows that *bd* is a configuration of rank 2 (with resultant *e*). But *bd* is not a Gladkiĭ configuration in *L*, since there is no word $\alpha \in \Gamma$ such that the replacement of α in any marked string also yields a marked string. In particular, *bd* is not a Gladkiĭ configuration with resultant *e*, since *aec* is marked, but *abdc* is not. Theorem 8 is proved.

Although Gladkiĭ configurations are a special kind of configurations, most configurations encountered in natural languages are Gladkiĭ configurations. For instance, Russian configurations *vysokii dom* (qualitative adjective + noun) and *novyi dom* (qualitative adjective + noun) are Gladkiĭ configurations of the same rank and with the same resultant (*dom*), but *očen vysokii* (adverb + qualitative adjective) is a. Gladkiĭ configuration with resultant *vysokii* and whose rank is less than the rank of the former, because in the marked string *na uglu stoit očen vysokii dom* the replacement of *vysokii dom* by *dom* yields an unmarked string. But in the same string the replacement of *dom* by *novyi dom* yields a marked string, although the first string contains the Gladkiĭ configuration of a lower rank *očen vysokii*.

A Gladkiĭ configuration *x* is said to be *of order n* if it is of rank *n*, but not of rank $n-1$. If no such integer *n* exists, we say that *x* is *of infinite order*. We may also define the *Gladkiĭ configurational type G of a language L* by the following two properties: There exists in *L* a Gladkiĭ configuration of order *G*; there exists in *L* no Gladkiĭ configuration of order $G-1$. In view of Proposition 21, most of the results established for customary configurations and concerning ranks, orders, configurational types, remain true for Gladkiĭ configurations.

If there exists an integer *n* such that the string *x* is a Gladkiĭ configuration of rank *n*, we say that *x* is a *Gladkiĭ configuration*; we recall that *x* is not parasitic if it is contained in at least one marked string.

In establishing Gladkiĭ configurations of a natural language, the following result may be useful.

Proposition 22. Let $L = \{\Gamma, \Phi\}$ and let *a* be a nonparasitic word in *L*. Then every Gladkiĭ configuration of *L*, with resultant *a*, is not parasitic.

PROOF. Since *a* is not parasitic, we find two strings *u* and *v*, such that $uav \in \Phi$. Therefore, $uxv \in \Phi$ and *x* is not parasitic.

The Gladkiĭ configuration *x* is said to be *simple of rank n* if it contains no Gladkiĭ configuration of rank *n* other than *x*. For instance, the English string *very great countries* is not a simple Gladkiĭ configuration of rank 3, although it is a Gladkiĭ configuration of rank 3. In exchange, *great countries* is a simple Gladkiĭ configuration of rank 3. (Configurations of the form *secondary adverb + adverb* are of rank 1; those of the form *adverb + qualitative adjective* are of rank 2; those of the form qualitative *adjective + noun* are of rank 3.)

The notions of minimal, semiregular, regular, or normal configuration may be transposed to Gladkiĭ configurations. Obviously, every minimal Gladkiĭ configuration of rank n is simple of rank n.

Unless a contrary assumption is made, all configurations considered in Sections 9 and 10 are Gladkiĭ configurations.

Given a language $L = \{\Gamma, \Phi\}$, we shall denote by $\mathcal{M}$ a set of ordered pairs of the form $\langle x, a \rangle$, where x is a configuration in L and a is a resultant of x. We shall suppose that $\mathcal{M}$ fulfills the following condition: If a and b are two resultants of x and $\langle x, a \rangle \in \mathcal{M}$, then $\langle x, b \rangle \in \mathcal{M}$.

If x runs over the set of all configurations (the set of all simple configurations, the set of all configurations of rank n, the set of simple configurations of rank n) of L, then $\mathcal{M}$ will be denoted by $K(L)(\Pi(L)$, $K_n(L)$, $\Pi_n(L)$, respectively). Further, we denote by $B(L)(B_n(L))$ the set of all strings of L which contain no configuration (configuration of rank n, respectively) of L. Strings belonging to $B(L)$ are said to be *irreducible*.

The ordered pair $\langle B(L), K(L) \rangle$ is said to be *the complete configurational characteristic of L*, whereas $\langle B(L), \Pi(L) \rangle$ is said to be *the reduced configurational characteristic of L*. It is natural to ask whether a language is completely determined by its configurational characteristics. Propositions 23 and 24 and Theorems 9 and 10 will give an affirmative answer.

Proposition 23.   Let $L_1 = \{\Gamma, \Phi_1\}$ and $L_2 = \{\Gamma, \Phi_2\}$. If $B(L_1) \subseteq B(L_2)$ and $\Pi(L_1) \subseteq K(L_2)$, then $\Phi_1 \subseteq \Phi_2$.

PROOF.   If Φ_1 contains strings of length 1, all these strings belong to $B(L_1)$; but $B(L_1) \subseteq B(L_2) \subseteq \Phi_2$.

Let us suppose that every string of Φ_1, whose length is less than or equal to n, belongs to Φ_2. Let $x = a_1 a_2 \ldots a_{n+1}$ be a string of length $n+1$, $x \in \Phi_1$. If $x \in B(L_1)$, we proceed as for $n = 1$. Suppose that x does not belong to $B(L_1)$. Denote by r the smallest rank of a configuration of L_1, contained in x. Then, x contains a simple configuration of rank r. Hence there exist two integers i, j ($1 \le i < j \le n+1$) and a word $a \in \Gamma$, such that $\langle a_i a_{i+1} \ldots a_j, a \rangle \in \Pi_r(L_1) \subseteq \Pi(L_1)$. Let $y = a_1 \ldots a_{i-1} a a_{j+1} \ldots a_{n+1}$. Since x contains no configuration of rank less than r, we have $y \in \Phi_1$; therefore, by our induction hypothesis, $y \in \Phi_2$. But $\langle a_i \ldots a_j, a \rangle \in K(L_2)$. Hence $x \in \Phi_2$.

Proposition 24. Let $L_1 = \{\Gamma, \Phi_1\}$, $L_2 = \{\Gamma, \Phi_2\}$. Let s be a positive integer. If $B_s(L_1) \subseteq B_s(L_2)$ and $\Pi_s(L_1) \subseteq K(L_2)$, then $\Phi_1 \subseteq \Phi_2$.

PROOF. We proceed as in the proof of Proposition 23, by taking into account that $r \leq s$ implies $K_r(L) \subseteq K_s(L)$.

Theorem 9. Let $L_1 = \{\Gamma, \Phi_1\}$, $L_2 = \{\Gamma, \Phi_2\}$. If $B(L_1) = B(L_2)$ and $K(L_1) = K(L_2)$ or if $B(L_1) = B(L_2)$ and $\Pi(L_1) = \Pi(L_2)$, then $\Phi_1 = \Phi_2$.

PROOF. We obviously have $\Pi(L) \subseteq K(L)$ for any language L; hence Theorem 9 follows immediately from Proposition 23.

Theorem 10. Let $L_1 = \{\Gamma, \Phi_1\}$, $L_2 = \{\Gamma, \Phi_2\}$ and let s be a positive integer. If $B_s(L_1) = B_s(L_2)$ and $K_s(L_1) = K_s(L_2)$ or if $B_s(L_1) = B_s(L_2)$ and $\Pi_s(L_1) = \Pi_s(L_2)$, then $\Phi_1 = \Phi_2$.

PROOF. We obviously have $\Pi_s(L) \subseteq K_s(L)$ for any language L. Thus Theorem 10 follows immediately from Proposition 24.

The notions and facts concerning configurations may be easily transposed from strings to S-structures. (We recall that S is the partition of Γ into families.) It is enough to replace words, strings, and marked strings by families, S-structures, and marked S-structures, respectively. (We recall that, in view of Corollary 6, Chapter I, each marked S-structure is perfect, that is, every corresponding string is marked.) In the same way one can define simple S-configurations and the sets $B^S(L)$, $K^S(L)$, $\Pi^S(L)$, $B_n^S(L)$, $K_n^S(L)$, $\Pi_n^S(L)$ corresponding to the notion of simple configurations and to the sets $B(L)$, $K(L)$, $\Pi(L)$, $B_n(L)$, $K_n(L)$, and $\Pi_n(L)$, respectively.

Proposition 25. Let $L = \{\Gamma, \Phi\}$ and $a \in \Gamma$; let $x = a_1 a_2 \ldots a_n$ be a string over Γ. Then the S-structure $S(a_1)S(a_2) \ldots S(a_n)$ is an S-configuration of rank m, with resultant $S(a)$ in L if and only if x is a configuration of rank m with resultant a in L.

PROOF. Since the unit partition E is regularly finer than S and since Theorem 7 is also valid after replacing customary configurations by Gladkiĭ configurations, Proposition 25 follows immediately from Theorem 7.

Proposition 26. Let $L_1 = \{\Gamma, \Phi_1\}$ and $L_2 = \{\Gamma, \Phi_2\}$. Suppose that (1) for every S-structure $\mathscr{P} \in B^S(L_1)$ there exists an S-structure $\mathscr{P} \in B^S(L_2)$ such that $\mathscr{P}$ is contained in $\mathscr{P}'$; (2) for every pair $\langle W, w \rangle \in \Pi^S(L_1)$ there exists a pair $\langle W', w' \rangle \in K^S(L_2)$ such that W is contained in W' and w is contained in w'. Then, $\Phi_1 \subseteq \Phi_2$.

PROOF.   This follows from Proposition 23 and 25.

Proposition 27. Let n be a positive integer and let $L_1 = \{\Gamma, \Phi_1\}$ and $L_2 = \{\Gamma, \Phi_2\}$ satisfying the following conditions: (1) for every S-structure $\mathscr{P} \in B_n^S(L_1)$ there exists an S-structure $\mathscr{P} \in B_n^S(L_2)$ such that $\mathscr{P}$ is contained in $\mathscr{P}'$; (2) for every pair $\langle W, w \rangle \in \Pi_n^S(L_1)$ there exists a pair $\langle W', w' \rangle \in K_n^S(L_2)$, such that W is contained in W' and w is contained in w'. Then, $\Phi_1 \subseteq \Phi_2$.

PROOF.   The proof follows from Propositions 24 and 25.

Propositions 26 and 27 show that Theorems 9 and 10 remains true when we replace $A(L_i)$ and $A_n(L_i)$ ($i = 1, 2; A = B, K, \Pi$) by $A^S(L_i)$ and $A_n^S(L_i)$, respectively. The theorems thus obtained will be called Theorem $9S$ and $10S$, respectively.

The following example shows that Propositions 23, 24, 26, and 27 and Theorems 9, 10, '$S6$ and $10S$ become erroneous if we replace Gladkiĭ configurations by customary configurations. Let $\Gamma = \{a, b, c, d, e, f, g\}$, $\Phi_1 = \{aec, gc, aef, gf, ec, bdc, ab, db\}$ and $\Phi_2 = \Phi_1 \cup \{abd\}$. The unique Gladkiĭ configuration of L_1 is ae (of rank 1, with resultant g) and the same is true for L_2. Thus, $B(L_2) = B(L_1) \cup \{abd\}$. From the standpoint of customary configurations, L_1 and L_2 also have configuration bd (of rank 2, with resultant e). Since for any word α we have $S(\alpha) = \{\alpha\}$ in L_1 as well as in L_2, it follows that from the standpoint of customary configurations we have $A^S(L_1) = A(L_1) = A(L_2) = A^S(L_2)$, where $A = B, K, \Pi$.

10. Gladkiĭ Configurations and Generative Grammars

Čulík observes that one of the main aims of mathematics is to characterize infinite classes by a structure using finite classes only ([10],

p. 14). Faithful to this principle, Gladkiĭ introduces the following definition: A language $L = \{\Gamma, \Phi\}$ is said to be *of finite type* if both the sets
$B(L)$ and $\Pi(L)$ are finite[13].

If Gladkiĭ configurations are replaced by customary configurations,
then $B(L) = \mathscr{S}_\infty(L)$. On the other hand, if the E-configuration of L is infinite, there are, for every positive integer n, E-configurations of order n.
Hence there exists, for each positive integer n, a simple E-configuration
of order n and $\Pi(L)$ is thus an infinite set. We have therefore proved
the next proposition.

Proposition 28. If we concern ourselves with the customary configurations, every language L of finite type is of finite E-configuration, and
$\mathscr{S}_\infty(L)$ is finite.

Languages of finite type are an interesting approximation to natural
languages, where, in any case, there are infinitely many configurations.
For instance, in most European languages there are, for any positive
integer n, configurations of the forms: transitive verb $+ n$ direct objects,
n qualitative adjectives $+$ noun, n adverbs $+$ qualitative adjective, etc.

To avoid insignificant results, we shall explicitly state an assumption
tacitly adopted more often then not. We shall suppose that the vocabulary
Γ contains no parasitic word, that is, for any $a \in \Gamma$ there exist two strings
u and v over Γ such that $uav \in \Phi$.

Languages of finite type are closely related to some kinds of languages
obtained in generative grammars. We wish particularly to point out the
relations between languages of finite type, on one hand, and context-
free languages and finite-state languages on the other. Although these
notions were already defined (see Section 1, Chapter I; Section 7,
Chapter II; Section 10, Chapter III), we shall give new definitions,
more suitable to our present purposes, but equivalent to the previously
definitions. (For this equivalence see Chomsky [9].)

Let Γ and Γ_1 be two mutually disjoint nonempty sets. Γ is the *basic
vocabulary*, whereas Γ_1 is the *auxiliary vocabulary*. Choose an element s
of Γ_1. A *generative grammar over* $\Gamma \cup \Gamma_1$ is a finite set of rules of the form
$x \to y$, where x and y are strings over $\Gamma \cup \Gamma_1$, whereas the symbol $\to$
does not belong to $\Gamma \cup \Gamma_1$. If there exist four strings u, v, z_1, and z_2
over $\Gamma \cup \Gamma_1$, such that $u = z_1 x z_2$ and $v = z_1 y z_2$ (where $x \to y$), we shall
say that v *is obtained from* u *by the rule* $x \to y$. A finite sequence x_0,
$x_1, \ldots, x_n$ of strings over $\Gamma \cup \Gamma_1$ is a *derivation of* x_n *from* x_0 *in the generative grammar* $\mathscr{G}$, if for $1 \leq i \leq n$ the string x_i is obtained from x_{i-1} by
a rule of $\mathscr{G}$ (this rule is said to be the ith rule of the considered derivation).

If there is a derivation of x_n from x_0 in $\mathscr{G}$, we shall say that x_n *is derived from* x_0 *in* $\mathscr{G}$. The set of all strings over Γ, which are derived from s in $\mathscr{G}$, is a language over Γ; it is *the language generated by* $\mathscr{G}$ and is denoted by $L(\mathscr{G})$.

A generative grammar is said to be a *context-free grammar* if, in every one of its rules $x \to y$, the string x is an element of Γ_1. A context-free grammar is a *finite-state grammar* if and only if, in every one of its rules $x \to y$, we have either $y \in \Gamma$, or $y = ab$, where $a \in \Gamma$ and $b \in \Gamma_1$ [8,9]. The language generated by a context-free grammar is said to be a *context-free language*, whereas the language generated by a finite-state grammar is a *finite-state language*.

Theorem 11. If the language $L = \{\Gamma, \Phi\}$ is of finite type, then Φ is a context-free language.

PROOF. Let γ be the set of distribution classes of L. Consider a symbol s which does not belong to $\Gamma \cup \gamma$ and put $\Gamma_1 = \gamma \cup \{s\}$. We shall define a generative grammar $\mathscr{G}$ over $\Gamma \cup \Gamma_1$, by the following rules: (1) $s \to b$, where $b \in B^S(L)$; (2) $t_0 \to t$, where $(t, t_0) \in \Pi^S(L)$; (3) $A \to a$, where $A \in \gamma$ and $a \in A$.

We shall show that $\Phi = L(\mathscr{G})$.

(1) Let $x \in L(\mathscr{G})$. Obviously, in each derivation of x from s, the first rule (and only this rule) has form (1). It is easily seen that there exists a derivation $x_0, x_1, \ldots, x_n$ ($x_0 = s$, $x_n = x$, $n \geq 2$) such that for some i ($1 \leq i \leq n$), all rules from the $(i+1)$th to the nth rule inclusively have form (3); moreover, if $i \geq 2$, all rules from the second to the ith rule inclusively have form (2). For every k ($1 \leq k \leq i$), x_k is an S-structure in L. Obviously, $x = x_n \in x_i$. Therefore, to prove that $x \in \Phi$, it is enough to establish that x_i is a marked S-structure in L. But this is true for every S-structure $x_1, x_2, \ldots, x_i$. Indeed, (a) x_i is obtained from $x_0 = s$ by one rule of form (1); hence $x_1 \in B^S(L)$ and, consequently, x_1 is a marked S-structure in L; (b) if $1 \leq k < i$ and if x_k is a marked S-structure in L, then x_{k+1} is also a marked S-structure in L, since it is obtained from x_k by introducing some S-configuration instead of its resultant. Thus, $L(\mathscr{G}) \subseteq \Phi$.

(2) Let x be a marked S-structure in L. We shall show that x is derived from s in $\mathscr{G}$. We proceed by induction with respect to the length of x.

If the length x is 1, then $x \in B^S(L)$. Hence x is obtained from s by a rule of form (1).

Let us admit that every marked S-structure of length less than or equal to n is derived from s in $\mathscr{G}$. Consider a marked S-structure x of length $n+1$. If $x \in B^S(L)$, we proceed as for $n=1$. If x does not belong to $B^S(L)$, let r be the smallest rank of an S-configuration of L, contained in x. Then, x contains a simple S-configuration of rank r in L. Therefore, if $x = x_1 \cdots x_{n+1}$ ($x_1, \ldots, x_{n+1} \in \gamma$), there exist two integers i and j ($1 \leqslant i < j \leqslant n+1$), and a family $x_0 \in \gamma$, such that $(x_i \cdots x_j, x_0) \in \Pi^S(L)$. The S-structure $y = x_1 \cdots x_{i-1} x_0 x_{j+1} \cdots x_{n+1}$ is marked in L. In view of our induction hypothesis, y is derived from s in $\mathscr{G}$. But x is obtained from y by a rule of form (2): $x_0 \rightarrow x_i \cdots x_j$.

Now let $z \in \Phi$. Denote by x the S-structure of z. Since $z \in \Phi$, x is a marked S-structure in L. Hence, in view of the result just obtained, x is derived from s in $\mathscr{G}$. On the other hand, z may be obtained from x, by a rule of form (3). Therefore, $z \in L(\mathscr{G})$ and $\Phi \subseteq L(\mathscr{G})$, and Theorem 11 is proved.

The converse of Theorem 11 is not true, as now shown.

Theorem 12. There exists a finite-state language Φ over Γ, such that $L = \{\Gamma, \Phi\}$ is not of finite type.

PROOF. Let $\Gamma' = \{a, b\}$, $\Phi' = \{bab, a, a^2, a^3, \ldots\}$. If we put $\Gamma_1' = \{s, A, D, H\}$ and $\mathscr{G}' = \{s \rightarrow aH, H \rightarrow aH, H \rightarrow a, s \rightarrow a, s \rightarrow bA, A \rightarrow aD, D \rightarrow b\}$, then $\Phi' = L(\mathscr{G}')$. Moreover, $K(L) = 0$ and $B(L') = \Phi'$ (where $L' = \{\Gamma', \Phi'\}$).

Let $\Gamma'' = \{c, d, e, f, g\}$, $\Phi'' = \{fg, cd^2eg, cd^3eg, \ldots\}$. If we put $\Gamma_1'' = \{s, C, F, E, G\}$ and $\mathscr{G}'' = \{s \rightarrow fG, s \rightarrow cC, C \rightarrow dF, F \rightarrow dF, F \rightarrow dE, E \rightarrow eG, G \rightarrow g\}$, then $\Phi'' = L(\mathscr{G}'')$. Obviously, every string of the form cd^ne ($n = 2, 3, \ldots$) is a simple configuration of order 1 in $L'' = \{\Gamma'', \Phi''\}$ (with resultant f); $B(L'') = \{fg\}$.

Now let us put $\Gamma = \Gamma' \cup \Gamma''$ and $\Phi = \Phi' \cup \Phi''$. The language Φ is a finite-state language over Γ but $L = \{\Gamma, \Phi\}$ is not of finite type, since both the sets $B(L)$ and $\Pi(L)$ are infinite. Theorem 12 is proved.

It is natural to ask whether Theorem 11 may be improved by replacing the words "context-free language" by "finite-state language". The answer is negative, as shown now.

Proposition 29. There exists a language $L = \{\Gamma, \Phi\}$ of finite type, such that Φ is not a finite-state language over Γ.

PROOF. Let $\Gamma = \{a, b\}$, $\Phi = \{b, aba, a^2ba^2, a^3ba^3, \ldots\}$. The unique simple configuration in L is aba (of rank 1, with resultant b); $B(L) = \{b\}$.

Therefore, L is of finite type. On the other hand, we shall show that Φ is not a finite-state language. Indeed, for $m \neq n$, the strings a^m and a^n are not E-equivalent, since the string $a^m b a^n$ does not belong to Φ. Thus, there exist infinitely many T-distribution classes with respect to Φ.

Theorem 12 and Proposition 29 make the following problem natural: Determine a class of languages which are both finite-state languages and languages of finite type. In this aim, we shall use a new type of grammar [13].

Let $\mathscr{G}$ be a finite-state grammar. Let $a \in \Gamma$, $b \in \Gamma_1$, $c \in \Gamma_1$, $d \in \Gamma_1$, $e \in \Gamma_1$, $f \in \Gamma_1$. We suppose that $\mathscr{G}$ fulfills the following two conditions: (1) If $b \to a$ and $c \to ad$ are rules in $\mathscr{G}$, then $b = c$; (2) if $c \to ad$ and $e \to af$ are rules in $\mathscr{G}$, then $c = e$. We shall say of such a grammar $\mathscr{G}$ that it is a *finite-state grammar without homonymy*. If we interpret the elements of Γ as words (or morphemes) and the elements of Γ_1 as grammatical categories, each of the rules $b \to a$, $b \to ac$ ($a \in \Gamma$, $b \in \Gamma_1$, $c \in \Gamma_1$) says that word a belongs to category b. If all rules occurring in $\mathscr{G}$ and containing the word a contain homogeneous grammatical categories (*masculine* and *feminine* are homogeneous; also, *nominative* and *genitive*, *singular* and *plural*, etc.; *masculine* and *genitive* are not homogeneous; also, *singular* and *present*, *nominative* and *plural*, etc.), then, in a grammar without homonymy, no word can belong to two homogeneous grammatical categories. This is precisely the meaning of grammatical homonymy in the customary grammar. Thus, the grammatical homonymy of the French adjective *maigre* is that it belongs to two homogeneous grammatical categories, the masculine and the feminine, whereas the grammatical homonymy of the Rumanian adjective *cumsecade* is that it belongs to two pairs of homogeneous grammatical categories: masculine-feminine and singular-plural.

A language which may be generated by a finite-state grammar without homonymy is said to be a *finite-state language without homonymy*. We give here without proof the following result due to Gladkiï ([13], p. 257).

Theorem 13.   Let Φ be a language over Γ. If Φ is a finite-state language without homonymy, then $\{\Gamma, \Phi\}$ is of finite type.

The problem of finding the configurations of a finite-state language has been completely solved by Gladkiï [15]. Indeed, we have another theorem.

Theorem 14.   If Φ is a finite-state language over Γ, then, for every $b \in \Gamma$ and every positive integer n, the set $K_n(b, L)$ of the configurations of rank n and having the resultant b in $L = \{\Gamma, \Phi\}$, is also a finite-state language. Starting from the finite-state grammar which generates Φ, from the word b and from the number n, we may effectively find a finite-state grammar which generates the language $K_n(b, L)$.

11. Quasi-Configurations and Syntagms

Configurational analysis is quite adequate for the description of the so-called connected or continuous constituents of a string x, that is, of constituents which are substrings of x. But there are also discontinuous constituents such as the German string *das Buch* in *das gute Buch*. On the other hand, we have concerned ourselves until now only with dependence relations; but there are also coordination relations, which remain outside the configurational analysis.

This section concerns itself precisely with these two problems which have not been previously discussed. To investigate discontinuous constituents, the notion of quasi-configuration will be introduced. Then, with the aid of quasi-configurations, two types of syntagms will be analyzed: dependence syntagms and coordination syntagms. All notions and results given in this section (as well as those given in Sections 9 and 10) are due to Gladkiĭ [14].

Two words a and b are said to be *related* if (1) for every pair of strings z_1 and z_2 and every positive integer m, the string $z_1 a z_2$ is a configuration of rank m with resultant a if and only if $z_1 b z_2$ is a configuration of rank m with resultant b; (2) there exists at least one configuration of the form $z_1 a z_2$, with resultant a.

In Russian, transitive verbs are related to the corresponding non-transitive forms. Thus, the configuration *horošo moet* corresponds to the configuration *horošo rabotaet*.

The following proposition is obvious.

Proposition 30. If $b \in S(a)$, then a and b are related.

The configuration x is said to be *decomposable* if for any resultant a of x there exists a word b related to a, such that $x = x_1 b x_2$ (that is, b is contained in x); b is said to be a *kernel of the configuration x, a* is called a *principal resultant of x*, and the string $x_1 x_2$ is said to be an *attribute of x*.

In Russian, *očen vysokū, vysokū dom, móju ruki* are decomposable configurations. In German, the configuration *der Tisch* (with resultant *er*) is not decomposable.

The string x is said to be a *quasi-configuration of rank m* if x admits a representation of the form $x = x_0 y_1 x_1 y_2 x_2$, where: the length of $y = y_1 y_2$ is greater than 1; at least one of the strings x_0, x_1, x_2 is not the zero string; given two strings z_1 and z_2, the following two conditions are fulfilled: if $z_1 y z_2 \in \Phi$ then $z_1 x z_2 \in \Phi$; if $z = z_1 x z_2 \in \Phi$, and if every configuration of rank less than m, contained in z and which meets x, is contained in x, then $z_1 y z_2 \in \Phi$. The string y is said to be the *kernel of the quasi-configuration x*, whereas the string $x_0 x_1 x_2$ is called an *attribute of x*.

In Russian, *za bolšim stolom* is a quasi-configuration with the kernel *za stolom*. In German, *das gute Buch* is a quasi-configuration with the kernel *das Buch*; *geht schnell voŕuber* is a quasi-configuration with the kernel *geht voŕuber*.

We recall that a string of Φ is said to be *irreducible* if it contains no configuration. A string (belonging or not belonging to Φ) in which a certain permutation of the terms yields an irreducible string is said to be a *source string*. Obviously, every irreducible string is a source string but the converse is not true. A word is said to be a *source word* if it is contained in at least one irreducible string, but it is not the attribute of a decomposable configuration or quasi-configuration.

In Russian, *čelovek idet* is a source string, whereas *idet* is a source word.

Given a string $x = a_1 a_2 \cdots a_n$, every string of the form $a_{i_1} a_{i_2} \cdots a_{i_k}$ ($1 \leqslant i_1 < \cdots < i_k \leqslant n$) is said to be a *part of the string x*. A connected part of x, that is, a part of the form $a_j a_{j+1} \cdots a_{j+p}$ ($1 \leqslant j \leqslant n, 0 \leqslant p \leqslant n-j$) is said to be a *substring of x*. It is obvious that a string y is a substring of x if and only if it is contained in x. A part of x other than x is said to be a *proper part of x*.

A string u is said to be *of degree m* if it contains no configuration of rank less than m or equal to m and no quasi-configuration of rank less than m or equal to m.

Two strings x and y are said to be *m-equivalent* if, for any pair of strings z_1 and z_2 such that the strings $u = z_1 x z_2$ and $v = z_1 y z_2$ are of degree m, u and v are E-equivalent.

If x and y are parts of the string w and if x and y are *m*-equivalent for any positive integer m such that w contains no configuration of rank less than or equal to m, we shall say that *x and y are w-equivalent*; if

w contains at least one configuration of rank 1, we define the w-equivalence between x and y as the E-equivalence between x and y.

Let x be a decomposable configuration or a quasi-configuration; x is said to be a *dependence syntagm* if the following five conditions are fulfilled: (a) its attribute has a unique component that is, if x is a decomposable configuration, only one of the strings x_1 and x_2 is not the zero string; if x is a quasi-configuration, only one of the strings x_0, x_1, and x_2 is not the zero string; (b) its kernel and its attribute are uniquely determined; (c) no substring of its kernel and no substring of its attribute is a decomposable configuration or a quasi-configuration; (d) no substring of its attribute is a source string; (e) if y and z are two disjoint parts of x, then y and z are neither x-equivalent nor source strings.

Every principal resultant of a decomposable configuration which is a dependence syntagm and every kernel of a quasi-configuration which is a dependence syntagm are said to be *substitutes of the corresponding dependence syntagms*.

A dependence syntagm x is said to be *of the first species* if its attribute contains no source string and no source word; x is said to be *of second species*, if it is not of the first species.

Russian dependence syntagms of the first species: *očen vysokiĭ; v vysokom dome; móju ruki;* of the second species: *dom, v kotorom ja živu; o teoreme, kotoraja dokazana; znal, čto on matematik; rasskažu, esli sumeju.* The following strings are not dependence syntagms: *vysokiĭ novyĭ* [condition (b) is not fulfilled]; *očen horošaja kniga* [condition (c) is not fulfilled]; *ja priehal včera* [condition (d) is not fulfilled]; *pročel gazetu i žurnal* [condition (e) is not fulfilled]. German dependence syntagms of the first species: *das gute Buch; sehr gutes Buch; geht schnell vorüber.*

Let x be the attribute of a dependence syntagm of the second species. Suppose that

$$x = y_0 x_1 y_1 \cdots x_n y_n \qquad (n \geqslant 1), \tag{5}$$

where (a) none of the strings $x_1, x_2, \ldots, x_n$ is the zero string; (b) the string $\bar{x} = x_1 x_2 \cdots x_n$ may be obtained from some string belonging to Φ, by a suitable permutation of its terms; (c) representation (5) is maximum, that is, if

$$x = y_0' x_1' y_1' \cdots x_p' y_p' \tag{6}$$

and if every x_i is contained in some x_j', then (6) does not fulfill conditions (a) and (b). In this case, we shall say that $\bar{x}$ is a *principal part of* x, whereas the string $y_0 * y_1 * \cdots * y_n$ (where the asterisk is a separating sign) is said to be an *auxiliary part of x*.

Let us consider an attribute x of a dependence syntagm of the second species. Suppose that x does not admit a representation (5) fulfilling conditions (a) and (b), that is, no substring of x is a source string. Then we find a source word a such that $x = z_0 a z_1$. In this case, we shall say that a is a *principal part of x*, whereas $z_0 * z_1$ is said to be an *auxiliary part of x*.

In the above Russian examples of dependence syntagms of the second species, the principal parts and the auxiliary parts of the corresponding attributes are, respectively, the following: (1) *ja živu* and *v kotorom* $* \theta$; (2) *dokazana* and *kotoraja* $* \theta$; (3) *on matematik* and *čto* $* \theta$; and (4) *sumeju* and *esli* $* \theta$, where θ is the zero string.

Kernels and principal resultants of dependence syntagms as well as attributes of dependence syntagms of the first species are said to be *elements of the first species*. Principal parts of attributes of dependence syntagms of the second species and strings $x \in \Phi$ admitting no pair of disjoint x-equivalent parts and containing no dependence syntagm are said to be *elements of the second species*.

The string x is said to be a *coordination syntagm of species j*$(j = 1, 2)$, if the following conditions are fulfilled: (a) x is a configuration or a quasi-configuration; (b) we have $x = y_0 x_1 y_1 \cdots x_k y_k$ $(k \geq 2)$, where: $x_1, \ldots, x_k$ are elements of species j; $x_1, \ldots, x_k$ are pairwise x-equivalent; if x is a quasi-configuration or a decomposable configuration with kernel x_i, then the same is true for every x_h $(1 \leq h \leq k)$; if $x = z_1 x' z_2$, where x' is an element of species j, then we have, for any $i = 1, 2, \ldots, k$, $x' = x_i$, $z_1 = y_0 \cdots x_{i-1} y_{i-1}$, $z_2 = y_i x_{i+1} \cdots y_k$.

The strings $x_1, \ldots, x_k$ are said to be *terms of the coordination syntagm x*, whereas the sequence of strings $y_0 * y_1 * \cdots * y_k$ (where the asterisk is a separating sign) is an *auxiliary part of x*.

The notion of a *substitute of a coordination syntagm* is defined as follows: (1) If x is a nondecomposable configuration, every resultant of x is a substitute of x; (2) If x is a decomposable configuration, every principal resultant of x is a substitute of x; (3) If x is a quasi-configuration, every kernel of x having a minimum length is a substitute of x.

Coordination syntagms in Russian: *Ivanov, Petrov i Sidorov* is a coordination syntagm of species 1, with the auxiliary part $\theta *, * i * \theta$. (We are concerned with written Russian; signs of punctuation are considered words; however, periods at the ends of the strings are omitted.) This syntagm is a nondecomposable configuration (for instance, with resultant *Ivanovy*). *Ne tolko Ivanov, no i Petrov* is a coordination syntagm of species 1, with the auxiliary part *ne tolko, no i* $* \theta$. This syntagm is a decomposable configuration. *Ivanov matematik, a Petrov fizik* and *esli Ivanov prišel, to Petrov ne prišel* are coordination syntagms of species 2, with the auxiliary parts $\theta *$, $a * \theta$ and *esli* $*$, to $* \theta$, respectively. Both these syntagms are quasi-configurations.

Given an element x of species 2, we shall say that the representation $x = z_1, \ldots, z_t$ is a *canon representation of* x if (a) every z_i is an element of species 1; (b) for any representation $x = z'_1 \cdots z'_u$ fulfilling condition (a), every z'_j is a substring of some z_i.

Obviously, an element of species 2 may have no more than one canon representation.

12. Final Remarks

Very interesting notions and facts concerning Gladkiĭ configurations are discussed by Padučeva [35]. Gladkiĭ configurations are also used in [16]. Another notion of configuration is used by Mološnaja in her algorithm of translation from English into Russian [30]; see also [31]. The determination of configurations in Russian sentences was made by Ceitin and Zasorina [7]. For various aspects concerning the analysis into immediate constituents see also Haugen [22], Hockett [23], and Nida [34]. The notion of rank (of a constituent or of a configuration) has its origin in Jespersen [24] and was used by De Groot [18, 19] and by Harris [21]. Some illustrations of configurations in the Czech language is given by Nebeský and Sgall ([33], pp. 97–98). A definition of the dependence relation, without using the notion of configuration, was given by Nebeský [32] and improved by Revzin [43]. This point of view will be discussed in the next chapter, together with the notion of subordination. Interesting notions and facts related to configurations, such as the norm of an S-structure and the notion of sentence are discussed by Revzin [39, 40]. For the notion of syntagm see also Stati [44]. A new model of grammatical description, which improves in some respects the model of immediate constituents, was given by Parker–Rhodes and members of the Cambridge language research unit [36]. A classification of syntactic relations is given by Bloch and Trager [3]. For some logical aspects of syntax see Carnap [6]. Some ideas closely related to that of configuration are developed by Harris [20].

REFERENCES

1. Y. Bar-Hillel, On recursive definitions in empirical sciences. *Proc. XIth Intern. Congr. Philosophy, Vol. V, Bruxelles 1953,* 160–165.
2. Y. Bar-Hillel, M. Perles, and E. Shamir, On formal properties of simple phrase structure grammars. *Z. Phonetik, Sprachwissenschaft Kommunikationsforschung* **14,** 143–172 (1961).
3. B. Bloch and G. L. Trager, "Outline of Linguistic Analysis." Baltimore, 1942, pp. 76–7.
4. L. Bloomfield, A set of postulates for the science of language. *Language* **XI** (3), pp. 26–31 (1926).
5. L. Bloomfield, "Language" Holt, Rinehart and Winston, New York, 1933.
6. R. Carnap, "Logical Syntax of Language." Harcourt, Brace, New York, 1937, p. 8.
7. G. S. Ceitin and L. N. Zasorina, Determining configurations in Russian sentences (in Russian). *Doklady na koferencii po obrabotke informacii, masinnomu perevodu i avtomatičeskomu čteniju teksta, No. 23,* Izd. VINITI, Moscow, 1961.
8. N. Chomsky, "Syntactic Structures," Mouton, Gravenhage, 1957.
9. N. Chomsky, Formal properties of grammars, *in* "Handbook of Mathematical Psychology," Vol. 2 (R. D. Luce, R. R. Bush, and E. Galanter, eds.). Wiley, New York, 1963, pp. 323–418.
10. K. Čulík, Applications of graph theory to mathematical logic and linguistics. Theory of graphs and its applications. *Proc. of the Symposium held in Smolenice in June 1963.* Publishing House of the Czechoslovak Academy of Sciences, Prague, 1964, pp. 13–20.
11. H. B. Curry, *Some logical aspects of grammatical structure, in* "Structure of Language and Its Mathematical Aspects." *Proc. Symp. Appl. Math.* **12,** 56–68 (1961).
12. P. Erdös, Some applications of Brun's method. *Acta Sci. Math. Szeged* **13,** 57–63 (1949).
13. A. V. Gladkiĭ, The configurational characteristics of languages (in Russian). *Probl. Kibernetiki* **10,** 251–260 (1963).
14. A. V. Gladkiĭ, On a method of formalizing the notion of syntactic link (in Russian). *Probl. Kibernetiki* **11,** 199–213 (1964).
15. A. V. Gladkiĭ, An algorithm of recognizing the configurations in automatic languages (in Russian). *Probl. Kibernetiki* **12,** 243–245 (1964).
16. A. V. Gladkiĭ, Some algorithmic problems for context-free grammars (in Russian). *Algebra i Logika Seminar* **4** (Fasc. 1), 1–13 (1965).
17. H. A. Gleason, Jr., "An Introduction to Descriptive Linguistics." Holt, Rinehart and Winston, New York, 1961.
18. A. W. De Groot, "Strukturelle Syntaxis." Den Haag, 1949.
19. A. W. De Groot, Structural linguistics and syntactic laws. *Word* **5** (1), (1949).
20. Z. S. Harris, From morpheme to utterance. *Language* **22** (3), 161–183 (1946).
21. Z. S. Harris, "Methods in Structural Linguistics." Univ. Chicago Press, Chicago, 1951. pp. 265–268.
22. E. Haugen, Directions in modern linguistics, *in* "Readings in Linguistics" (M. Joos, ed.). New York, 1958. p. 359.
23. C. Hockett, "A Course in Modern Linguistics." Macmillan, New York, 1958.
24. O. Jespersen, "The Philosophy of Grammar." Allen and Unwin, New York, 1951.
25. S. C. Kleene, Representation of events in nerve nets and finite automata, *in* "Automata Studies (C. E. Shannon and J. McCarthy, eds.). Princeton Univ. Press, Princeton N.J., 1956. pp. 3–41.
26. O. S. Kulagina, On one method of defining grammatical notions on the basis of set theory (in Russian). *Probl. Kibernetiki* **1,** 203–214 (1958).

27. S. Marcus, "Gramatici şi Automate Finite." Editura Academiei R. P. R., Bucureşti, 1964.
28. S. Marcus, Sur un modèle de H. B. Curry pour le langage mathématique. *Compt. Rend.* 2 (7), 1954–1956 (1964).
29. R. F. Mikuš, Die Klassische Grammatik und der syntagmatische Strukturalismus. *Z. Phonetik, Sprachwissenschaft und Kommunikationsforschung* 15 (1–2), (1962).
30. T. N. Mološnaja, Algorithm of translation from English to Russian (in Russian). *Probl. Kibernetiki* 3, 209–272 (1960).
31. T. N. Mološnaja, On the notion of grammatical configuration (in Russian), *in* "Strukturno-tipologiceskie issledovanija," Izd. Akad. Nauk SSSR, Moscow, 1962, pp. 46–59.
32. L. Nebeský, O jedné formalizaci vetného rozboru. *Slovo a Slovesnost* 1962 (2), 104–107.
33. L. Nebeský and P. Sgall, Algebraická lingvistika, *in* "Cesty moderni jazykovedy. Malá moderni encyklopedie" (P. Sgall a kolektiv), Orbis, Praha, 1964. pp. 72–102.
34. E. A. Nida, "Morphology. The Descriptive Analysis of Words." Univ. Michigan Press, Ann Arbor, Mich., 1957.
35. E. V. Padućeva, On the notion of configuration (in Russian). *Vopr. Jazykoznanija* XIV (1), 56–68 (1965).
36. A. F. Parker-Rhodes and members of the Cambridge language research unit, "A Lattice Model of Syntactic Description." Cambridge Language Research Unit, Cambridge, England, 1961.
37. K. L. Pike, Taxemes and immediate constituents. *Language* 19 (2), 70 (1943).
38. R. S. Pittman, Nuclear structures in linguistics. *Language* 24 (3), 287–293 (1948).
39. I. I. Revzin, Formal and semantic analysis of syntactic links in the language (in Russian), *in* "Primenenie Logiki v Nauke i Tehniki." Moscow, 1960, pp. 119–139.
40. I. I. Revzin, "Language Models" (in Russian). Izd. Akad. Nauk SSSR, Moscow, 1962.
41. I. I. Revzin, On some questions of distributional analysis and its further formalization (in Russian), *in* "Problemy Strukturnoi Lingvistiki." Izd. Akad. Nauk SSSR, Moscow, 1962, pp. 13–21.
42. I. I. Revzin, The basic units of syntactic analysis and the establishment of relations between them (in Russian), *in* "Strukturno-Tipologiceskie Issledovanija." Izd. Akad. Nauk SSSR, Moscow, 1962, pp. 118–123.
43. I. I. Revzin, On a syntactic model (letter to the editors) (in Russian). *Vopr. Jazykoznanija* 1963 (2), 148–150.
44. S. Stati, Sintagma şi sistemul sintactic al limbii. *Studii Cercetări Lingvistice* 8 (4), p. 431–452 (1957).
45. R. S. Wells, Immediate constituents. *Language* 23, 81–117 (1947).

NOTE ADDED IN PROOF

Some remarks concerning the notion of configuration are made by F. Kiefer (Bemerkungen zur Anwendung Mengentheoretischer Methoden in der Sprachwissenschaft, in "Colloquium on the Foundations of Mathematics, Mathematical Machines and their Applications," Tihany, 1962. Akadémiai Kiado, Budapest, 1965, 173–176.) New results concerning Gladkiĭ configurations and their relations with generative grammars are given by M. Novotný (Über endlich charakterisierbare Sprachen, *Časopis pro pěstování matematiky*, 91 (1), 92–94 (1966) and *Publ. Fac. Sci. Univ. Y. E. Purkyně Brno*, 468, 495–502 (1965)).

Chapter VI

Subordination and Projectivity

1. Introduction

In the preceding chapter, we analyzed in a constructive and recursive way the dependence relations occurring in a string, and we introduced a hierarchy of dependencies, the order of a dependence relation being the order of the corresponding configuration. In the present chapter, we continue the study of syntactic relations, but from another point of view. The dependence structure of a string will be considered either as given (Sections 3, 7, and 8) or as a derived notion, the main notion being that of subordination (Sections 4 and 5). In the first case, we shall obtain the subordination relation as the transitive closure of the dependence relation. In the second we shall insist on an axiomatic treatment of syntactic relations and various modes of representing a structured string by means of strings of a rudimentary structure. In both cases, we shall investigate various types of restrictions concerning the dependence and the subordination relations in a string. In this respect, the main properties we shall deal with will be the property of simplicity of a string (Sections 3–5) and the projectivity property (Sections 7–10).

2. Some Notions and Results concerning Graph Theory

The main mathematical tool we use in Sections 3 and 4 of this chapter is graph theory, and we give without proof some results which will be used subsequently. All these notions and results may be found in books and monographs concerning graph theory: Berge [7], Berge and Ghouila-Houri [8], Ore [46]. We wish to point out that we make particular use

200

of the variant of [8], which differs in some respects from that of [7] (for instance, in the definition of a chain or a cycle) However, theorems of [7] remain valid with the definitions of [8].

When two sets V_1 and V_2 are given, one can form the set of all ordered pairs $\langle v_1, v_2 \rangle$, $v_1 \in V_1$, $v_2 \in V_2$. This set is called the *product space* and denoted by $V_1 \times V_2$.

Let V be a set and let U b a subset of $V \times V$. The couple $G = \langle V, U \rangle$ is called a *graph*. V is the *vertex set* of G. The elements of V are said to be *vertices*, whereas the elements of U are called *arcs*. Thus, an arc is an ordered pair $\alpha = \langle a, b \rangle$ of vertices; a is called the *initial vertex* of α, and b is its *terminal vertex*. a and b are the *end points* of α; the arc α *starts in* a and *arrives in* b. An arc $\langle a, b \rangle$ such that $a = b$ is called a *loop*.

A graph is said to be *finite* if its vertex set is finite. The cardinal number of V is called the *order of* G.

A *subgraph* $\langle V_1, U_1 \rangle$ of G is a graph such that $V_1 \subseteq V$ and U_1 contains precisely the arcs in G whose end points are in V_1. A *partial graph* $\langle V_2, U_2 \rangle$ of G is a graph for which $V_2 = V$ and $U_2 \subseteq U$. A *partial subgraph* of G is a partial graph of a subgraph of G.

Two arcs are said to be *adjacent* if they have a common end point. Two distinct vertices are said to be *adjacent* if they are the end points of an arc.

A *finite path* in a graph is a finite sequence of arcs such that the terminal vertex of each arc coincides with the initial vertex of the next arc. The *length* $l(\mu)$ of a path $\mu = (u_1, u_2, \ldots, u_k)$ is the number of its terms; here, $l(\mu) = k$. The *initial extremity* of a finite path is the initial vertex of its first arc, whereas the *terminal extremity* of a path is the terminal vertex of its last arc. Given a path p having a and b as its initial and terminal extremities, respectively, we say that p *starts in* a and *arrives in* b; p is a path between a and b.

A graph $G = \langle V, U \rangle$ is said to be *symmetric* if $\langle a, b \rangle \in U$ implies $\langle b, a \rangle \in U$. G is said to be *antisymmetric* if $\langle a, b \rangle \in U$ implies $\langle b, a \rangle \notin U$. G is said to be *complete* if $\langle a, b \rangle \notin U$ implies $\langle b, a \rangle \in U$. G is *strongly connected* if for any two distinct vertices a and b there exists a path between a and b.

The notions just defined depend in actuality upon the orientation of arcs. We also have some nonoriented notions, as follows.

An *edge* is a (nonordered) couple of adjacent vertices. A *finite chain* is a finite sequence of arcs $\mu = (u_1, u_2, \ldots, u_k, u_{k+1}, \ldots, u_q)$ such that each of its intermediate arcs u_k is adjacent to u_{k-1} by one of its end points and adjacent to u_{k+1} by the other. Thus, every finite path is a finite chain, but the converse is not true.

In the following we shall use *path* (*chain*) instead of *finite path* (*finite chain*).

Let $u_1 = \langle a_1, b_1 \rangle$, $u_q = \langle a_q, b_q \rangle$. Let us denote by c_1 the end point (if it exists) of u_1 which is not an end point of u_2; if such an end point does not exist (for instance, u_1 may be a loop), we put $c_1 = a_1$. Let us denote by c_q the end point (if it exists) of u_q which is not an end point of u_{q-1}; if such an end point does not exist, we put $c_q = b_q$. The vertices c_1 and c_q are called the *initial extremity* and the *terminal extremity* of the considered chain μ. We say that μ *starts in* c_1 and *arrives in* c_q or that μ *connects* c_1 and c_q.

A graph is said to be *connected* if for any two distinct vertices a and b there exists a chain which starts in a and arrives in b. Every strongly connected graph is connected, but the converse is not true.

Given a vertex a, the set formed by a and by all vertices which may be connected with a by a chain is called a *connected component*, the connected component of a. A graph is connected if and only if it has a unique connected component.

A *cycle* of a graph is a chain fulfilling the following two conditions: (1) no arc occurs twice in the chain; (2) the initial extremity of the chain coincides with its terminal extremity.

A cycle $\mu = (u_1, u_2, \ldots, u_q)$ is said to be a *circuit* if the terminal vertex of each arc u_k ($1 \leqslant k < q$) is the initial vertex of u_{k+1}, whereas the terminal vertex of u_q is the initial vertex of u_1.

A *tree* is a connected graph without cycles and having at least two vertices.

Theorem A ([8], p. 131).   Let $G = \langle V, U \rangle$ be a graph of order $n \geqslant 2$. The following propositions are pairwise equivalent:

(1) G is connected and without cycles (that is, G is a tree);

(2) G has no cycle and admits $n - 1$ arcs;

(3) G is connected and admits $n - 1$ arcs;

(4) G has no cycle, but if we add an arc, we obtain a (unique) cycle;

(5) G is connected, but it becomes nonconnected if we remove an (arbitrary) arc;

(6) given two vertices a and b of G, there exists a (unique) chain starting in a and arriving in b.

A *suspended vertex* of a graph is a vertex which is the endpoint of a unique arc.

Theorem B ([8], p. 132). A tree admits at least two suspended vertices.

Theorem C ([8], p. 132). A graph G contains a partial graph which is a tree if and only if G is connected. (The proof of this theorem gives a simple algorithm for obtaining a tree in a connected graph.)

A *center* of a graph is a vertex a such that for any other vertex b *there exists a path starting in a* and arriving in b. There exist graphs which admit no center.

A graph is *quasi-strongly connected* if for any two vertices a and b there exists a vertex c, a path between c and a and a path between c and b. It follows that any strongly connected graph is quasi-strongly connected (since we may take $c = a$) but the converse is not true. Every quasi-strongly connected graph is connected.

A *proper tree* (for the French *arborescence*) is a tree endowed with a center.

Theorem D (Roy [52]; see also [8], p. 135). Let G be a graph of order $n > 1$; each of the following conditions is both necessary and sufficient that G be a proper tree:

(1) G is quasi-strongly connected and without cycles;

(2) G is quasi-strongly connected and admits $n - 1$ arcs;

(3) G is a tree with a center a;

(4) There exists a vertex a such that for any other vertex b there exists a unique path starting in a and arriving in b;

(5) G is quasi-strongly connected, but it becomes nonquasi-strongly connected if we remove an arbitrary arc.

Theorem E ([8], p. 137). A graph G admits a partial graph which is a proper tree if and only if G is quasi-strongly connected.

3. Simple Strings and Proper Trees

The automatic syntactic analysis is frequently made within the framework of a geometric representation. In this respect, graph theory and especially the theory of trees is of great utility. We shall first define the notion of a structured string. Then we shall associate a certain graph to each structured string.

Consider a language $L = \{\Gamma, \Phi\}$ and let $x \in \Phi$, $x = a_1 a_2 \ldots a_n$. We associate to the string x a binary relation R_x defined in the set $\mathscr{N}_x = \{1, 2, \ldots, n\}$, that is, a subset of the cartesian product $\mathscr{N}_x \times \mathscr{N}_x$. (We recall that the cartesian product $A \times B$ of two sets A and B is the set of all ordered pairs $\langle a, b \rangle$, with $a \in A$ and $b \in B$.) R_x is said to be a *dependence relation*. We may obtain this relation in a constructive manner, with the aid of configurations of various orders, as in Chapter V. But the dependence structure of a string is often considered given.

If $\langle i, j \rangle \in R_x$, we shall also write $a_i R_x a_j$. In fact, by a_i $(1 \le i \le n)$ we mean the ordered pair $\langle a_i, i \rangle$. Thus $a_i \ne a_j$ if and only if $i \ne j$, and we may consider that R_x is defined in the set $\{a_1, a_2, \ldots, a_n\}$. If $a_i R_x a_j$, we shall say that a_j *depends upon* a_i (with respect to the string x and the language L). The ordered pair $\langle x, R_x \rangle$ is said to be a *structured string*; it is a structured string associated with x.

Given a binary relation ρ defined in the set A, we define in A the binary relation $\bar{\rho}$ as $\langle a, b \rangle \in \bar{\rho}$ if and only if there exists a finite sequence $a_1, a_2, \ldots, a_n$ of elements of A, such that $a_1 = a$, $a_n = b$, and $\langle a_i, a_{i+1} \rangle \in \rho$ for any i, $1 \le i \le 1$. $\bar{\rho}$ is called the *transitive closure of* ρ. It is obvious that $\bar{\rho}$ is a transitive relation in A.

Let us consider the transitive closure $\bar{R}_x$ of R_x in $\mathscr{N}_x$. If $a_i \bar{R}_x a_j$, we shall say that a_j *is subordinate to* a_i (with respect to x). $\bar{R}_x$ is said to be a *subordination relation*; it is the subordination relation induced by R_x.

We say that the structured string $\{x, R_x\}$ is *simple* if the following three conditions are fulfilled: (a) there exists a term a_i of x which depends upon no term of x; (b) for any $j \ne i$ $(1 \le j \le n)$ there exists an integer k $(1 \le k \le n)$, uniquely determined, such that a_j depends upon a_k; (c) for any integer $m \ne i (1 \le m \le n)$, a_m is subordinate to a_i. It follows immediately that the term a_i occurring in conditions (a) and (c) is uniquely determined; by definition, a_i (or i) is the *center of the considered simple structured string*. On the other hand, it is easily seen that we always have $k \ne j$ in condition (b).

For the sake of simplicity, we shall often say *a simple string* instead of *a simple structured string*; but it is tacitly assumed that every simple string is also a structured string.

Various notions very closely related to the notion of simple string may be found in Hays [22–25], Lecerf [35], Fitialov [16], Gaifman [18], and others. Condition (b) owes its origin to Tesnière [57].

The notion of a simple string is a model of first approximation of the classical syntactic notion of sentence. The center of a simple string corresponds to the predicative element of a sentence.

Let $\{x, R_x\}$ be a structured string, $x = a_1 a_2 \cdots a_n$. We associate with this string a graph G_x defined as follows. The vertices of G_x are the elements of $\mathcal{N}_x$ (that is, the integers $1, 2, \ldots, n$). The ordered pair $\langle i, j \rangle$ is an arc of G_x if and only if $\langle i, j \rangle \in R_x$. It follows that the order of G_x is equal to the length of x. Since by a_i we mean in fact the ordered pair $\langle a_i, i \rangle$, we may equally consider that the vertices of G_x are a_1, $a_2, \ldots, a_n$.

Theorem 1. Let G be a finite graph of order greater than 1. G is a proper tree of center α if and only if the following three conditions are fulfilled:

(1) every vertex other than α is the terminal vertex of an arc, but of a single arc;

(2) no arc has its terminal vertex in α;

(3) G has no circuit.

PROOF. Let G be a proper tree of center α and let us verify conditions (1, 2), and (3). By Theorem D, for every vertex $\beta \neq \alpha$ there will exist an arc having β as terminal vertex. This arc is unique, because if there were two such arcs, then the existence of the center would imply the existence of a cycle, in contradiction to the assumption that G is a proper tree. Thus, condition (1) is fulfilled. If there were an arc $\langle \gamma, \alpha \rangle$, then, since α is the center of G (and thus a path exists starting in α and arriving in γ), there would exist a circuit passing through α and γ. But any circuit is a cycle; we again obtain a contradiction with the assumption that G is a proper tree; thus condition (2) is fulfilled. Since every circuit is a cycle and because G, being a proper tree, contains no cycle, condition (3) is also fulfilled.

Now suppose that the finite graph G (of order > 1) contains no circuit, but G has a vertex α satisfying conditions (1 and 2). We shall show that G is a proper tree of center α. In view of the hypotheses, there exists for every vertex $\beta \neq \alpha$ a path starting in α and arriving in β; thus, by theorem D, α is a unique center of G and G is a proper tree (another way: by (1) and since G has no circuit, G has no cycle. Hence in view of Theorem A, G is a tree. But a tree having a center is a proper tree.) and thus Theorem 1 is proved.

REMARK. Theorem 1 establishes the equivalence, for finite graphs, between two definitions of the notion of a proper tree: that of [7] (Chap. 16) and that of [8] (p. 135). The first of these definitions is given for finite graphs only, whereas the second does not introduce such a restriction.

It should be observed that this equivalence holds and is interesting only if both the definitions consider the notion of cycle in the sense of Berge and Ghouïla-Houri ([8], p. 122); as we have already remarked, this is not the case in [7].

Theorem 2.   A structured string $\{x, R_x\}$ is simple if and only if the graph G_x associated with $\{x, R_x\}$ is a proper tree. The center of $\{x, R_x\}$ is precisely the center of G_x.

PROOF.   Let $x = a_1 a_2 \cdots a_n$. Assume that $\{x, R_x\}$ is a simple string, with center a_i. To prove that G_x is a proper tree with center a_i, it is enough to show that conditions (1), (2), and (3) of Theorem 1 are fulfilled with $\alpha = a_i$ and to take into account Theorem 1. In view of (a) (see the definition of a simple string), no arc of G_x arrives in a_i. Hence G_x satisfies condition (2). In view of (b), condition (1) is also fulfilled. To prove (3), we shall establish a stronger result: G_x contains no cycle. This property is a consequence of another, that: G_x is a tree. To prove that G_x is a tree, it is enough to show that G_x is connected and has $n-1$ arcs (Theorem A). The connectedness of G_x follows from property (c) of a simple string, that is, from the fact that for any two integers j, k ($1 \leqslant j, k \leqslant n$) there exists a chain between a_j and a_k (indeed, we have a chain between a_i and a_j and another chain between a_i and a_k). On the other hand, since G_x has n vertices and by taking into account properties (a) and (b) of a simple string, it follows that G_x has $n-1$ arcs.

Now suppose that G_x is a proper tree with center a_i. We shall show that $\{x, R_x\}$ is a simple string, with center a_i. Properties (a) and (b) follow from conditions (1) and (2), fulfilled by every proper tree (see Theorem 1). To establish (c), let a_j be a term of x ($j \neq i$). In view of (1), there exists an integer j_i such that we may find in G_x an arc starting in a_{j_1} and arriving in a_j. If $j_1 \neq i$, then, in view of (1), there exists an integer j_2 such that we may find in G_x an arc starting in a_{j_2} and arriving in a_{j_1}. Continuing in this way, we find a finite sequence $j_1, j_2, \ldots, j_s = i$ of positive integers such that, for $1 \leqslant k \leqslant s-1$, there exists in G_x an arc starting in $a_{j_{k+1}}$ and arriving in a_{j_k}. The existence of an integer s such that $j_s = i$ is assured; indeed, if if there were no such integer, then by properties (1) and (2) of a proper tree and since G_x is finite, G_x would have a circuit, in contradiction to property (3) of proper trees (see Theorem 1). Thus, there exists in G_x a path starting in a_i and arriving in a_j. This implies that a_j is subordinate to a_i (with respect to x). Property (c) is fulfilled and Theorem 2 is proved.

Theorem 2 enables us to use all results concerning proper trees in the investigation of simple strings.

Two structured strings may be compared from the standpoint of their dependence and subordination. To this aim, we introduce two types of syntactic isomorphism.

Two structured strings $\{x, R_x\}$ and $\{y, R_y\}$ where $x = a_1 a_2 \cdots a_n$, $y = b_1 b_2 \cdots b_m$, are said to be δ-*isomorphic* if the following two conditions are fulfilled: (1) x and y have the same length $(m = n)$; (2) we have $a_i R_x a_j$ if and only if $b_i R_y b_j$. If condition (2) is replaced by condition (3) [(3) we have $a_i \bar{R}_x a_j$ if and only if $b_i \bar{R}_y b_j$], then we say that the considered structured strings are σ-*isomorphic*. The δ-isomorphism is called the *dependence isomorphism*, whereas the σ-isomorphism is called the *subordination isomorphism*. These two types of syntactic isomorphism are related by a theorem.

Theorem 3. If two structured strings are δ-isomorphic, they are also σ-isomorphic, but the converse is not true.

PROOF. Let $x = a_1 a_2, \ldots, a_n$, $y = b_1 b_2, \ldots, b_n$. The first part of Theorem 3 follows immediately from the fact that, if a_i depends upon a_j (with respect to x), then a_i is subordinate to a_j (with respect to x) and the same is true for y. It is also necessary to take into account the transitivity of subordination relations. To prove the second part of Theorem 3, let $x = a_1 a_2 a_3$, $y = b_1 b_2 b_3$, $R_x = \{\langle a_1, a_2 \rangle, \langle a_2, a_3 \rangle\}$, $R_y = \{\langle b_1, b_2 \rangle, \langle b_2, b_3 \rangle, \langle b_1, b_3 \rangle\}$. The structured strings $\{x, R_x\}$ and $\{y, R_y\}$ are σ-isomorphic, since we have $\bar{R}_x = \{\langle a_1, a_2 \rangle, \langle a_2, a_3 \rangle, \langle a_1, a_3 \rangle\}$, and $\bar{R}_y = R_y$. But they are not δ-isomorphic, since $\langle b_1, b_3 \rangle \in R_y$, whereas $\langle a_1, a_3 \rangle$ does not belong to R_x. This example also yields a proposition.

Proposition 1. There exist two σ-isomorphic structured strings such that one of them is a simple string but the other is not.

On the other hand, the following proposition is obvious.

Proposition 2. If two structured strings are δ-isomorphic and if one of them is simple, the other is also simple.

Proposition 1 admits a significant illustration in Rumanian. Let us consider the following Rumanian strings: $x = $ *zgomotoşii copii vin* and $y = $ *zgomotoşi copiii vin*. These two strings present the dependencies $R_x = \{\langle copii, zgomotoşii \rangle, \langle vin, copii \rangle\}$, $R_y = \{\langle copiii, zgomotosi \rangle, \langle vin, zgomotoşi \rangle, \langle vin, copiii \rangle\}$. Hence x and y are σ-isomorphic, but not δ-

isomorphic. x is a simple string, its center being *vin*. *Copii* depends upon *vin*, and thus is subordinated to *vin*; *zgomotoşii* is also subordinated to *vin*, by means of two dependencies. On the other hand, y is not a simple string since condition (b) of the definition of a simple string is not fulfilled; there exists a term of y(*zgomotoşi*) other than the center *vin*, which depends upon two terms of x, *copiii* and *vin*. This fact has an interesting grammatical significance. The string x has the P'-structure *adjective + noun + verb*, whereas in the string y the first term is both an adjective (it depends upon *copiii*) and an adverb (it depends upon *vin*). Such phenomena often have stylistic value; they are often encountered in belletristic texts (see Marcus [40]).

4. An Axiomatic Description of Simple Strings

In the preceding section, the subordination relation was defined as the transitive closure of a dependence relation. There is another way, due to Beleckiĭ *et al.* [4], who define the subordination relation by means of a system of axioms; then, as a derived notion, we obtain the dependence relation.

We consider given a set of elements called words and two binary relations defined in this set: (1) the word *a precedes the word b* $(a \leqslant b)$ and (2) the word *b is subordinated to the word a* $(a \Rrightarrow b)$. The coincidence of two words a and b is denoted by $a = b$; the noncoincidence, by $a \neq b$. We consider nine axioms, as follows.

ORDER AXIOMS: (1.1).   If $a \leqslant b$ and $b \leqslant a$, then $a = b$; (1.2) if $a \leqslant b$ and $b \leqslant c$, then $a \leqslant c$; (1.3) given two words a and b, we have either $a \leqslant b$ or $b \leqslant a$.

SUBORDINATION AXIOMS: (2.1).   For any word a we have $a \Rrightarrow a$; (2.2) if $a \Rrightarrow b$ and $b \Rrightarrow a$, then $a = b$; (2.3) if $a \Rrightarrow b$ and $b \Rrightarrow c$, then $a \Rrightarrow c$.

AXIOM OF THE SEMILATTICE CHARACTER: (3.1).   Given two words a and b, there exists a word c such that $c \Rrightarrow a$ and $c \Rrightarrow b$.

AXIOMS OF CORRECTNESS: (4.1).   If $a \Rrightarrow c$ and $b \Rrightarrow c$, then we have $a \Rrightarrow b$ or $b \Rrightarrow a$.

AXIOM OF FINITENESS: (5.1). The set of words is finite.

If $a \leqslant b$, but $a \neq b$, we say that a *strictly precedes* b and we write $a < b$. If $a \Rrightarrow b$, $a \neq b$, and there exists no word c such that $a \Rrightarrow c \Rrightarrow b$, $a \neq c$, $b \neq c$, we write $a \rightarrow b$ and we say that b *depends upon* a.

Each realization of the above system of axioms is said to be a *B-string* (*B* from Beleckiĭ). If we consider order axioms only, a corresponding realization is said to be a *string*.

Although not explicitly specified, all theorems, propositions and corollaries given in this section concern *B*-strings.

Theorem 4. Given two words a and b, there exists a word c fulfilling $c \Rrightarrow a$, $c \Rrightarrow b$, such that for every word d for which $d \Rrightarrow a$, $d \Rrightarrow b$, we have $d \Rrightarrow c$.

PROOF. In view of (3.1) there exists a word d_0 such that $d_0 \Rrightarrow a$, $d_0 \Rrightarrow b$. If it does not fulfill conditions of Theorem 4, there exists a word d_1 such that $d_1 \Rrightarrow a$, $d_1 \Rrightarrow b$, but we do not have $d_1 \Rrightarrow d_0$. Then, by Axiom (4.1), $d_0 \Rrightarrow d_1$. If d_1 is not the required word c, there exists a word d_2, such that $d_2 \Rrightarrow a$, $d_2 \Rrightarrow b$, but we do not have $d_2 \Rrightarrow d_1$; then $d_0 \Rrightarrow d_1 \Rrightarrow d_2$. In this way we obtain a sequence $d_0 \Rrightarrow d_1 \Rrightarrow \cdots \Rrightarrow d_n$ and, by Axioms (2.2) and (2.3) none of the terms of this sequence may be repeated. In view of Axiom (5.1), this sequence is finite; its last term d_n is the required word c.

Proposition 3. If $a \Rrightarrow b$, then either $a = b$, or there exists a sequence $a = a_0 \rightarrow a_1 \rightarrow \cdots \rightarrow a_n = b$.

PROOF. Let $a \Rrightarrow b$ and $a \neq b$. If $a \rightarrow b$, Proposition 3 is proved; if not, we may find a word a_1 such that $a = a_0 \Rrightarrow a_1 \Rrightarrow a_2 = b$, the words a_0, a_1, and a_2 being mutually distinct. If $a_0 \rightarrow a_1$ and $a_1 \rightarrow a_2$, Proposition 3 is proved; if not, we may find a sequence of four mutually distinct words $a_0 \rightarrow a_1 \rightarrow a_2 \rightarrow a_3$. In view of Axiom (5.1), this process may be continued only finitely many times, and we find after n steps the desired sequence.

Proposition 4. If $a \rightarrow c$ and $b \rightarrow c$, then $a = b$.

PROOF. Since $a \Rrightarrow c$ and $b \Rrightarrow c$, we have $a \Rrightarrow b$ or $b \Rrightarrow a$ [see Axiom (4.1)]; let us suppose that $a \Rrightarrow b$. Then, since $a \rightarrow c$ and $a \Rrightarrow b \Rrightarrow c$, we have $a = b$ or $b = c$; but the last equality is not possible, because $b \rightarrow c$. Thus, $a = b$. The case $b \Rrightarrow a$ may be analyzed in the same way.

Proposition 5. Let $a \Rightarrow b$, $b \Rightarrow c$. If $a < b$, then $a < c$; if $b < a$, then $c < a$.

PROOF. Let $a < b$. If $c \leqslant a$, then $c \leqslant a \leqslant b$ and, since $b \Rightarrow c$, it follows that $b \Rightarrow a$ and, in view of Axiom (2.2), we have $b = a$, which contradicts the assumption that $a < b$. Hence, $a < c$. In the same way one can prove the second assertion of Proposition 5.

The word a is said to be a *nonsubordinated word* if there exists no word b such that $b \Rightarrow a$ and $b \neq a$.

The word a is said to be a *nonsubordinating word* if there exists no word b such that $a \Rightarrow b$ and $b \neq a$.

Proposition 6. A word a is a nonsubordinated (nonsubordinating) word if and only if there exists no word b such that $b \to a$ ($a \to b$, respectively).

PROOF. Proposition 6 follows immediately from Proposition 3.

Proposition 7. In every nonempty B-string there exist a nonsubordinated word and a nonsubordinating word.

PROOF. Let us prove the existence of a nonsubordinated word. Let a be an arbitrary word. If a is not a nonsubordinated word, there exists a word a_1 such that $a_1 \to a_0 = a$. By continuing in this way and in view of Axioms (2.3), (2.2), and (5.1), we find a finite sequence of words $a_n \to a_{n-1} \to \cdots \to a_1 \to a_0 = a$ such that a_n is a nonsubordinated word.

In an analogous way we can prove the existence of a nonsubordinating word.

Proposition 8. If a is a nonsubordinated word, we have $a \Rightarrow b$ for any word b.

PROOF. Let b be an arbitrary word. By Axiom (3.1), there exists a word c such that $c \Rightarrow a$ and $c \Rightarrow b$. Since a is a nonsubordinated word, we have $c = a$. Hence $a \Rightarrow b$.

Corollary 1. The nonsubordinated word of a B-string is uniquely determined. [This follows immediately from Axiom (2.2).]

Corollary 2. If a B-string x possesses a word a which is both a nonsubordinated and a nonsubordinating word, then x is formed by a single word.

PROOF. Let us suppose that x contains a word $b \neq a$; then $a \Rrightarrow b$, in contradiction to the fact that a is a nonsubordinating word.

The words a and b are said to be *comparable* if $a \Rrightarrow b$ or $b \Rrightarrow a$.

Proposition 9. If $a \to b$, $a \to c$ and $b \neq c$, then b and c are not comparable.

PROOF. Let us suppose that b and c are comparable; for instance, $b \Rrightarrow c$. Then, since $a \Rrightarrow b \Rrightarrow c$ and $a \to c$, we have $a = b$ or $b = c$. But each of these equalities is false, because $a \to b$ and $b \neq c$. Thus, b and c are not comparable.

Proposition 10. If a and b are not comparable and if $a \Rrightarrow c$ and $b \Rrightarrow d$, then c and d are not comparable.

PROOF. Let us suppose that c and d are comparable, for instance, $c \Rrightarrow d$. Then, by Axiom (2.3), we have $a \Rrightarrow d$ and, in view of Axiom (4.1), a and b should be comparable, in contradiction to the hypothesis.

Corollary 3. If a and b are not comparable and if $a \Rrightarrow c$ and $b \Rrightarrow d$, then $c \neq d$.

In the following, the relation $\leq$ will be interpreted as the linear order of words (from the left to the right). Thus, every realization of the order axioms becomes a customary string.

Theorem 5. If the string $x = a_1 a_2 \cdots a_n$ endowed with the relation $\Rrightarrow$ is a B-string, then, by putting $a_i R_x a_j$ if and only if $a_i \to a_j$, the structured string $\{x, R_x\}$ is simple.

PROOF. We shall prove that conditions (a), (b), and (c) from the definition of a simple string are fulfilled. Let a_j be a term of x. In view of Proposition 6, the existence of a word a_k such that $a_k \to a_j$ implies the existence of a word a_p such that $a_p \Rrightarrow a_j$ and conversely, if $a_p \Rrightarrow a_j$, there exists a word a_k such that $a_k \to a_j$. Moreover, if $a_k \to a_j$, then $k \neq j$ (see the definition of $\to$). By Proposition 7, there exists a term a_i of x such that $a_k \Rrightarrow a_i$ for no k ($1 \leq k \leq n$). Thus, we have $a_k \to a_i$ for no $k (1 \leq k \leq n)$. By Corollary 1, the term a_i is uniquely determined. Hence a_i is the unique term for which $a_k R_x a_i$ for no k ($1 \leq k \leq n$). Condition (a) is thus fulfilled.

Consider now a term a_j such that $j \neq i$. In view of Proposition 6 and Corollary 1, there exists a term a_k such that $a_k \to a_j$. By Proposition 4, this term is uniquely determined. Condition (b) is thus fulfilled. Proposition 8 shows that condition (c) is also fulfilled and Theorem 5 is proved.

The converse of Theorem 5 is also true and we have Theorem 6.

Theorem 6. If the structured string $\{x, R_x\}$ $(x = a_1 a_2 \cdots a_n)$ is simple, by putting $a_k \Rrightarrow a_j$ if $k = j$ or $a_k \bar{R}_x a_j$, the string x endowed with the relation $\Rrightarrow$ is a B-string.

PROOF. The order axioms are obviously satisfied. Axiom (2.1) follows immediately from the hypothesies. To verify Axiom (2.2), let us remark that $a_j \Rrightarrow a_k$ implies the existence, in G_x, of a path starting in a_j and arriving in a_k; conversely, the existence of such a path implies $a_j \Rrightarrow a_k$. Assume that $a_j \Rrightarrow a_k$ and $a_k \Rrightarrow a_j$. If there were $k \neq j$, there would exist in G_x a cycle passing through a_j and a_k. But since $\{x, R_x\}$ is a simple string, it follows from Theorem 2 that G_x is a proper tree. Hence, by Theorem D, G_x contains no cycle. We deduce that $j = k$, and Axiom (2.2) is fulfilled.

Axiom (2.3) follows from the transitivity of subordination relation $\bar{R}_x$.

Axiom (3.1) is also fulfilled. Indeed, if a_j and a_k are two terms of x, then, by denoting by a_i the center of x (which is a simple string), we have $a_i \Rrightarrow a_j$ and $a_i \Rrightarrow a_k$ (see the definition of $\Rrightarrow$).

To prove Axiom (4.1), let us assume the existence of j, k, and m such that $a_j \Rrightarrow a_m$, $a_k \Rrightarrow a_m$, and $j \neq k$ and let a_i be the center of the simple string x. Then, $a_i \Rrightarrow a_j$, $a_i \Rrightarrow a_k$ and we deduce the existence of a cycle in G_x. But this fact contradicts the hypothesis that G_x is a proper tree (see Theorem 2). Thus, $k = j$, and Axiom (4.1) is proved. Since Axiom (5.1) is obviously fulfilled, Theorem 6 is proved.

Theorems 5 and 6 establish, in some sense, the equivalence between simple strings and B-strings.

5. Elementary Strings and Operations with Simple Strings

In this section we define two classes of strings of a very rudimentary structure. Then we define some operations with B-strings.

These notions will be used in Section 7, where we shall show that an important category of B-strings may be represented by means of the operation of superposition, using only strings of a rudimentary structure. In view of the equivalence between simple strings and B-strings, we may investigate B-strings and apply the obtained results to simple strings.

A B-string is said to be *elementary* if from $a \Rightarrow b$, $c \Rightarrow d$, $a \neq b$, and $c \neq d$ it follows that $a = c$. A B-string is said to be *strongly elementary* if from $a \Rightarrow b$, $c \Rightarrow d$, $a \neq b$, and $c \neq d$, it follows that $b = d$.

Proposition 11. Every strongly elementary B-string x is elementary.

PROOF. Let $a \Rightarrow b$, $c \Rightarrow d$, $a \neq b$, and $c \neq d$. We shall show that $a = c$. Since x is strongly elementary, we have $b = d$. Then by Axiom (4.1), we have $a \Rightarrow c$ or $c \Rightarrow a$. Assume that $a \Rightarrow c$. In view of Axiom (2.3) we have $a \Rightarrow d$ and, since $a \Rightarrow c$, $a \Rightarrow d$, and $c \neq d$, we also have $a = c$ or $a = d$. if $a = c$, Proposition 11 is proved; if $a = d$, then, since $a \Rightarrow c$ and $c \Rightarrow a$, we deduce, by Axiom (2.2), that $a = c$ and Proposition 11 is proved.

Proposition 12. Every word of an elementary B-string is a nonsubordinated word or a nonsubordinating word.

PROOF. Let a be an arbitrary word. Assume that a is not a nonsubordinated word. Thus, there exists a word b such that $b \neq a$ and $b \Rightarrow a$. Suppose we may find a word c such that $a \Rightarrow c$ and $a \neq c$. Then, since $b \Rightarrow a$, $a \Rightarrow c$, $b \neq a$, and $a \neq c$ and since the considered B-string is elementary, we have $b = a$, in contradiction to $b \neq a$. Thus, no word c with $a \Rightarrow c$ and $a \neq c$ exists, and a is a nonsubordinating word.

Proposition 13. If a is a nonsubordinated word of a B-string x of length greater than 1 and if b is a nonsubordinating word of x, then $a \rightarrow b$.

PROOF. By Proposition 8, we have $a \Rightarrow b$; by Corollary 2, $a \neq b$. Assume the existence of a word c such that $a \Rightarrow c \Rightarrow b$, $a \neq c$, $c \neq b$. From $c \neq a$, we deduce, in view of Corollary 1, that c is a nonsubordinating word, in contradiction to $c \Rightarrow b$, $c \neq b$. Thus, no word c exists with the required properties and we have $a \rightarrow b$.

Proposition 14. A strongly elementary B-string may not have more than one nonsubordinating word.

PROOF. Assume there are two nonsubordinating words a and b and let c be a nonsubordinated word. By Proposition 8, we have $c \Rightarrow a$, $c \Rightarrow b$

and, since a and b are nonsubordinating words, we also have $c \neq a$, $c \neq b$. Thus, $c \Rightarrow a$, $c \Rightarrow b$, $c \neq a$, $c \neq b$. Hence, since the considered B-string is strongly elementary, we deduce $a = b$.

Corollary 4. A strongly elementary B-string has at most two terms.

PROOF. It follows from Corollary 1 and Propositions 11, 12, and 14.

Proposition 15. Every B-string of length less than or equal to 2 is a strongly elementary B-string.

PROOF. Obvious.

Let y be a subset of a B-string x. If y is a B-string with respect to the order relation and the subordination relation of x, then y is said to be a *B-substring of* x.

Proposition 16. Let a be an arbitrary term of a B-string x. The set y of words subordinated to a form a B-substring of x.

PROOF. It is immediately seen that each axiom occuring in the definition of a B-string is fulfilled by y.

We shall define four operations with B-strings. These operations will always be concerned with B-strings without common words. To show that the word a precedes the word b in the B-string x we shall write $a \leqslant b(x)$. Analogously, $a \Rightarrow b(x)$ means that b is subordinated to a in the B-string x.

OPERATION OF RIGHT UNION. Let x and y be two B-strings; let a and b be the nonsubordinated words of x and y, respectively (if such words do exist). Let x' and y' be the sets obtained from x and y after removing a and b, respectively (if a or b does not exist, we put $x = x'$ or $y = y'$, respectively). Let α be a word occurring neither in x' nor in y'. Let z be the set containing precisely the words of x', the words of y', and the word α. We define in z the relations $\leqslant$ and $\Rightarrow$, as follows:

(1) If both c and d belong either to x' or to y', then $c \leqslant d(z)$ [or $c \Rightarrow d(z)$] if and only if the same relation holds in x or in y, respectively.

(2) If $c \in x'$ and $d \in y'$, then $c \leqslant d(z)$ and we have neither $c \Rightarrow d(z)$ nor $d \Rightarrow c(z)$.

(3') For every word $c \in z$ we have $c \leqslant \alpha(z)$ and $\alpha \Rightarrow c(z)$.

It is easily seen that z, endowed with $\leqslant$ and $\Rightarrow$, fulfills all axioms defining a B-string in z. The B-string z so obtained is said to be *the right union of* x *and* y.

OPERATION OF LEFT UNION. This operation differs from the right union in formulation of rule (3′) only; (3′) is replaced here by (3″). (3″) For every word $c \in z$, we have $\alpha \leqslant c(z)$ and $\alpha \Rightarrow c(z)$.

OPERATION OF CENTRAL UNION. This operation differs from the right union in formulation of rule (3′) only; (3′) is replaced here by (3). (3) For every word $c \in x'$, we have $c \leqslant \alpha(z)$ and $\alpha \Rightarrow c(z)$; $\alpha \leqslant \alpha$; $\alpha \Rightarrow \alpha$; for every word $d \in y'$ we have $\alpha \leqslant d$ and $\alpha \Rightarrow d$.

OPERATION OF SUPERPOSITION. Let us consider the B-strings $x, y_1, y_2, \ldots, y_m$. We shall define the superposition between x, on one hand, and $y_1, y_2, \ldots, y_m$, on the other.

If x is the empty string, the superposition string is the empty string.

If x is not empty, then x contains some nonsubordinating words $a_1, a_2, \ldots, a_n$. If $m < n$, then we add to $y_1, y_2, \ldots, y_m$ the strings $y_{m+1}, \ldots, y_n$ of length 1, such that the superposition of x and $y_1, y_2, \ldots, y_m$ be equivalent to the superposition of x and $y_1, y_2, \ldots, y_m, \ldots, y_n$. If $m \geqslant n$, then our superposition will be supposed equivalent to the superposition between x and $y_1, \ldots, y_n$. Thus, we may always assume that $m = n$.

Let x' be the set obtained from x by removing the words $a_1, a_2, \ldots, a_n$. Let z be the set of all words belonging to at least one of the sets x', $y_1, y_2, \ldots, y_n$. We define in z the relations $\leqslant$ and $\Rightarrow$, as follows:

(1) If both c and d belong either to x' or to one of the sets y_i, then $c \leqslant d(z)$ [or $c \Rightarrow d(z)$] if and only if the same relation holds in x or in one of the sets y_i, respectively.

(2) If $i \neq j$, then for any $c \in y_i$ and $d \in y_j$ we have not $c \Rightarrow d(z)$; we have $c \leqslant d(z)$ if and only if $a_i < a_j$.

(3) If $c \in x'$ and $d \in y_i$, then $c \Rightarrow d(z)$ if and only if $c \Rightarrow a_i(x)$; $d \leqslant c(z)$ if and only if $a_i \leqslant c(x)$.

(4) If $d \in y_i$ and $c \in x'$, we have not $d \Rightarrow c(z)$; we have $c \leqslant d(z)$ if and only if $c < a_i(x)$.

It is easily seen that all axioms defining a B-string are fulfilled in z, with the above definition of $\leqslant$ and $\Rightarrow$.

6. Subordination in the Sense of Nebeský

Nebeský [62] has proposed a new way for the analysis of subordination relation which uses some semantic aspects but, as Revzin has pointed out, one can remove the reference to semantics and obtain a more formalized description [64]. This remark of Revzin suggested to Nebeský a new and more general description of syntactic subordination, which we now present [63].

Let x be a string over Γ. Denote by T the free semigroup generated by Γ. Let $\tilde{x} = \{x_1, x_2, \ldots, x_n\}$, where x_i denotes the position i in the string x and n is the length of x. Let $\hat{x}$ be a mapping of $\tilde{x}$ into Γ; this mapping associates with $x_i \in \tilde{x}$ the word which stands in x at position i. If we denote by $\bar{x}$ the binary relation which associates to each $x_i \in \tilde{x}$ the element x_{i+1} ($1 \leq i < n$), it is easily seen that the ordered set $\langle \tilde{x}, \bar{x}, \hat{x} \rangle$ uniquely determines the string x.

EXAMPLE 1. Let $\Gamma = \{a, b, c, d\}$; $x = caababdc$. We have $\tilde{x} = \{x_1, x_2, x_3, x_4, x_5, x_6, x_7, x_8\}$, $x_i \bar{x} x_{i+1}$ ($1 \leq i < n$), $\hat{x}(x_1) = \hat{x}(x_8) = c$, $\hat{x}(x_2) = \hat{x}(x_3) = \hat{x}(x_5) = a$, $\hat{x}(x_4) = \hat{x}(x_6) = b$, $\hat{x}(x_7) = d$.

Let x and y be two strings over Γ. Suppose that y may be obtained from x by removing at least one term. Denote by x_y the set of elements in $\tilde{x}$ which are used in any derivation of y from x, by removing some terms.

EXAMPLE 2. Let us adopt the assumptions of Example 1 and let $y = cabdc$. We have $\tilde{y} = \{y_1, y_2, y_3, y_4, y_5\}$, $y_i \bar{y} y_{i+1}$ ($1 \leq i < 5$). The string y may be derived from x in four modes: (1) by removing the elements x_2, x_4, x_5; (2) by removing x_3, x_4, x_5; (3) by removing x_2, x_5, x_6; (4) by removing x_3, x_5, x_6. Thus, $x_y = \{x_1, x_7, x_8\}$.

Consider a language Φ over Γ. We define a set Ω of mappings ω of Φ into 2^Φ such that, if $x \in \Phi$, $y \in \omega(x)$, then either $y = x$ or y may be derived from x by removing at least one term. Let us denote by k the mapping of Φ into 2^Φ which associates to every $x \in \Phi$ the set $k(x)$ containing x as well as all strings derived from x by removing at least one term. Obviously, $k \in \Omega$ and $\omega(x) \subseteq k(x)$. Let us denote by r the mapping of Φ into 2^Φ which associates to each string x in Φ the set $r(x)$ of all $y \in \Phi$ fulfilling one of the conditions (1) $y = x$ or (2) there exists $z \in r(x)$ such that y may be derived from z by removing a unique word. Obviously, for any $x \in \Gamma$ we have $x \in r(x) \subseteq k(x)$.

EXAMPLE 3. Let $\Gamma = \{a, b, c, d\}$, $\Phi = \{caababdc, ac, cabdc, caabbdc, abdc\}$. We have $k(caabadc) = \Phi \neq r(caababdc) = \{caababdc, caabbdc\}$; $k(caabdc) = \{caabdc, cabdc, abdc\} = r(caabdc)$; $k(ac) = r(ac) = \{ac\}$.

Let $x \in \Phi$, $\omega \in \Omega$. We shall define in $\tilde{x}$ a binary relation x_ω, as follows. Let $x_i, x_j \in \tilde{x}$. We have $x_i x_\omega x_j$ if and only if the following conditions are both fulfilled: (1) $i \neq j$; (2) for any $y \in \omega(x)$ we have that if $x_j \in x_y$, then $x_i \in x_y$.

EXAMPLE 4. Let $\Gamma = \{a, b, c, d\}$, $\Phi = \{a, abd, abcd, abccd\}$. If $x = abccd$, then $\tilde{x} = \{x_1, \ldots, x_5\}$ and we have, for $\omega = k$, $x_1x_kx_2$, $x_1x_kx_5$, $x_1x_kx_4$, $x_1x_kx_3$, $x_2x_kx_3$, $x_2x_kx_4$, $x_2x_kx_5$, $x_3x_kx_4$, $x_4x_kx_3$, $x_5x_kx_3$, $x_5x_kx_2$, $x_5x_kx_4$; for $\omega = r$, $x_1x_rx_2$, $x_2x_rx_1$, $x_1x_rx_5$, $x_1x_rx_3$, $x_1x_rx_4$, $x_2x_rx_3$, $x_2x_rx_4$, $x_2x_rx_5$, $x_3x_rx_4$, $x_4x_rx_3$, $x_5x_rx_2$, $x_5x_rx_4$, $x_5x_rx_3$.

We shall associate now with every string $x \in \Phi$ a binary relation x^+ defined in $\tilde{x}$; x^+ will be called the *subordination relation of x*. Let $\omega \in \Omega$. If for any $x \in \Phi$ we have $x^+ = x_\omega$ we say that $\{\Gamma, \Phi\}$ is a ω-language.

Let $\Phi = \{x, x', x''\}$, where $x = x_1 \cdots x_i x_{i+1} x_{i+2} \cdots x_p$, $x' = x_1 \cdots x_i x_{i+2} \cdots x_p$, $x'' = x_1 \cdots x_i x_{i+1} x_{i+3} \cdots x_p$ (or $x = x_1 \cdots x_{i-2} x_{i-1} x_i \cdots x_p$, $x' = x_1 \cdots x_{i-2} x_i \cdots x_p$, $x'' = x_1 \cdots x_{i-3} x_{i-1} x_i \cdots x_p$). Suppose we have $x_i x^+ x_{i+1}$, but we do not have $x_i x^+ x_{i+2}$ (or we have $x_i x^+ x_{i-1}$ but not $x^+ x_{i-2}$); suppose also that $\hat{x}(x_{i+1}) = \hat{x}(x_{i+2})[\text{or } \hat{x}(x_{i-1}) = \hat{x}(x_{i-2})]$

It follows that $x' = x''$, $x = \{x_1, \ldots, x_p\}$ and $x_{x'} = x_{x''} = \tilde{x} = \{x_{i+1}, x_{i+2}\}$ (or $= \tilde{x} = \{x_{i-1}, x_{i-2}\}$). We see that, for any $\omega \in \Omega$, we have $x^+ \neq x_\omega$. Hence a language containing strings of the form x, x', and x'' may be a ω-language for no $\omega \in \Omega$.

For the sake of simplicity, we shall suppose that no word occurs several times in a string belonging to Φ.

Nebeský makes several interesting remarks concerning the application of his description to the Czech language. He observes that Czech is neither a k-language, nor an r-language, but some portions of Czech may be k-languages or r-languages. In this respect, he gives the following examples.

EXAMPLE 5. Let $x = $ *zpíval dávno zapomenutou píseň*. We have $k(x) = $ {*zpíval dávno zapomenutou píseň, zpíval zapomenutou píseň, zpíval píseň, zpíval dávno, zpíval*}. It follows that *zpíval x_k dávno, zpíval x_k zapomenutou, zpíval x_k píseň, píseň x_k zapomenutou*; *zpíval x^+ dávno, zpíval x^+ zapomenutou, zpíval x^+ píseň, zapomenutou x^+ dávno, píseň x^+ dávno, píseň x^+ zapomenutou*. It follows that x_k and x^+ are different, but x_r and x^+ are identical.

EXAMPLE 6. Let $y = $ *vidím bratra otce*. We have $k(y) = r(y) = $ {*vidím bratra otce, vidím otce, vidím bratra, vidím*}, *vidím y_r bratra, vidím y_r otce, vidím y_k bratra, vidím y_k otce*. Hence $y_k = y_r$. On the other hand, *vidím y⁺ bratra, vidim y⁺ otce, bratra y⁺ otce.* Hence y_k and y^+ are different.

The next example belongs to a mathematical language.

EXAMPLE 7. Let $\Gamma = \{1, 2, 3\}$, $\Phi = \{1, 2, 12, 13, 21, 23, 31, 32, 123, 132, 213, 231, 321, 312\}$. We interpret every string of Φ as the result of some mathematical operations, as follows: Every term of a string is the exponent of the preceding term. For instance, 12, 23, 123, 231, 312 mean, respectively,

$$1^2, 2^3, 1^{23}, 2^{31}, 3^{12}.$$

Hence

$$1^2 = 1, \quad 2^3 = 8, \quad 1^{23} = 1^{(23)} = 1, \quad 2^{31} = 2^{(31)} = 8, \quad 3^{12} = 3^{(12)} = 3.$$

Using the analogy with natural languages, we may define in each of the strings of Φ a subordination relation corresponding to the following principles: Each exponent is subordinated to its base; the subordination relation is transitive. Thus, in the string $x = 213$ we have $2x^+1$, $1x^+3$, $2x^+3$, but also $2x_k1$, $2x_k3$, $2x_r1$, $2x_r3$. It follows that $x^+ \neq x_k = x_r$.

An important common peculiarity of the mappings k and r is their independence of the elements of Γ. The exact meaning of this assertion follows from the next definition. The mapping $\omega \in \Omega$ is said to be *independent of the elements of* Γ if for every mapping φ of Γ into Γ we have if $x_1 \cdots x_m \in \Phi$ and $y_1 \cdots y_n \in \omega(x_1 \cdots x_m)$, that $\varphi(y_1) \cdots \varphi(y_n) \in \omega(\varphi(x_1) \cdots \varphi(x_m))$.

EXAMPLE 8. Let $\Gamma = \{a, b, c, d, e, f\}$, $\Phi = \{ab, ac, abc, dc, df, dcf\}$, $x = abc$ and $y = def$. Define x^+ and y^+ as follows: bx^+a, cx^+b, cx^+a; fy^+d, fy^+e. The considered language is an ω-language for no mapping ω independent of the elements of Γ.

EXAMPLE 9. Example 8 may be applied to Czech. Let $x = $ *často dlouho četl*, $y = $ *včera dobře spal*. We have $k(x) = \{$*často dlouho četl, často četl, dlouho četl, četl*$\}$, $k(y) = \{$*včera dobře spal, včera spal, dobře spal, spal*$\}$, *dlouho x⁺ často, četl x⁺ dlouho, četl x⁺ často, spal y⁺ včera, spal y⁺ dobře*. It follows that Czech is an ω-language for no mapping ω independent of the Czech vocabulary.

All notions and examples in this section are due to Nebeský [63].

It would be interesting to establish the precise connection between Nebeský's description and the other syntactic descriptions given previously.

7. Various Types of Projectivity. Properties of Montonically Projective Strings

We adopt here the definitions and the conventions of Section 3. Thus a dependence relation is considered given; a subordination relation is defined as the transitive closure of the dependence relation. Moreover, we suppose that the subordination relation is reflexive, that is, every term of a string is subordinated to itself. Let $x = a_1 a_2 \cdots a_i \cdots a_n$. We adopt the notations of Section 4: $a_i < a_j$ means that a_i strictly precedes (eventually, not immediately) a_j, that is, $i < j$; $a_i \leqslant a_j$ means that $i \leqslant j$; $a_i \to a_j$ means that a_j depends upon a_i; $a_i \Rightarrow a_j$ means that a_j is subordinated to a_i. We tacitly assume that all strings considered in Sections 7–9 are structured strings, that is, strings endowed with three binary relations: $\leqslant$, $\to$, and $\Rightarrow$.

There are some restrictions which considerably reduce the possible dependencies and subordinations between the terms of a string belonging to a natural language. Among these restrictions, the projectivity restrictions are very important. The word *projectivity* suggests a geometric situation, which will be explained in Section 10.

The string x is said to be regressively projective if for $i \neq j$ we have $a_i \Rightarrow a_j$ if and only if $a_j < a_i$. The English string *very clearly projected pictures appeared* (Yngve [61], p. 136) is regressively projective, since every term depends upon the following term. Hence every term is subordinated to any term situated to its right and only to these terms.

The string x is said to be *progressively projective* if for $i \neq j$ we have $a_i \Rightarrow a_j$ if and only if $a_i < a_j$. The Rumanian string *citesc cărti frumoase* is progressively projective, since we have only two dependencies: *citesc* $\to$ *cărti* $\to$ *frumoase*. Hence there are only three subordinations: *citesc* $\Rightarrow$ *cărți* $\Rightarrow$ *frumoase*, *citesc* $\Rightarrow$ *frumoase*.

The string x is said to be *monotonically projective* if it is progressively projective or regressively projective. If we consider $\to$ antisymmetric (that is, if $a_i \to a_j$ is true, then $a_j \to a_i$ is false), no string exists which is both progressively and regressively projective. The hypothesis of antisymmetry of $\to$ agrees with most situations occurring in natural languages. However, for the sake of generality, we do not always adopt this hypothesis.

The string x is said to be *strongly projective* if from $a_i \Rightarrow a_j$ and $\min(i, j) < k < \max(i, j)$ it follows that $a_i \to a_k$. The Russian string *vesma malenkaja devočka* is strongly projective, since we have *devočka* $\to$ *malenkaja* $\to$ *vesma*.

The string x is said to be *projective in the restricted sense* if from $a_i \rightarrow a_j$ and $\min(i,j) < k < \max(i,j)$ it follows that $a_i \rightarrow a_k$. The German string *ein steiler, sandiger, schwieriger Weg* (Tesnière [57], Chap. 8) is projective in the restricted sense, since we have $Weg \rightarrow ein$, $Weg \rightarrow steiler$, $Weg \rightarrow sandiger$, $Weg \rightarrow schwieriger$.

The string x is said to be *projective in the sense of Harper and Hays* (or *H-projective*) if from $a_i \rightarrow a_j$ and $\min(i, j) < k < \max(i, j)$ follows $a_i \Rrightarrow a_k$. The German string *ein sehr schwieriger Weg* is H-projective, since we have $sehr \rightarrow ein$, $Weg \rightarrow schwieriger$, $Weg \rightarrow ein$.

The string x is said to be *projective in the sense of Lecerf and Ihm* (or *L-projective*) if from $a_i \Rrightarrow a_j$ and $\min(i, j) < k < \max(i, j)$ it follows that $a_i \Rrightarrow a_k$. The Rumanian string *o foarte frumoasă casă* is L-projective, since we have $casă \rightarrow o$, $casă \rightarrow frumoasă \rightarrow foarte$.

The string x is said to be *projective in the sense of Fitialov* (or *F-projective*) if, for $a_m \Rrightarrow a_i$, $a_m \Rrightarrow a_j$ and $\min(i, j) < k < \max(i, j)$, it follows that $a_m \Rrightarrow a_k$. The Russian string *v eto vremja molodoi čelovek byl v teatre* (Fitialov [16], p. 105) is F-projective, since we have $byl \rightarrow v \rightarrow vremja \rightarrow eto$, $byl \rightarrow čelovek \rightarrow molodoi$, $v \rightarrow teatre$. It should be remarked that the dependence $byl \rightarrow v$ is true both for the first v and for the second v of the considered string, whereas the dependence $v \rightarrow teatre$ is true only for the second v and the dependence $v \rightarrow vremja$ is true only for the first v.

REMARK.   The so-called condition $Pr(I)$ of Lecerf and Ihm ([35], p. 8) is in fact the condition of F-projectivity. Thus, F-projectivity originates with Lecerf and Ihm.

The string x is said to be *quasi-projective* if from $a_m \Rrightarrow a_i$, $a_m \Rrightarrow a_j$, $i \neq m \neq j$, $\min(i, j) < k < \max(i, j)$, it follows that $a_m \Rrightarrow a_k$. The Russian string *primerom možet služit sledujuščii fakt* (Padučeva [48], p. 112) is quasi-projective, since we have *služit* $\rightarrow$ *primerom*, *možet* $\rightarrow$ *služit*, *možet* $\rightarrow$ *fakt* $\rightarrow$ *sledujuščii*. The French string *nous avons tous étudié* (Hirschberg [26], example 3) is quasi-projective, since we have *étudié* $\rightarrow$ *nous* $\rightarrow$ *tous*, *étudié* $\rightarrow$ *avons*.

We establish now some properties of monotonically projective strings.

Proposition 17.   If x is a regressively projective string, we have $a_{i+1} \rightarrow a_i$ for $1 \leqslant i \leqslant n-1$ and $a_j \rightarrow a_i$ implies $i < j$.

PROOF.   Let us admit the existence of an integer j ($1 \leqslant j \leqslant n-1$) such that a_j does not depend upon a_{j+1}. Then, since x is regressively projective, we have $a_{j+1} \Rrightarrow a_j$. Hence there exists a finite sequence $b_1, \ldots, b_m$ of terms of x, such that $a_j = b_1$, $a_{j+1} = b_m$, and $b_{k+1} \to b_k$ for $1 \leq k \leq m-1$. Since the dependence relation is a particular case of the subordination relation, we have $b_k < b_{k+1}$ for $1 \leq k \leq m-1$. Hence $b_1 < b_2$ and $a_j < b_2$. We also have $b_2 \to a_j$. Therefore $b_2 \neq a_{j+1}$. Hence $a_{j+1} < b_2$. It follows that $a_{j+1} < b_s$ for $s \geq 2$. Hence $a_{j+1} < b_m = a_{j+1}$. The contradiction so obtained shows that for every i, $1 \leq i \leq n-1$, a_i depends upon a_{i+1}.

Now let $a_j \to a_i$ $(i \neq j)$. We have $a_j \Rrightarrow a_i$ and, since x is regressively projective, it follows that $a_i < a_j$. Therefore $i < j$.

Proposition 18. Let x be a string such that $a_{i+1} \to a_i$ for $1 \leq i \leq n-1$. If $a_j \to a_i (i \neq j)$ implies $i < j$, then x is regressively projective.

PROOF.   We shall show that $a_j \Rrightarrow a_i$ $(i \neq j)$ if and only if $a_i < a_j$. Suppose first that $a_j \Rrightarrow a_i$. There exists a sequence $b_1, \ldots, b_m$ of terms of x such that $b_1 = a_i$, $b_m = a_j$, and $b_{k+1} \to b_k$ for $1 \leq k \leq m-1$. It follows that $b_k < b_{k+1}$ for $1 \leq k \leq m-1$. Hence $a_i < a_j$.

Suppose now that $a_i < a_j$. In view of the hypothesis, we have $a_j \to a_{j-1} \to \cdots \to a_{i+1} \to a_i$. Therefore, by the transitivity of $\Rrightarrow$, we deduce that $a_j \Rrightarrow a_i$.

Propositions 17 and 18 yield the following result.

Theorem 7.   The string x is regressively projective if and only if the following two conditions are fulfilled:
(1) $a_{i+1} \to a_i$ for $1 \leq i \leq n-1$;
(2) the relation $a_j \to a_i$ $(i \neq j)$ implies $a_i < a_j$.
In a similar way we obtain another result.

Theorem 7'.   The string x is progressively projective if and only if the following two conditions are fulfilled:
(1) $a_{i-1} \to a_i$ for $2 \leq i \leq n$;
(2) the relation $a_j \to a_i$ $(i \neq j)$ implies $a_j < a_i$.
The regressive projectivity corresponds to the *regressive structures* in the sense of Yngve [61] [*phrases centripètes* in the sense of Tesnière ([57], Chap. 8)]. The progressive projectivity corresponds to the *progressive structures* in the sense of Yngve [61] [*phrases centrifugues* in the sense of Tesnière ([57], Chap. 8)]. These facts are clearly shown by Theorems 7 and 7'.

It is known (see, for instance, Tesnière [57]) that Turkish is very rich in regressive structures, whereas Hebrew is very rich in progressive structures. English and German are less regressive than Turkish, Latin is less regressive than English and German, whereas French and Rumanian are more progressive than Latin, but less progressive than Hebrew. It follows that Hebrew and Turkish are the most suitable languages to be described with the aid of a monotonically projective model.

Important results concerning progressive and regressive structures are due to Yngve. We shall try to explain his ideas, by using his own considerations [60, 61].

Psychologists have measured what they call the span of immediate memory. We are able to memorize at a glance and repeat correctly about seven random digits, about seven nonsense words, about seven items. This has been known for a long time and has been summarized by Miller [45]. Apparently we have to live with this restriction when we speak. We can remember only about seven grammatical or syntactic constraints at one time. Yngve has proposed a depth hypothesis, which states that much of the syntactic complexity of a natural language such as English (in contrast to the simplicity of mathematical notation) can be understood in terms of this memory restriction. The syntax of English contains many devices for automatically keeping utterances within the bounds of this restriction, and it contains many devices for effectively circumventing the restriction so as to regain the loss of expressive power that this restriction on immediate memory span would imply. The depth hypothesis predicts that all languages have extensive syntactic complications for the same purpose. A restriction on immediate memory span would not, however, be expected to have any influence on the structure of mathematical notations because they are written.

In producing a sentence, we have a device such as a phrase-structure grammar which must remember somehow its next step by the rules of the language. Having expanded S(sentence) into a subject NP(noun phrase) and a predicate VP (verb phrase), it goes on to expand the leftmost constituent, NP. But somewhere in its memory it has to store the information that when it gets finished with all the branches of the NP, it is committed to expand a VP, otherwise it will not have a grammatical English sentence. Similarly, after expanding NP into T (article) and N (noun), it must store away the N while it is expanding the T. In this way, every time the device goes down a left branch, it must store in its temporary memory one symbol for each step taken down the branch.

Now a question arises: If the set of sentences is infinite, how much temporary memory will have to be provided in the device? Here there appears an essential difference between regressive structures and progressive structures.

Let us consider a regressive structure such as *Very clearly projected pictures appeared* (secondary adverb + adverb + adjective + noun + verb). In producing this structure (see Fig. 1), the machine has to go

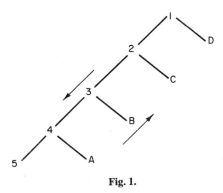

Fig. 1.

down the stem expanding 1, 2, 3, 4, and 5, storing a number of symbols in its memory — here four (A, B, C, and D), because there are four unexpanded branches. Then it has to go back, expanding in turn the branches growing from A, B, C, and D. This regressive structure has a depth of four, the depth of a node being numerically equal to the number of symbols in temporary memory when that node is about to be expanded.

A quite different situation arises when progressive structures are considered. In producing such a structure, the machine can continue down the main stem (see Fig. 2), expanding as it goes, and never retracing its steps. It puts only one symbol away in its temporary memory

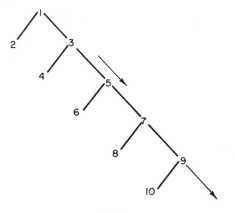

Fig. 2.

each time, and each time it takes it right out again and expands upon it. It is clear that as regressive structures grow longer they require more and more memory, but progressive structures do not. They can continue indefinitely with a minimum of memory.

Yngve's hypothesis is an interesting contribution concerning the problem of syntactic complexity in natural languages. Other significances and applications of Yngve's ideas are discussed in an interesting paper of Varga [58]. To apply these ideas to some questions concerning mechanical translation (especially in syntactic analysis of languages with progressive structure), Varga has used an algorithm of Dömölki [14].

8. Relations between Various Types of Projectivity

We shall establish in this Section the logical relations existing between the various types of projectivity defined in Section 7. As in that section, we always put $x = a_1 a_2 \cdots a_n$; all considered strings are tacitly assumed to be structured strings.

Theorem 8.   Every monotonically projective string is L-projective.

PROOF.   First let x be regressively projective. Assume that $a_j \Rrightarrow a_i$ and min $(i, j) < k < \max(i, j)$. We have $a_i < a_j$. Hence $i < j$ and $i < k < j$. By Theorem 7, we have $a_j \rightarrow a_{j-1} \rightarrow \cdots \rightarrow a_{k+1} \rightarrow a_k \rightarrow a_{k-1} \rightarrow \cdots \rightarrow a_{i+1} \rightarrow a_i$. Since $\rightarrow$ is a particular case of $\Rrightarrow$ and $\Rrightarrow$ is transitive, we deduce that $a_j \Rrightarrow a_k$. Thus, x is L-projective.

Now let x be progressively projective and assume that $a_j \Rrightarrow a_i$ and $\min(i, j) < k < \max(i, j)$. We deduce that $a_j < a_i$. Hence $j < i$ and $j < k < i$. By Theorem 7', we have $a_j \rightarrow a_{j+1} \rightarrow \cdots \rightarrow a_{k-1} \rightarrow a_k \rightarrow a_{k+1} \rightarrow \cdots \rightarrow a_{i-1} \rightarrow a_i$. Hence $a_j \Rrightarrow a_k$ and x is L-projective.

Proposition 19.   There exists an L-projective string which is not monotonically projective.

PROOF.   Consider the string $x = a_1 a_2 a_3 a_4$ and let $\rightarrow$ be defined as follows: $a_4 \rightarrow a_3 \rightarrow a_2$, $a_4 \rightarrow a_1$. This string is obviously L-projective, but, by Theorems 7 and 7', x is neither regressively nor progressively projective. A French illustration of x is *une très belle fille*.

Proposition 20. There exists a monotonically projective string which is not strongly projective. There exists a strongly projective string which is not monotonically projective.

PROOF. The string $x = a_1a_2a_3a_4$, with $\rightarrow$ defined by $a_4 \rightarrow a_3 \rightarrow a_2 \rightarrow a_1$, is monotonically projective (in view of Theorem 7), but it is not strongly projective, since we have $a_4 \Rightarrow a_1$, without having $a_4 \rightarrow a_2$. (An English illustration of x is *very clearly projected pictures*.)

The string $y = a_1a_2a_3$, with $\rightarrow$ defined by $a_1 \rightarrow a_2$ and $a_1 \rightarrow a_3$, is strongly projective, but, in view of Theorems 7 and 7', y is not monotonically projective. (A Rumanian illustration of y is *dau elevului cartea*.)

Proposition 21. There exists a monotonically projective string which is not projective in the restricted sense. There exists a string which is projective in the restricted sense, but not monotonically projective.

PROOF. The string $x = a_1a_2a_3a_4$, with $\rightarrow$ defined by $a_4 \rightarrow a_3 \rightarrow a_2 \rightarrow a_1$ and $a_4 \rightarrow a_1$, is regressively projective, since conditions (1) and (2) of Theorem 7 are fulfilled. But x is not projective in the restricted sense, since we have $a_4 \rightarrow a_1$ without having $a_4 \rightarrow a_2$.

The string $y = a_1a_2a_3$, with $\rightarrow$ defined by $a_1 \rightarrow a_2$, $a_1 \rightarrow a_3$, is projective in the restricted sense, but, in view of Theorems 7 and 7', y is not monotonically projective. (See a Rumanian illustration of y in the proof of Proposition 20.)

We shall now compare strong projectivity and projectivity in the restricted sense.

Proposition 22. Every strongly projective string is projective in the restricted sense, but the converse is not true.

PROOF. Let x be strongly projective and assume that $a_j \rightarrow a_i$ and $\min(i, j) < k < \max(i, j)$. It follows that $a_j \Rightarrow a_i$. Hence, since x is strongly projective, we have $a_j \rightarrow a_k$ and x is projective in the restricted sense.

The string $x = a_1a_2a_3a_4a_5$, with $\rightarrow$ defined by $a_1 \rightarrow a_3 \rightarrow a_5$, $a_2 \rightarrow a_1$ and $a_3 \rightarrow a_4$, is projective in the restricted sense, but it is not strongly projective, since we have $a_1 \Rightarrow a_5$ without having $a_1 \rightarrow a_4$. (Rumanian illustration: $x = da\c{t}i\ elevului\ caietul\ meu\ gros$.)

Another example is the string $z = a_1a_2a_3a_4a_5$ with $\rightarrow$ defined by $a_5 \rightarrow a_4 \rightarrow a_3 \rightarrow a_2 \rightarrow a_1$; z is projective in the restricted sense, without being strongly projective (since we have $a_5 \Rightarrow a_1$ without having $a_5 \rightarrow a_2$). An

English illustration of z was given in Section 7 after the definition of regressive projectivity.

Proposition 23.   If the length of a monotonically projective string x is not less than 4 and if $a_j \to a_i$ implies $|i-j| \leq 1$, then x is projective in the restricted sense, but it is not strongly projective.

PROOF.   Projectivity in the restricted sense is obviously fulfilled. Assume that x is regressively projective. We have $a_j \Rightarrow a_i$ for $i < j$. Take $i = 1$ and $j = 4$. (This is possible because the length of x is not less than 4.) We deduce that $a_4 \Rightarrow a_1$ but, in view of the hypothesis, we do not have $a_4 \to a_2$; thus, x is not strongly projective.

If x is progressively projective, we reason in a similar manner; we have $a_1 \Rightarrow a_4$ without having $a_1 \to a_3$.

We now compare projectivity in the restricted sense and L-projectivity.

Theorem 9.   If the string x is projective in the restricted sense, then x is L-projective, but the converse is not true.

PROOF.   Let x be projective in the restricted sense and let $a_j \Rightarrow a_i$ ($1 \leq i$, $j \leq n$). Consider an integer k such that $\min(i,j) < k < \max(i,j)$. By definition of $\Rightarrow$ there exists a sequence $b_1, b_2, \dots, b_t$ of terms of x, such that $a_i = b_1$, $a_j = b_t$, and $b_{m+1} \to b_m$ for $1 \leq m \leq t-1$. If there exists an integer m such that $a_k = b_m$, we have $a_j \Rightarrow a_k$; if such an integer m does not exist, we distinguish two possibilities:

(1) $i < j$. Let s be the smallest integer m such that $a_k < b_m$. We have $1 < s \leq t$ and $b_{s-1} < a_k < b_s$. Since $b_s \to b_{s-1}$ and by taking into account that x is projective in the restricted sense, we deduce that $b_s \to a_k$. Hence $b_s \Rightarrow a_k$. On the other hand, we have $a_j \Rightarrow b_s$. Therefore, by the transitivity of $\Rightarrow$, $a_j \Rightarrow a_k$.

(2) $i > j$. Let s be the greatest integer m such that $a_k < b_m$. We have $1 \leq s < t$ and $b_{s+1} < a_k < b_s$. Since $b_{s+1} \to b_s$ and by taking into account that x is projective in the restricted sense, we deduce that $b_{s+1} \to a_k$. Hence $b_{s+1} \Rightarrow a_k$. On the other hand, we have $a_j \Rightarrow b_{s+1}$. Therefore, by the transitivity of $\Rightarrow$, $a_j \Rightarrow a_k$.

We have proved that, from $a_j \Rightarrow a_i$ and $\min(i,j) < k < \max(i,j)$, it follows that $a_j \Rightarrow a_k$, that is, x is L-projective.

The string $y = a_1 a_2 a_3 a_4$, with $\to$ defined by $a_4 \to a_3 \to a_2$ and $a_4 \to a_1$, is L-projective; but y is not projective in the restricted sense, because we have $a_4 \to a_1$ without having $a_4 \to a_2$. (German illustration of y: *ein sehr alter Mann.*)

Corollary 5. Every strongly projective string is L-projective, but the converse is not true.

PROOF. This is an immediate consequence of Proposition 22 and Theorem 9.

We now compare H-projectivity, L-projectivity, and F-projectivity. Theorems 10 and 11 will show that these three types of projectivity are pairwise equivalent.

Theorem 10. Every H-projective string is L-projective; every L-projective string is H-projective.

PROOF. Let x be H-projective. Assume that $a_j \Rrightarrow a_i\,(1 \leqslant i, j \leqslant n)$ and let k be an integer such that $\min(i,j) < k < \max(i,j)$. By definition of $\Rrightarrow$, there exists a sequence $b_1, b_2, \ldots, b_t$ of terms of x, such that $a_i = b_1$, $a_j = b_t$, and $b_{m+1} \to b_m$ for $1 \leqslant m \leqslant t-1$. If there exists an integer m such that $a_k = b_m$, we obviously have $a_j \Rrightarrow a_k$. If such an integer m does not exist, we distinguish two possibilities:

(1) $i < j$. Let s be the smallest integer m such that $a_k < b_m$. We have $1 < s \leqslant t$ and $b_{s-1} < a_k < b_s$. Since $b_s \to b_{s-1}$ and since x is H-projective, we deduce that $b_s \Rrightarrow a_k$. But we also have $a_j \Rrightarrow b_s$. Therefore $a_j \Rrightarrow a_k$.

(2) $i > j$. Let s be the greatest integer m such that $a_k < b_m$. We have $1 \leqslant s < t$ and $b_{s+1} < a_k < b_s$. Since $b_{s+1} \to b_s$ and since x is H-projective, we deduce that $b_{s+1} \Rrightarrow a_k$. But we also have $a_j \Rrightarrow b_{s+1}$. Therefore $a_j \Rrightarrow a_k$.

Since in both (1) and (2) we have $a_j \Rrightarrow a_k$, x is L-projective; thus, H-projectivity implies L-projectivity.

Consider now an L-projective string x. Let $a_j \to a_i$ and $\min(i, j) < k < \max(i, j)$. We have $a_j \Rrightarrow a_i$ and, in view of the L-projectivity, we deduce that $a_j \Rrightarrow a_k$. We have so shown that x is H-projective. Theorem 10 is proved.

Theorem 11. The string x is F-projective if and only if it is L-projective.

PROOF. Let x be F-projective. Let $a_j \Rrightarrow a_i$ and consider an integer k such that $\min(i, j) < k < \max(i, j)$. Since $\Rrightarrow$ is reflexive, we also have $a_j \Rrightarrow a_j$. By the definition of F-projectivity (with $m = j$) we deduce that $a_j \Rrightarrow a_k$. Therefore x is L-projective.

Assume now that x is L-projective. Suppose that $a_m \Rrightarrow a_i$, $a_m \Rrightarrow a_j$ and $\min(i, j) < k < \max(i, j)$. We distinguish three cases:

(1) $k = m$; by reflexivity of $\Rrightarrow$, we have $a_m \Rrightarrow a_k$.

(2) $k < m$. If $i < k$, then $a_i < a_k < a_m$ and, since x is L-projective and

because $a_m \Rrightarrow a_i$, we deduce that $a_m \Rrightarrow a_k$. If $i > k$, then $j < k$. Therefore, $a_j < a_k < a_m$. Since x is L-projective and because $a_m \Rrightarrow a_j$, we deduce that $a_m \Rrightarrow a_k$.

(3) $k > m$. If $j > k$, then $a_m < a_k < a_j$. Since x is L-projective and $a_m \Rrightarrow a_j$, it follows that $a_m \Rrightarrow a_k$. If $j < k$, then $i > k$. Hence $a_m < a_k < a_i$. Since x is L-projective and $a_m \Rrightarrow a_i$, we have $a_m \Rrightarrow a_k$.

Thus, we have in all cases $a_m \Rrightarrow a_k$ and x is F-projective. Theorem 11 is proved.

REMARK.   In another way, Theorem 11 was outlined by Lecerf and Ihm [35].

We now compare quasi-projectivity and L-projectivity.

Theorem 12.   Every L-projective string is quasi-projective, but the converse is not true.

PROOF.   By Theorem 11, L-projectivity and F-projectivity are equivalent; thus, it is enough to show that every F-projective string is quasi-projective but not conversely. Let x be F-projective and assume $a_m \Rrightarrow a_j$, $a_m \Rrightarrow a_i$, and min $(i, j) < k < $ max (i, j). It follows that $a_m \Rrightarrow a_k$. This means, among other things, that from $a_m \Rrightarrow a_i$, $a_m \Rrightarrow a_j$, min$(i, j) < k < $ max(i, j), and $i \neq m \neq j$ it follows that $a_m \Rrightarrow a_k$. Therefore, x is quasi-projective.

An example of a quasi-projective string which is not L-projective is $x = a_1a_2a_3a_4a_5$, with $\rightarrow$ defined by $a_2 \rightarrow a_3 \rightarrow a_1$ and $a_2 \rightarrow a_5 \rightarrow a_4$. Since $a_3 \Rrightarrow a_1$ and $a_1 < a_2 < a_3$, but we do not have $a_3 \Rrightarrow a_2$, x is not L-projective. On the other hand, it is easily seen that x is quasi-projective. (A Russian illustration of x may be found in Section 7, after the definition of quasi-projectivity.)

Proposition 24.   There exist strings which are not quasi-projective.

PROOF.   Let $x = a_1a_2a_3a_4a_5$, with $\rightarrow$ defined by $a_1 \rightarrow a_3 \rightarrow a_2 \rightarrow a_5$, $a_4 \rightarrow a_5$. We have $a_3 \Rrightarrow a_2$, $a_3 \Rrightarrow a_5$, and $a_2 < a_4 < a_5$, but we do not have $a_3 \Rrightarrow a_4$. Thus, x is not quasi-projective. [Russian illustration of x: *goda čerez tri ja vedu* (Beleckiĭ *et al.* [4], p. 73).]

We now make several remarks concerning the invariance of various types of projectivity by the dependence isomorphism or by the subordination isomorphism. It is obvious that every type of projectivity is invariant by the dependence isomorphism, that is, if the strings x and

y are δ-isomorphic and x is projective in some sense, then y is projective in the same sense. But we also have the following result.

Theorem 13. If the strings x and y are σ-isomorphic and if x is monotonically projective (L-projective, H-projective, F-projective, quasi-projective), then y is also monotonically projective (L-projective, H-projective, F-projective, quasi-projective, respectively). Strong projectivity and projectivity in the restricted sense are not invariant by σ-isomorphism.

PROOF. The definitions of monotone projectivity, L-projectivity, F-projectivity, and quasi-projectivity involve only the relations $<$ and $\Rightarrow$; since both these relations are invariant by σ-isomorphism, it follows that the corresponding types of projectivity are also invariant by σ-isomorphism. What concerns H-projectivity, it is equivalent to L-projectivity (in view of Theorem 10). Hence it is invariant by σ-isomorphism.

To prove the second part of Theorem 13, let us consider the strings $x = a_1 a_2 a_3 a_4$, with $\rightarrow$ defined by $a_1 \rightarrow a_2 \rightarrow a_3 \rightarrow a_4$, $a_1 \rightarrow a_3$, $a_2 \rightarrow a_4$, $a_1 \rightarrow a_4$, and $y = b_1 b_2 b_3 b_4$ with $\rightarrow$ defined by $b_1 \rightarrow b_2 \rightarrow b_3 \rightarrow b_4$ and $b_1 \rightarrow b_4$. The strings x and y are obviously σ-isomorphic, but not δ-isomorphic. String x is strongly projective. Hence, by Proposition 22, x is projective in the restricted sense. On the other hand, y is not projective in the restricted sense, because we have $b_1 \rightarrow b_4$, but we do not have $b_1 \rightarrow b_2$. In view of Proposition 22, y is not strongly projective and Theorem 13 is proved.

The most interesting and important type of projectivity is L-projectivity. When we speak of projectivity, without otherwise specifying, we tacitly assume that we mean L-projectivity.

9. Projectivity in Natural Languages

Let us now remark on projectivity in natural languages. A language is said to be *projective* if each of its strings is projective. There are some close connections between projective languages and context-free phrase-structure languages. These two types of language are in some sense equivalent (Gaifman [18], Bar-Hillel [2]; for context-free languages see also [3]), but we shall not deal here with this problem.

Most of the strings belonging to natural languages are projective, which is a very restrictive property. As has been shown by Lecerf ([31], p. 2–3), almost 100 percent of French strings are projective. The same seems to be true for German, Italian, Danish, and other languages. The projectivity of a string in a natural language is in some sense equivalent to the absence of discontinuous immediate constituents. In this respect, very interesting remarks are made by Padučeva [48] and Iordanskaja [28], who have made a deep analysis of dependence and subordination structures in Russian, as well as of the connections between these structures and the description in terms of immediate constituents. According to an investigation of Hays, among 30,000 Russian strings only 2 strings are not projective ([23], p. 4). On the other hand, Šreider ([56], p. 38) says that among 10,500 English strings only 610 are not projective. However, it seems that all these statistics refer to simple strings only.

It is interesting to remark that there are about 117,000 structured strings which may be formed with seven given words, but only 3876· of these strings are projective. If we identify two σ-isomorphic strings and we call a class of σ-isomorphic strings an *abstract structured string*, we may say that there are about 117,000 abstract structured strings of length 7, but only 3876 of them are projective. Projectivity becomes more useful when we are concerned with strings of greater length. Thus, there are about 1,000,000,000 abstract structured strings of length 10; there are about 2×10^{25} abstract structured strings of length 20. Projectivity enables us to select a relatively small number of these strings (Lecerf [31], p. 6). A complete study of the number of projective strings, when the length of the strings is less than 8, is given in Table 5 (Lecerf [31], p. 21).

TABLE 5

Length of strings	p = number of projective solutions	n = number of nonprojective solutions	Total number of solutions	$\dfrac{n}{n+p}$
1	1	0	1	0
2	2	0	2	0
3	7	2	9	22
4	30	34	64	53
5	143	482	625	77
6	728	7048	7776	90.6
7	3876	113,773	117,649	96.7

Three concrete linguistic problems will now be discussed in the light of projectivity: the position of separable particle in German (Lecerf-Ihm [35], pp. 12–15); the dependencies in a certain French string (Lecerf-Ihm [35], pp. 15–17); the so-called supplementary predicative element in Rumanian (Marcus [40]).

THE SEPARABLE PARTICLE IN GERMAN. Let us consider the German strings (1) *ich gehe sofort aus*, (2) *ich bin sofort gegangen*, and (3) *ich bin sofort ausgegangen*. In each of these three strings there exists a verb having a separable particle. We wish to establish how many words may be inserted between the verb and its separable particle without affecting the projectivity of the string. In (1) we have *gehe → ich, gehe → sofort*, and *gehe → aus*. Hence any word of (1), other than *gehe* and *aus*, may be inserted between *gehe* and *aus*, without affecting the projectivity of (1)—and even the strong projectivity of (1). Thus, the interrogative construction *gehe ich sofort aus?* is strongly projective. A similar situation arises in (2), where we have *bin → ich, bin → sofort*, and *bin → gegangen*. Any word of (2), other than *bin* and *gegangen*, may be inserted between *bin* and *gegangen* without affecting the projectivity—or even the strong projectivity. Thus, the interrogative construction *bin ich sofort gegangen?* is strongly projective. A quite different situation arises in (3), where we have *bin → ich, bin → sofort*, and *bin → gegangen → aus*. Here, none of the words *ich, bin*, and *sofort* may be inserted between the verb *gegangen* and its separable particle *aus*, without affecting the projectivity of the string. For instance, the string *ich bin gegangen sofort aus* is not projective, since we have *gegangen → aus* without have *gegangen → sofort;* the string *bin sofort gegangen ich aus* is not projective, since we have *gegangen → aus* without have *gegangen → ich*. This fact agrees with the known rules of German grammar, which require that *gegangen* and *aus* always be neighbors. In exchange, projectivity permits us to insert between *bin* and *gegangen* any word of (3) other than *bin* and *gegangen;* German allows us great liberty in forming the interrogative constructions.

ESTABLISHING THE DEPENDENCIES IN A CERTAIN FRENCH STRING. In most cases, the dependencies occurring in a string are established in an intuitive way. But in many situations the intuition is not sufficient, and we must use some *a posteriori* criteria, having an explanatory power. Projectivity may sometimes be such a criterion. Consider, for instance, the French string *x = je ne le rencontre généralement pas.*

The group of words $\alpha = ne\ rencontre\ pas$ is customarily considered a single one and we have the following dependencies: $\alpha \to je$, $\alpha \to le$, and $\alpha \to généralement$. But we wish to investigate the dependence structure of the nucleus α. Many solutions are intuitively plausible, but only a few of them fulfill the projectivity condition. Consider, for instance, the following four possibilities: (a) $rencontre \to je$, $rencontre \to le$, $rencontre \to généralement$, $rencontre \to ne \to pas$; in this case, x is not projective, since we have $ne \to pas$ and $ne < rencontre < pas$, without having $ne \Rrightarrow rencontre$; (b) $rencontre \to je$, $rencontre \to le$, $rencontre \to généralement$, $rencontre \to pas \to ne$; in this case x is not projective, since we have $pas \to ne$ and $ne < rencontre < pas$, without having $ne \Rrightarrow rencontre$; (c) $rencontre \to je$, $rencontre \to le$, $rencontre \to généralement$, $rencontre \to pas$, $ne \to rencontre$; in this case, x is not projective since we have $rencontre \to je$ and $je < ne < rencontre$, without having $rencontre \Rrightarrow ne$; (d) For every word e of x, other than $rencontre$, we have $rencontre \to e$; in this case, x is projective and even strongly projective. This fact does not mean that the dependence structure of x is undoubtedly that given by (d), but only says that solution (d) agrees with the projectivity condition. Hence it is more plausible than (a), (b), and (c).

THE SUPPLEMENTARY PREDICATIVE ELEMENT IN RUMANIAN. Let us consider the Rumanian string $zgomotoşi\ copiii\ vin$. Some facts concerning Rumanian grammar require us to consider the word $zgomotoşi$ as dependent both upon $copiii$ and upon vin; thus, we have $vin \to zgomotoşi$, $vin \to copiii \to zgomotoşi$. Condition (b) of the definition of simple strings (see Section 3) is not fulfilled; the considered string is not simple, but, as is easily seen, this string is projective and even strongly projective. But let us consider the string $y = o\ pisică\ trecu\ albă$. As $zgomotoşi$ in the preceding string, $albă$ has a double nature in y: one adjectival, the other adverbial. Indeed, $albă$ depends both upon the noun $pisică$ and upon the verb $trecu$ and we have the following dependencies: $trecu \to pisică \to albă$, $trecu \to albă$. String y is neither simple nor projective, since condition (b) of the definition of simple strings is not fulfilled ($trecu \to albă$, $pisică \to albă$, and we have $pisică \Rightarrow albă$ and $pisică < trecu < albă$, without having $pisică \Rightarrow trecu$). It is interesting to remark that such strings as y were considered earlier with another dependence structure, which differs from the above dependence structure by the abscence of the relations $copiii \to zgomotoşi$ (in the first string) and $pisică \to albă$ (in the second string). In other words, the double nature of *zgomotoşi* and of *albă* was not recognized. But without this double nature, each considered string is both simple and projective. Thus, simplicity and projectivity are hypotheses of first approximation, which correspond to an elementary level of grammatical analysis. A finer analysis, which also takes into account some stylistic facts, must abandon both simplicity and projectivity. But we know very little about these more complex situations. Most of the known results concern strings which are both simple and projective. Some of these results will be presented in the next Section.

10. Simple Projective Strings

In the investigation of strings which are both simple and projective, we shall use the axiomatic description of simple strings given in Section 4. We add a further axiom to the system of axioms introduced there.

AXIOM OF PROJECTIVITY: (6.1). If $a \Rightarrow b$ and $a \leqslant c \leqslant b$ or $b \leqslant c \leqslant a$, then $a \Rightarrow c$.

It is easy to recognize in Axiom (6.1) the property of L-projectivity. The system of Axioms (1.1), (1.2), (1.3), (2.1), (2.2) (2.3), (3.1), (4.1), (5.1), and (6.1) defines the projective B-strings. In view of Theorems 5 and 6, we shall identify B-strings and simple strings; thus, instead of projective B-strings we shall speak of simple projective strings.

Proposition 25. If the words a and b of a simple projective string are not comparable and if $a \Rightarrow c$ and $b \Rightarrow d$, then from $a < b$ it follows that $c < d$ and from $b < a$ it follows that $d < c$.

PROOF. Let $a < b$. By Axiom (4.1), we have $c \neq d$. Hence, in view of Axiom (1.3), we have either $c < d$ or $d < c$. Assume that $d < c$; since a and b are not comparable, we deduce from Axiom (6.1) that we have neither $b \leqslant c$, nor $d \leqslant a$. Therefore, $a < d < c < b$. Then, since $a \Rightarrow c$, we have $a \Rightarrow d$; by taking into account the relation $b \Rightarrow d$, we obtain a contradiction to Axiom (4.1). Hence, the relation $d < c$ is false and we have $c < d$.

If $b < a$, we find in a similar way that $d < c$.

Proposition 26. Axiom (1.1) is a consequence of Axioms (2.1), (2.2), and (6.1) ([4], pp. 84–85).

PROOF. Assume that $a \leqslant b$ and $b \leqslant a$. We have $a \leqslant b \leqslant a$ and $b \leqslant a \leqslant b$. By Axiom (2.1) we have $a \Rightarrow a$ and $b \Rightarrow b$. Hence, by Axiom (6.1), we have $a \Rightarrow b$ and $b \Rightarrow a$; further, by Axiom (2.2), we deduce that $a = b$, and Axiom (1.1) is proved.

It may be seen, by suitable examples, that each of the other nine axioms is independent.

Theorem 14. None of the axioms (1.2), (1.3), (2.1), (2.2), (2.3), (3.1), (4.1), (5.1), and (6.1) follows from the other axioms (Beleckiĭ et al. [4], pp. 83–84).

PROOF. For every axiom α we shall give an example of a set A where α is not fulfilled, but all other axioms are fulfilled.

AXIOM (1.2). $A = \{1, 2, 3, 4\}$; $1 \leqslant 1$, $2 \leqslant 2$, $3 \leqslant 3$, $4 \leqslant 4$, $1 \leqslant 2$, $1 \leqslant 3$, $1 \leqslant 4$, $2 \leqslant 3$, $3 \leqslant 4$, $4 \leqslant 2$; $1 \Rightarrow 1$, $2 \Rightarrow 2$, $3 \Rightarrow 3$, $4 \Rightarrow 4$, $1 \Rightarrow 2$, $1 \Rightarrow 3$, $1 \Rightarrow 4$.

AXIOM (1.3). $A = \{1, 2, 3\}$; $1 \leqslant 1$, $2 \leqslant 2$, $3 \leqslant 3$, $1 \leqslant 2$, $1 \leqslant 3$; $1 \Rightarrow 1$, $2 \Rightarrow 2$, $3 \Rightarrow 3$, $1 \Rightarrow 2$, $1 \Rightarrow 3$.

AXIOM (2.1). $A = \{1, 2\}$; $1 \leqslant 1$, $2 \leqslant 2$, $1 \leqslant 2$; $1 \Rightarrow 1$, $1 \Rightarrow 2$.

AXIOM (2.2). $A = \{1, 2\}$; $1 \leqslant 1$, $2 \leqslant 2$, $1 \leqslant 2$, $1 \Rightarrow 1$, $1 \Rightarrow 2$, $2 \Rightarrow 1$, $2 \Rightarrow 2$.

AXIOM (2.3). $A = \{1, 2, 3, 4\}$; $1 \leqslant 2 \leqslant 3 \leqslant 4$; $1 \Rightarrow 1$, $2 \Rightarrow 2$, $3 \Rightarrow 3$, $4 \Rightarrow 4$, $1 \Rightarrow 2$, $1 \Rightarrow 3$, $1 \Rightarrow 4$, $2 \Rightarrow 3$, $3 \Rightarrow 4$.

AXIOM (3.1). $A = \{1, 2\}$; $1 \leqslant 1$, $1 \leqslant 2$, $2 \leqslant 2$; $1 \Rightarrow 1$, $2 \Rightarrow 2$.

AXIOM (4.1). $A = \{1,2,3,4\}$; $1 \leqslant 2 \leqslant 3 \leqslant 4$; $1 \Rightarrow 1$; $2 \Rightarrow 2$: $3 \Rightarrow 3$: $4 \Rightarrow 4$, $1 \Rightarrow 2$, $1 \Rightarrow 3$, $1 \Rightarrow 4$, $2 \Rightarrow 3$, $4 \Rightarrow 3$.

AXIOM (5.1). A = the set of positive integers; $m \leqslant n$ if and only if m is not greater than n; $m \Rightarrow n$ if and only if $m \leqslant n$.

AXIOM (6.1). $A = \{1, 2, 3\}$; $1 \leqslant 2 \leqslant 3$; $1 \Rightarrow 1$, $2 \Rightarrow 2$, $3 \Rightarrow 3$, $2 \Rightarrow 1$, $1 \Rightarrow 3$, $2 \Rightarrow 3$.

In Section 5 we defined some operations with simple strings. When these operations are applied to simple projective strings, the resulting simple strings are also projective, that is, Axiom (6.1) is fulfilled (see also [4], p. 76).

In the following, we shall show that every simple projective string may be obtained from elementary strings, by means of finitely many superpositions. Theorems 15–17 are due to Beleckiï *et al.* ([4], pp. 81–82).

Theorem 15. Let x be a simple projective string of length greater than 1 and let a_0 be its nonsubordinated word. Let $a_1 < a_2 < \cdots < a_n$ be the words of x which are subordinated to a_0. Denote by x_i ($1 \le i \le n$) the set of words subordinated to a_i; denote by θ the set of words $a_0, a_1, a_2, \ldots, a_n$. Then, $\theta, x_1, \ldots, x_{n-1}$ and x_n are simple projective strings, whereas the string x is σ-isomorphic to the superposition between θ and x_1, $x_2, \ldots, x_n$.

PROOF. Obviously, θ is a simple projective string. Proposition 16 implies that $x_1, x_2, \ldots, x_n$ are simple projective strings. By Proposition 9, the words $a_1, a_2, \ldots, a_n$ are pairwise noncomparable; then, by Corollary 3, the sets x_i ($1 \le i \le n$) are pairwise disjoint. Denote by θ' the set obtained from θ as x' is obtained from x in the definition of superposition (see Section 5). It is easily seen that θ' contains a unique word: a_0. Therefore, the sets $\theta', x_1, x_2, \ldots, x_n$ are pairwise disjoint and, by Propositions 3 and 8, each word of x belongs either to θ' or to one of the strings x_i ($1 \le i \le n$). Thus, the set z (see the definition of superposition) on which the superposition between θ and $x_1, x_2, \ldots, x_n$ is defined, may be settled in a 1 : 1 correspondence with x.

By Proposition 10, two words belonging to different sets x_i are not comparable [see rule (2) in the definition of superposition]. By rule (4) of the definition of superposition, the word a_0 may be subordinated to no word of $x_1, x_2, \ldots, x_n$. In view of Proposition 25, if $a_i < a_j$, any word of x_i precedes any word of x_j [see rule (2) in the definition of superposition]. By Proposition 5, if b is an arbitrary word of x_i and $a_i < a_0$ ($a_i > a_0$), then $b < a_0$ ($b > a_0$, respectively). [See rules (2) and (4) of the definition of superposition.] Thus, the relations $\le$ and $\Rightarrow$ fulfill in x all conditions required by the definition of superposition between θ and $x_1, x_2, \ldots, x_n$. Theorem 15 is proved.

Theorem 16. Every simple projective string may be obtained from elementary strings, by means of finitely many superpositions.

PROOF. We proceed by induction with respect to the length of the string. If the length of x is less than or equal to 2, then, by Propositions 11 and 15, our assertion is immediate. Assume the assertion is proved for any string of length less than n ($n \geqslant 3$) and let us prove the validity of the assertion for strings of length n. Since $n \geqslant 3$, we may apply Theorem 15 to x and represent x as a superposition between θ and $x_1, x_2, \ldots, x_m$. It is easily seen that, in the construction given by the proof of Theorem 15, the string θ is elementary, whereas each of the strings $x_1, x_2, \ldots, x_m$ is of length less than n, since no x_i contains the nonsubordinated word of x. By the induction hypothesis, the strings $x_1, x_2, \ldots, x_m$ may be represented as superpositions of elementary strings; thus, this is also true for x.

We may improve the above result by representing every elementary string by means of strongly elementary strings. Indeed, we have the next theorem.

Theorem 17. Every elementary string may be obtained from strongly elementary strings, by means of finitely many operations of left union, right union, and central union.

PROOF. We proceed by induction with respect to the length of the string. If the length of x is less than or equal to 2, the assertion is immediate (see Proposition 15). Assume the validity of the assertion for every elementary string of length less than $n(n \geqslant 3)$ and let us prove its validity when the length is n.

By Proposition 12 and Corollaries 1 and 2, the elementary string x is formed by one nonsubordinated word a_0 and $n - 1$ nonsubordinating words $a_1, a_2, \ldots, a_{n-1}$; in view of Proposition 13, we deduce that $a_0 \rightarrow a_k$ ($1 \leqslant k \leqslant n - 1$).

Let us prove that x may be represented as a (left, right, or central) union of elementary strings, each of which is of length less than n. Without loss of generality, we may admit that $a_1 < a_2 < \cdots < a_{n-1}$. Three cases are possible: (1) $a_0 < a_1$; (2) $a_{n-1} < a_0$; (3) $a_k < a_0 < a_{k+1}$, where $0 < k < n - 1$. In the first case, we consider the strings $x_1 = a_0 a_1$ and $x_2 = a_0 a_2 \cdots a_{n-1}$. It is easily seen that x is σ-isomorphic to the left union of x_1 and x_2. In (2) we consider the strings $x_1 = a_0 a_1 \cdots a_{n-2}$ and $x_2 = a_0 a_{n-1}$. It is easily seen that x is σ-isomorphic to the right union of x_1 and x_2. In (3) we consider the strings $x_1 = a_0 a_1 \cdots a_k$ and $x_2 = a_0 a_{k+1} a_{k+2} \cdots a_{n-1}$. It is easily seen that x is σ-isomorphic to the central union of x_1 and x_2. In the first case, x_1 and x_2 are of length 2 and $n - 1$, respectively; in (2)

x_1 and x_2 are of length $n-1$ and 2, respectively; in (3) x_1 and x_2 are of lengths $k+1$ and $n-k$, respectively. Thus, in every case we may represent the string x as a union of strings whose length is less than the length of x. It is sufficient we now refer to our induction hypothesis.

Corollary 6. Every simple projective string may be obtained from strongly elementary strings by means of finitely many operations of superposition and left, right, and central union.

We now give a geometric interpretation of the projectivity condition. This interpretation is due in essence to Lecerf and Ihm [35] and concerns only simple strings; that is, in view of Theorem 2 it concerns only strings whose associated graph is a proper tree. According to this interpretation, we shall justify the presence of the word "projective" in describing this restriction.

Let us consider a simple string x and denote by G_x the associated graph. By Theorem 2, G_x is a proper tree. We represent G_x in the plane as follows.

Consider a straight line ω in the plane and let us represent the center of x by a point a_1^1 situated above ω; a_1^1 will be the center of G_x. Denote by A_1^1 the orthogonal projection of a_1^1 on ω (see Fig. 3).

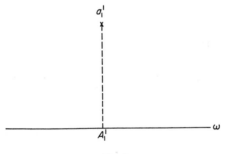

Fig. 3.

Consider a straight line ω_1 parallel to ω, situated below the point a_1^1 and above the line ω. On ω_1 we shall represent all vertices $a_1^2, a_2^2, \ldots, a_{n_2}^2$ of G_x, corresponding to words which depend upon the center of x. These vertices will be disposed from the left to the right, in their linear order in x and such that for every word a for which $a < a_1^1$ $(a_1^1 < a)$ the corresponding vertex is situated at the left (at the right, respectively) with respect to the projection line $a_1^1 A_1^1$. Denote by $A_1^2, A_2^2, \ldots, A_{n_2}^2$ the orthogonal projections of $a_1^2, a_2^2, \ldots, a_{n_2}^2$, respectively, on the line ω and let us consider the projection line $a_i^1 A_i^1$ ($1 \le i \le n_2$; see Fig. 4 for $n_2 = 5$).

Consider now a straight line ω_2 parallel to ω, situated below the line ω_1 but above the line ω. On ω_2 we shall represent all vertices $a_1^3 a_2^3 \cdots a_{n_3}^3$ of G_x, corresponding to words which depend upon one of the words

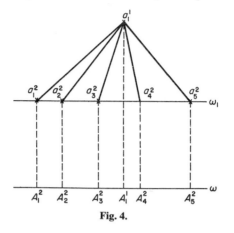

Fig. 4.

corresponding to $a_1^2, a_2^2, \ldots, a_{n_2}^2$. These vertices will be disposed from the left to the right, in their linear order in x and such that, for every word a for which $a < a_i^1, a_i^1 < a < a_{i+1}^1$, or $a_{i+1}^1 < a$, the corresponding vertex is

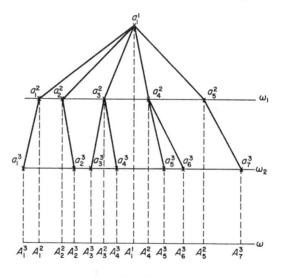

Fig. 5.

situated at the left with respect to the projection line $a_i^1 A_i^1$, at the right with respect to the projection line $a_i^1 A_i^1$, and at the left with respect to the projection line $a_{i+1}^1 A_{i+1}^1$, or at the right with respect to the projection line $a_{i+1}^1 A_{i+1}^1$, respectively ($1 \leq i \leq n_2 - 1$). Denote by $A_1^3, A_2^3, \ldots, A_{n_3}^3$ the orthogonal projections of $a_1^3, a_2^3, \ldots, a_{n_3}^3$, respectively, on the line ω and consider the projection lines $a_i^3 A_i^3$ ($1 \leq i \leq n_3$; see Fig. 5 for $n_3 = 7$).

Further, we consider a straight line ω_3 parallel to ω, situated below the line ω_2 but above the line ω. On ω_3 we shall represent, as in the preceding steps, the vertices of G_x corresponding to words which depend upon one of the words $a_1^3, a_2^3, \ldots, a_{n_3}^3$. We continue in the same way until we exhaust all vertices of G_x. It is easily seen that the projection points so obtained on ω keep the linear order of the corresponding words in x.

We also make the convention that every arc in G_x is represented by a straight line segment.

We shall say that G_x is a *proper tree without intersections* if in the above construction every intersection point between two arcs of G_x or between an arc and a projection line is a vertex of G_x. (By the projection line $a_i^j A_i^j$ we mean the corresponding segment.)

It is easily seen that the defined property does not depend upon the position of ω and of the other points and lines considered, but only upon x.

Theorem 18. The simple string x is projective if and only if the corresponding proper tree is without intersections.

We shall not give here the proof of this theorem, which can easily be accomplished by the reader. (A proof of this theorem was given by Lecerf and Ihm [35], pp. 11–12, 17–19.) Figures 6 and 7 contain two

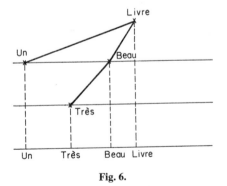

Fig. 6.

examples for which Theorem 18 decides, in the first case, the projectivity and, in the second case, the nonprojectivity of a simple string (Example 14 of [26]).

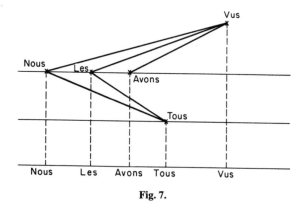

Fig. 7.

We close the discussion concerning simple projective strings with the following theorem which follows immediately from Theorems D and 2.

Theorem 19. Let $x = a_1 a_2 \cdots a_n$. The structured string $\{x, R_x\}$ is simple if and only if there exists a term a_i of x such that any other term is subordinated to a_i in a unique manner; that is, for $j \neq i$ there exists a unique sequence $k_1, k_2, \ldots, k_p$ such that $i = k_1, j = k_p$, and $a_{k_1} \to a_{k_2} \to \cdots \to a_{k_p}$.

Some modifications of the geometric criteria of projectivity, which lead to a notion more general than that of simple projective string but less general than that of simple string, have been proposed by Lynch [37] and Hirschberg [26]. The first is concerned particularly with Russian, whereas the second one considers primarily French.

11. Bibliographic Remarks

Theorems 1-3, 5 and 19, Propositions 1 and 2, and all theorems and propositions contained in Sections 7 and 8 are due to Marcus. Some of these results have already been published [38, 39, 41]. Theorem 4,

Propositions 3–10, Corollaries 1 and 2, and all results exposed in Sections 5 and 10, with the exception of Theorems 18 and 19 are due to Beleckiĭ *et al.* [4].

In an implicit manner, the notion of projectivity may be found in Harper and Hays [21]. The program described by these authors generates projective strings only, but they explicitly mention the hypothesis of compactness. In 1960, Hays introduced dependency grammars ([23]; see also [22, 24]). The description of these grammars contains a condition equivalent to L-projectivity. A survey of dependency grammars is given by Hays [25]. At almost the same time as Hays, Lecerf and Ihm introduced the hypothesis of projectivity and made a detailed study of this notion [27, 31–35]. An algebraic analysis of a projectivity criterion of Lecerf and Ihm was made by Camion [10]. The projectivity condition is very important in mechanical translation ([31], p. 8; [29]), but its origin is of a purely linguistic nature (see, for instance, [57]). A hierarchy of projectivity types has been investigated by Šreider [56]. For the semantic aspects of dependence and subordination, see Tesnière [57], De Boer [13], and Buydens-Ruvinschii [9]. The idea of the dependence relation as a function of several variables may be found in Reichenbach [50]. Some interesting formal aspects of dependence and subordination were investigated by Padučeva and Šumilina [49], Dreizin [15], and Iordanskaja [28]. Algorithmic aspects of syntactic analysis are studied by Melčuk [42], who also refers to projectivity in the study of internal flection in Indo-European and Semitic languages [43]. Some aspects of dependence and projectivity arising in the translation of an information logic language into Russian are discussed by Padučeva [47]. The same author discusses, in another paper, the relative equivalence between description by immediate constituents and description by dependence and subordination [48]. This problem was previously investigated by Lecerf [31] and Lecerf and Leroy [36]; in the terminology of these authors, we may speak of "graphes de Chomsky" and "graphes de Tesnière." Chomsky's graphs are the geometric representation of analysis of immediate constituents, whereas Tesnière's graphs are the geometric representation of dependence relations occurring in a string. Continuity of immediate constituents, in the first representation, corresponds to the projectivity in the second one. But, as Lecerf pointed out. Chomsky and Tesnière representations do not give the same information; each contains additional information with respect to the other. Analogously, continuity of immediate constituents and projectivity are not reducible one to the other. They are two aspects of the same syntactic mechanism. A synthesis of these two aspects is given by the so-called "modèle des conflits" (Lecerf [31]).

Another interesting relation concerns dependency systems viewed as generative grammars, on one hand, and phrase-structure systems, on the other. Dependency systems are formally defined by Gaifman [18]. The same author shows that every dependency system has a "naturally corresponding" phrase-structure system but not vice versa; he gives an effective necessary and sufficient condition for the existence of a "naturally corresponding" dependency system for a given phrase-structure system and an effective way to construct it when it exists. Nevertheless, as Gaifman shows [18], every set of strings defined by means of a grammar of one type is also defined by means of a grammar of the other type, which can be found effectively. (In this respect see also Gross [20].) However, this result implies that there will be cases in which the second system will not be "naturally correlated" with the first system from a structural point of view.

Another method for discovering the grammars of phrase-structure languages is given by the calculus of parentheses due to Solomonoff [55]. Fitialov has shown that to every immediate constituent calculus corresponds an equivalent Solomonoff calculus, but the converse is not true [17].

There are many other variants of syntactic analysis. Among the most formalized, we recall the description given by Vauquois with the aid of syntactic operators [59] and the very original conception of Benzécri [5, 6]. Closely connected to the presentation given in Chapter V are the notions and the results of Gladkiĭ [19], continuing the considerations exposed in Section 11, Chapter V.

Since projective languages, languages defined by dependency systems (in the sense of Gaifman), categorial languages (exposed in Chapter III), and context-free phrase-structure languages are approximatively pairwise equivalent, it is important to give some extensions of dependency theory. As Hays [25] remarks, two major avenues for extension of syntactic models have been opened in contemporary linguistic theory. One is transformation theory, which extends context-free phrase-structure grammars by admitting additional kinds of rules (see, in this respect, [1] and [11]. The other is stratification theory, which extends immediate constituent grammars by combining them in sequences (see Lamb [30]). Concerning the link between various levels of language, which is fundamental in stratification theory, see also the interesting papers of Sgall [54] and Daneš]12].

Many examples of graphs describing dependence relations are collected by Scheffer [53]. These examples may be useful for illustrating various dependence structures. The formal aspects of tree representations in linguistics are analyzed by Meyers and Wang [44].

REFERENCES

1. E. Bach. "An Introduction to Transformational Grammars." Holt, Rinehart and Winston, New York, 1964.
2. Y. Bar-Hillel, Four lectures on algebraic linguistics and machine translation. A revised version of a series of lectures given in July, 1962, before a NATO Advanced Summer Institute, Venice, Italy, on automatic translation of languages.
3. Y. Bar-Hillel, M. Perles, and E. Shamir, On formal properties of simple phrase structure grammars. Z. Phonetik, Sprachwissenschaft und Kommunikationsforschung 14, 143–172 (1961).
4. M. I. Beleckiĭ, V. M. Grigorjan, and I. D. Zaslavskii, An axiomatic description of the order and government of words in certain types of sentences (in Russian), in "Matematičeskie Voprosy Kibernetiki i Vyčislitelnoĭ Tekniki," Erevan, 1963, pp. 71–85.
5. J. P. Benzécri, Physique et langue, La Traduction Automatique, 4 (2), 31–50 (1963).
6. J. P. Benzécri, "Linguistique Mathématique." Université de Rennes, 1964.
7. C. Berge, "Theórie des graphes et ses applications." Dunod, Paris, 1958, 1963.
8. C. Berge, and A. Ghouila-Houri, "Programmes, jeux et réseaux de transport." Dunod, Paris, 1962.
9. J. Buydens-Ruvinschii, Liens de dépendance grammaticale et classification sémantique. Rapport CETIS No. 38, Euratom, 1961.
10. P. Camion, Analyse algébrique élémentaire du critère de Lecerf-Ihm. Rapport CETIS No. 3, Euratom, 1960, pp. 3–7.
11. N. Chomsky and G. Miller, Introduction to the formal analysis of natural languages, in "Handbook of Mathematical psychology," Vol. 2 (R. D. Luce, R. R. Bush and E. Galanter, eds.). Wiley, New York, 1963, pp. 269–321.
12. F. Daneš, A three-level approach to syntax. Trav. Linguistiques Prague 1, 225–240 (1964).
13. C. De Boer, "Syntaxe du Français Moderne." Leyden, 1954.
14. B. Dömölki, An algorithm for syntactic analysis. Computational Linguistics 3, 29–46 (1964).
15. F. A. Dreizin, On one method of syntactic analysis of simple sentences (in Russian). Naučnye Trudy Taškentskogo Gosudarstvennogo Universiteta 1962 (208), 76–81.
16. S. J. Fitialov, On modelling syntaxis in structural linguistics (in Russian), in "Problemy Strukturnoi Lingvistiki." Izd. Acad. Nauk SSSR, Moscow, 1962, pp. 100–114.
17. S. J. Fitialov, On two types of calculus (in Russian). Naučn. Tekh. Inform. 1964 (7), 30–36.
18. H. Gaifman, Dependency systems and phrase-structure systems. Mathematics Department, RAND Corp., Santa Mouica, Calif., P–2315, 1961.
19. A. V. Gladkii, On a method of formalizing the notion of syntactic link (in Russian). Probl. Kibernetiki 11, 199–213 (1964).

20. M. Gross, On the equivalence of models of language used in the fields of mechanical translation and information retrieval. *Inform. Storage Retrieval* **2**, 43–57 (1964).

21. K. E. Harper and D. G. Hays, The use of machines in the construction of a grammar and computer program for structural analysis. *Proc. Intern. Congr. Information Processing,* UNESCO, Paris, 1959.

22. D. G. Hays, Grouping and dependency theories. RAND Corp., Santa Monica, Calif. P–1910, 1960.

23. D. G. Hays, Basic principles and technical variations in sentence structure determination. RAND Corp., Santa Monica, Calif., P–1984, 1960.

24. D. G. Hays, Automatic language-data processing, *in* "Computer Applications in the Behavioral Sciences" (Harold Borko, ed.). Prentice-Hall, Englewood Cliffs, N.J., 1962, pp. 394–421.

25. D. G. Hays, Dependency theory: A formalism and some observations. *Language* **40** (4), 511–525 (1964).

26. L. Hirschberg, Le relachement conditionnel de l'hypothèse de projectivité. *Rapport CETIS No. 35,* Euratom, 1961.

27. P. Ihm and Y. Lecerf. Zu einer Theorie der G-Ordnungen. *Rapport CETIS, No. 2,* Euratom, 1960, pp. 12–15.

28. L. N. Iordanskaja, Peculiarities of correct syntactic structure and an algorithm for its discovery — on Russian language material (in Russian). *Probl. Kibernetiki* **11**, 215–244 (1964).

29. J. Kunze, Zur syntaktischen Synthese, *Kibernetika* **1** (1), 85–101 (1965).

30. S. M. Lamb, "Outline of Stratificational Grammar." Univ. California Press, Berkeley, Calif., 1962.

31. Y. Lecerf, Programme des conflits-modèle desconflits. *Rapport CETIS No. 4,* Euratom, 1960, pp. 1–26.

32. Y. Lecerf, "Analyse automatique. Renseignements préparatoires aux techniques de la documentation automatique." Euratom, Bruxelles, 1960.

33. Y. Lecerf, L'adressage intrinsèque en traduction automatique. *La Traduction Automatique* **2** (2–3), 31–47 (1961).

34. Y. Lecerf, Une représentation algébrique de la structure des phrases dans diverses langues naturelles. *Compt. Rend. Académie des sciences de Paris,* **252** (2) 232–234 (1961).

35. Y. Lecerf and P. Ihm, Eléments pour une grammaire générale des langues projectives. *Rapport CETIS No. 1,* Euratom, pp. 1–19.

36. Y. Lecerf and A. Leroy, Description d'un algorithme d'analyse documentaire. *Rapport CETIS No. 6,* Euratom, 1960.

37. I. Lynch, Suggestions for modification of Lecerf theory of projectivity and of his stemmas, for the purposes of their application to "non-projective" Russian sentences. *Rapport CETIS No. 35,* Euratom, 1961.

38. S. Marcus, Sur la notion de projectivité. *Computational Linguistics* **3**, 75–92 (1964).

39. S. Marcus, Sur une description axiomatique des liens syntaxiques. *Z. mathematische Logik und Grundlagen der Mathematik* **11** (4), 291–296 (1965).

40. S. Marcus, Dependenţă şi subordonare, *in* "Omagiu lui A. Rosetti la 70 de ani." Editura Academiei R.S.R., Bucureşti, 1965, 529–533.

41. S. Marcus, Phrases arborescentes. *Rev. Roumaine Math. Pures Appl.* **11** (6), (1966).

42. I. A. Melčuk, On the algorithm of syntactic analysis of linguistic texts (General principles and some results) (in Russian). *Mašinnyi perevod i prikladnaja lingvistika* **1962** (7) 45–87.

43. I. A. Melčuk, On "internal flexion" in Indoeuropean and Semit languages (in Russian). *Vopr. Jazykoznanija* **1963** (4) 27–40.

44. L. F. Meyers and W. S. Y. Wang, Tree representations in linguistics. The Ohio State University Project on Linguistic Analysis, *Report No. 3,* National Science Foundation. Washington, D.C., 1963.

45. G. A. Miller, Human memory and the storage of information. *IRE Trans. Information Theory,* **2** (3) 129–137 (1965).

46. O. Ore, Theory of graphs. American Mathematical Society, Providence, R.I., Colloquim Publications, Vol. 38, 1962.

47. E. V. Padučeva, Some problems in translation from an information-logic language into Russian (in Russian). *Naučn. Tekhn. Inform.* **1964** (2) 20–27.

48. E. V. Padučeva, On various modes of representing the syntactic structure of sentences (in Russian). *Vopr. Jazykoznanija,* **1964** (2) 99–113.

49. E. V. Padučeva, and A. L. Šumilina, Description of Russian syntagms (in connection with the construction of an algorithm of mechanical translation) (in Russian). *Vopr. Jazykoznanija* **1961** (4) 105–115.

50. H. Reichenbach, "Elements of Symbolic Logic." New York, 1948.

51. I. Rhodes, A new approach to the mechanical syntactic analysis of Russian. *Mechanical Translation* **6,** 33–50 (1961).

52. B. Roy, Cheminement et connexité dans les graphes, application aux problèmes d'ordonnancement. Thèse, Paris, 1962.

53. E. Scheffer, Recueil de stemmas. *Rapport CETIS No. 29,* Euratom, 1961.

54. P. Sgall, Zur Frage der Ebenen in Sprach system. *Trav. Linguistiques Prague* **1,** 95–106 (1964).

55. R. Solomonoff, A new method for discovering the grammars of phase-structure languages. *Proc. Intern. Congr. Information Processing,* UNESCO, Paris, 1959, pp. 285–289.

56. J. A. Šreider, The property of projectivity of language (in Russian). *Naučn. Tekhn. Inform.* **1964** (8), 38–41.

57. L. Tesnière, Éléments de syntaxe structurale." C. Klincksieck, Paris, 1959.

58. D. Varga, Yngve's hypothesis and some problems of the mechanical analysis. *Computational Linguistics* **3,** 47–74 (1964).

59. B. Vauquois, "Langages artificiels, systèmes formels et traduction automatique." CNRS, Grenoble, 1962.

60. V. H. Yngve, A model and an hypothesis for language structure. *Proc. Am. Phil. Soc.* **104,** 444–466 (1960).

61. V. H. Yngve, The depth hypothesis, *in* "Structure of Language and its Mathematical Aspects." *Proc. Symp. Appl. Math.* 130–138 (1961).

62. L. Nebeský, O jedne formalizaci vetného rozboru. *Slovo a slovesnost* **1962** (2), 104–107.

63. L. Nebeský, On a model of analysing of a sentence (in Russian). *Prague Bull. Math. Linguistics* **1964** (2), 3–10.

64. I. I. Revzin, On a syntactic model (letter to the editors) (in Russian). *Vopr. Jazykoznanija* **1963** (2), 148–150.

NOTE ADDED IN PROOF

A model of some simple Russian sentences is given by M. I. Beleckiĭ (A model of Russian, describing simple sentences without homogeneity (in Russian), *Naučn. Tekh. Inform.* **1964** (7), 37–42). For the bibliography concerning dependency theory, see D. G. Hays, An annotated bibliography of publications on dependency theory, RM-4479-PR, RAND Corp., Santa Monica, Calif., 1965. For a new version of [18] see H. Gaifman, Dependency systems and phrase-structure systems, *Inform. Control* **8** (3), 304–337 (1965). Some links between projectivity and graph theory are shown by V. V. Firsov (On isometric immersion of a graph in the Boolean cube (in Russian), *Kibernetika* (Akad. Nauk Ukrainsk. SSR), **1965** (6), 95–96). For various aspects of formal syntactic analysis see W. S. Cooper (Set theory and syntactic description, Mouton, The Hague, 1964), K. Mc Conlogue and R. B. Simmons (Analyzing English syntax with a pattern-learning parser, *Comm. Ass. Comp. Mach.* **8** (11), 687–698 (1965)) and L. Uhlířová (Some aspects of word order in categorial and transformational grammars, *Prague Studies Math. Linguistics* **1**, 159–166 (1966)). Concerning the notion of projectivity see also P. Sgall, Ein mehrstufiges generatives System, *Kybernetika* **2** (2), 181–190 (1966) and J. Kunze, Theoretische Probleme der Automatische Übersetzung, *Z. math. Logik und Grundl. der Math.* **12** (1/2), 85–130 (1966).

Author Index

Subject Index

A

AB-chain, 24
AB-connected set of words, 24
Absolutely adequate language, 63
Absolutely completely adequate language, 63
Absolutely completely homogeneous language, 64
Absolutely homogeneous language, 64
Absolutely inadequate language, 63
Absolutely noncompletely adequate language, 63
Absolutely noncompletely homogeneous language, 64
Absolutely nonhomogeneous language, 64
Absolutely nonperfect language, 64
Absolutely nonsimple language, 64
Absolutely nonwell adequate language, 63
Absolutely perfect language, 64
Absolutely simple language, 64
Absolutely well adequate language, 63
Abstract personal feminine gender, 151
Abstract personal masculine gender, 149
Abstract structured string, 230
Adequate language, 36
Adequate word, 39
Adjacent arcs, 201
Adjacent vertices, 201
Adjunct of a normal configuration, 173
Amorphic language, 9, 48
Amorphic word, 48
Analytic grammar, 1
Antisymmetric graph, 201
Archigender, 128
Associative syntactic calculus, 102

Atomic phrase, 104
Attribute of a configuration, 193
Automatic partition, 29
Auxiliary part of a coordination syntagm, 196
Auxiliary part of the attribute of a dependence syntagm, 196
Auxiliary vocabulary, 189

B

Base of a topology, 130
Basic vocabulary, 189
Bidirectional categorial grammar, 108
Bidirectional categorial language, 108
B-string, 209
B-substring of a B-string, 214

C

Category, 139
Cell of a partition, 8
Center of a graph, 203
Center of a normal configuration, 173
Center of a string, 204
Chain, 23, 201
Circuit of a graph, 202
Class of a word, 25
Closed set, 129
Comparable words, 211
Complete configurational characteristics of a language, 234
Complete graph, 201
Completely adequate language, 49
Completely adequate word, 50
Complementary distribution, 7
Completely homogeneous language, 44

250